Culturally and Linguistically Diverse Learners and STEAM

Culturally and Linguistically Diverse Learners and STEAM

Teachers and Researchers Working in Partnership to Build a Better Tomorrow

edited by

Pamela Spycher
WestEd

Erin F. Haynes
Engage Language, LLC

INFORMATION AGE PUBLISHING, INC.
Charlotte, NC • www.infoagepub.com

Library of Congress Cataloging-in-Publication Data

A CIP record for this book is available from the Library of Congress
http://www.loc.gov

ISBN: 978-1-64113-605-1 (Paperback)
       978-1-64113-606-8 (Hardcover)
       978-1-64113-607-5 (ebook)

Printed in the United States of America

CONTENTS

Preface: An Invitation ix

PART I
SCIENCE FOR DIVERSE LEARNERS

1 SUPERMOON! Literacy Infused STEAM 3
Kevin M. Carr and Lena Baucum

2 Fostering English Learners' Academic Language in a Science-
Themed Summer School Program 27
Lauren Artzi, Diane August, and Jennifer Letcher Gray

3 Concept-Based Teaching in Dual Language
Science Classrooms: Using Oral Language Routines
to Develop Scientific Descriptions and Arguments 45
Zenaida Aguirre-Muñoz and Maria O. Gregory

4 Supporting Linguistically Diverse Students in Scientific
Argumentation Across Writing and Speaking 77
María González-Howard and Katherine L. McNeill

5 Using Functional Grammar to Talk and Write About Science 95
*Mary Schleppegrell, Jason Moore, Catherine O'Hallaron,
and Annemarie Palincsar*

6 Scaffolding Young Children's Science Writing 117
  Pamela Spycher, Danielle Garegnani, and Thea Fabian

7 Supporting 3rd–8th Grade English Learners With Science
  Informational Texts Through Summer School Teacher
  Professional Learning...145
  Karin Linn-Nieves

8 Balancing Cultural and Science Identity Frameworks
  for American Indian/Alaska Native High School Students:
  A Summer Research Journey...169
  Carolee Dodge Francis, Noehealani Bareng-Antolin, and Kira Tran

9 Welcoming African Immigrant Students Into U.S. K–12
  STEAM Classrooms Through Culturally Relevant Teaching 189
  Sherilynn Nidever-Jordan and Michael Takafor Ndemanu

10 Making Everyday Phenomena Phenomenal: Next Generation
  Science Standards-Aligned Instructional Materials Using
  Local Phenomena With Diverse Student Groups............................211
  *Okhee Lee, Marcelle Goggins, Alison Haas, Rita Januszyk,
  Lorena Llosa, and Scott Grapin*

PART II

TECHNOLOGY, ENGINEERING, ARTS, AND MATHEMATICS FOR DIVERSE LEARNERS

11 Improving Students' Mathematics Dispositions and
  Participation Through Caring Mathematics Instruction...............231
  Nancy Tseng

12 Engaging New Americans in STEAM: Project-Based Learning
  Using Genre-Based Pedagogy 249
  James Nagle and Will Andrews

13 Full STEAM Ahead! Secondary Teachers' Artful Support
  of ELs Through Science Photography...267
  Alandeom W. Oliveira and Luciana C. de Oliveira

14 Facilitating Diverse Students' Discourse During Mathematics
  Discussions: What Do Teacher Questions Have to Do With It? 291
  Mary A. Avalos and Loren Jones

15 Integrating Coding and Composition: Linking English Language
Arts, Computer Programming, and Mathematics to Develop
English Learners' Strengths Across the Content Areas 313
Suzie Dollesin, Harry Cheng, and Porfirio Loeza

16 Exploring Scaffolds and Feedback for Improving Communication
in a Water Resources Engineering Laboratory Course........................ 333
Cristina Poindexter and Barbara J. Merino

17 What's Language Got to Do With It? Theory and Evidence
Linking Multilingualism and Mathematics Skills........................... 357
Rachel Garrett and Erin F. Haynes

18 Appendix: Developing Successful Projects Within a Research–
Practice Partnership by Using Stakeholder Advisory Groups........ 377
Julie Kochanek and Carrie Scholz

About the Editors 389

About the Contributors... 391

AN INVITATION

Culturally and linguistically diverse students, including those who are multilingual, multidialectal, and learning English as an additional language, constitute a substantial and growing demographic (McFarland et al., 2017). But these groups of students tend to receive unequal access to and inadequate instruction in advanced secondary math and science classes, including elective science, technology, engineering, arts, and mathematics (STEAM) courses (Feldman & Malagon, 2017; National Science Teachers Association, 2017). In many elementary schools, with the exception of math, STEAM education has not been a priority (Bybee, 2010). Compounding the issue, many STEAM teachers feel underprepared to meet the needs of culturally and linguistically diverse students (Stoddart, Bravo, Solis, Mosqueda, & Rodriguez, 2011). This situation is especially unfortunate given that a growing body of research suggests that multilingual students have an advantage in acquiring skills in mathematics (e.g., Golash-Boza, 2005; Garrett, 2010; Reardon & Galindo, 2007, 2009), logic (e.g., Bacolod & Rangel, 2017) and in cognitive processes such as control of attention (e.g., Bialystok & Majumder, 1998). These assets go largely unacknowledged and underutilized.

The need for more information about quality STEAM education for culturally and linguistically diverse students is pressing. This book seeks to address this need, with chapters from asset-oriented researchers and practitioners whose work offers promising teaching and learning approaches in the STEAM subjects in K–16 education settings. Authors share innovative ways in which classroom teachers integrate disciplinary reading, writing, discussion, and language development with content knowledge development in STEAM subjects. Also shared are approaches for integrating indigenous epistemologies, culturally sustaining pedagogy, and students' linguistic resources and life experiences into classroom teaching.

Guidance is provided throughout this book to support teachers to implement culturally sustaining, intellectually rich, relevant, and engaging STEAM teaching and learning to ensure that all classrooms are supportive, inclusive, and inspiring for all students. The book also serves to shape a research agenda in this important area and provide practical next steps for moving the agenda forward. It approaches these twin goals by demonstrating the outcomes of action research and researcher–practitioner collaborations and by concluding each chapter with a list of inquiry or theory-driven questions for researchers, as well as action research or practice-based questions for teachers and administrators. The distinction between these question types is a useful organizing structure for a book, but we recognize that it also creates a false dichotomy: Many people in the education field play multiple roles throughout their career, at times acting primarily as practitioners and at other times primarily as education researchers. Many practicing teachers engage routinely in action research processes. Furthermore, some of the strongest findings in the field arise from research–practice partnerships. (For people interested in developing such collaborations, Appendix A provides guidance, with information about forming and utilizing stakeholder advisory groups.)

There are three primary audiences for this book: teachers (both in-service and preservice teachers), teacher educators (both preservice preparation and professional learning); and applied researchers. Teachers have an immediate need to serve their students, and the chapters in this volume could form the basis for teacher professional learning, professional learning communities, and book study groups. It is also hoped that it will spur action research and collaborations with researchers. This volume could also serve as a resource for teacher preparation programs. Although the book will provide an overview of current promising practices, more research is urgently needed. We anticipate that researchers can use the research agenda laid forth in this book to guide their research in the area.

ABOUT THE BOOK

In accordance with its goal of promoting cultural and linguistic diversity as an asset to STEAM education, this volume eschews attempts at presenting a single, unified voice. As such, you will encounter many communication styles and conventions. In order to avoid confusion, the authors do not use acronyms, with the exception of English learner (EL); science, technology, engineering, art, and mathematics (STEAM); and any acronyms used to name specific education programs (defined in each chapter as relevant). The one theme that does unify all of the chapters is an asset orientation to learning. Each chapter considers the many strengths and skills that diverse learners contribute to their classrooms, schools, and communities, in addition to what students require for success in a multicultural world.

In the first section, chapter authors primarily address science. Most of these chapters are related to what authors Carr and Baucum call the "STEAM Club," a community of specialized knowledge and practice to which many underserved students do not have automatic access. Carr and Baucum discuss the importance of providing support to acquire specialized STEAM academic language, illustrated through a middle school science lesson for ELs called SUPERMOON! Similarly, Artzi, August, and Grey demonstrate academic language support about key scientific concepts concurrent with science instruction. Aguirre-Muñoz and Gregory argue that ELs must learn disciplinary discourse to support deep content learning, describing a three-step approach to develop students' skills in producing scientific descriptions and arguments. Gonzalez-Howard and McNeill's chapter and Schleppegrell, Moore, O'Hallaron, and Palincsar's chapter also focus on scientific discourse, the former describing linguistic practices middle school teachers can use to impart the science practice of argumentation, and the latter describing a systemic functional linguistics approach to support 4th grade students' science argument writing. Chapters by Spycher, Fabian, and Garegnani, and Linn-Nieves employ the teaching and learning cycle, a framework for scaffolding science learning and literacy. Spycher, Fabian, and Garegnani describe its use in a bilingual kindergarten classroom, and Linn-Nieves illustrates its use in a summer professional learning context and with ELs and long-term ELs in Grades 3–8.

The section ends with chapters that discuss an equity approach to science education, demonstrating how to achieve deep content learning with students from diverse backgrounds. Dodge Francis, Bareng-Antolin, and Tran tackle the larger culture of the science disciplines, describing summer research experiences with American Indian and Alaska Native high school students, developed to help the students explore and shape their own scientific identify. Nidever-Jordan and Ndemanu discuss the challenges that African immigrant students and their families encounter in schools and describe how to meet these students' needs through culturally responsive teaching. And Lee, Goggins, Haas, Januszyk, Llosa, and Grapin illustrate how using local phenomena can promote access to science and inclusion in the science classroom for diverse student groups, and they offer guidance on how to select and use local phenomena in developing Next Generation Science Standards-aligned instructional materials.

In the second section of the volume, chapter authors primarily address technology, engineering, art, and mathematics. Through her own action research project as a teacher, Tseng explores the role of caring student–teacher relationships in the mathematics classroom and how this relationship influences student learning and how students come to identify with the discipline. Nagle and Andrews describe a project-based learning environment for high school students called iLab, where new American students explore STEAM-related projects of their own choosing and communicate their experiences and findings through several scientific genres of writing and speech. Oliveira and de Oliveira describe how they infused art into science with high school ELs, resulting in aesthetically rich chemistry learning where students made a photographic record of their experiments and data and then engaged in whole-class critique of the photographs. Avalos and Jones present a case study in which a middle school mathematics teacher incorporated new talk moves around the claim–evidence–reasoning structure to facilitate discourse with her linguistically diverse students, who engaged in markedly higher level discussions and problem-solving by the end of the semester.

Another case study is provided by Dollesin, Cheng, and Loeza, in which they describe how Dollesin improved secondary students' English language arts and math skills concurrently through the use of computer coding and making metacognitive connections between writing academic compositions and writing code in a project-based learning environment. Poindexter and Merino explore how scaffolding for college level engineering lab report preparation influences effective communication and conceptual understanding of writing lab reports, and they offer suggestions for adapting the methods they use for younger students. Finally, to advance recognition of the assets multilingual students bring to math learning, Garrett and Haynes offer a theoretical framework to explain that multilingualism is a salient factor related to the underlying cognitive processes that contribute to mathematics achievement, suggesting that ELs may bring unrecognized abilities to the process of mathematics learning.

NEXT STEPS

This book aims to make quality STEAM education a reality for all students, taking into account the many perspectives, bodies of knowledge, and skills they bring from a range of cultural and linguistic backgrounds, with the ultimate goal of strengthening the fields that will drive our society towards the future. We recognize, however, that we were unable to address every aspect of student diversity in this volume, or every practice that might help a diverse body of students succeed. And that is where our invitation to you, the reader, comes in. As we noted at the beginning of this invitation, more research is urgently needed. We invite you to use this volume as a guide to continue this important work.

Whatever your current or evolving role, we encourage you to use this book and the inquiry questions provided at the end of each chapter as a launching point for your own important work. If you are working as a teacher or a preservice teacher in a K–12 school setting, use the practices described in the chapters, or form a reading group with other teachers to try out the practices and report back to each other, perhaps developing action research processes and a community of practice together. If you are a K–12 school administrator, create a safe space for teachers to engage in this work and allocate resources to support their activities. If you provide instruction to in-service or preservice teachers or administrators, encourage them to read this book and incorporate new practices into their school settings. If you work primarily as an education researcher, develop research–practice partnerships with K–12 school practitioners and design research projects that further the goal of increasing diversity in STEAM fields. And finally, if you are a policy maker or district leader, prioritize funding and resources to help culturally and linguistically diverse students succeed in STEAM subjects.

The value of quality STEAM education for all students is an equity issue, a civics issue, and an economic issue (Bybee, 2010). Our technologically-driven, scientifically-oriented, innovative society should be led by diverse people with diverse ways of approaching and being in the world, but if diverse people are denied the opportunity to participate in quality STEAM education, we will lose their crucial voices. STEAM subjects can be important drivers of school engagement, too, as for many children and youth, these classes are the reasons for coming to school. STEAM is where students can engage their full curiosity, get their hands dirty, and collaborate authentically with their peers as they explore how the world works. We view this book is a contribution to social justice efforts that seek to disrupt the status quo, which is a good thing for everyone.

REFERENCES

Bacolod, M, & Rangel, M. A. (2017). Economic assimilation and skill acquisition: Evidence from the occupational sorting of childhood immigrants. *Demography, 54,* 571–602.

Bialystok, E., & Majumder, S. (1998). The relationship between bilingualism and the development of cognitive processes in problem-solving. *Applied Psycholinguistics, 19,* 69–85.

Bybee, R. W. (2010). Advancing STEM education: A 2020 vision. *Technology and Engineering Teacher, 70*(1), 30–35.

Feldman, S., & Malagon, V. F. (2017). *Unlocking learning: Science as a lever for English learner equity*. Oakland, CA: The Education Trust–West.

Garrett, R. (2010). *Multilingualism, mathematics achievement, and instructional language policy* (Doctoral dissertation). Retrieved from ProQuest Dissertations and Theses (Accession Order No. 3419635).

Golash-Boza, T. (2005). Assessing the advantages of bilingualism for children of immigrants. *International Migration Review, 39*(3), 721–753.

McFarland, J., Hussar, B., de Brey, C., Snyder, T., Wang, X., Wilkinson-Flicker, S.,...Hinz, S. (2017). *The Condition of Education 2017* (NCES 2017-144). Washington, DC: U.S. Department of Education, National Center for Education Statistics.

National Science Teachers Association. (2017). *NSTA position statement: Science for English language learners*. Retrieved July 3, 2017 from http://www.nsta.org/about/positions/ell.aspx

Reardon, S., & Galindo, C. (2007). Patterns of Hispanic student's math skill proficiency in the early elementary grades. *Journal of Latinos and Education, 6*(3), 229–251.

Reardon, S., & Galindo, C. (2009). The Hispanic-White achievement gap in math and reading in the elementary grades. *American Educational Research Journal, 46*(3), 853–891.

Stoddart, T., Bravo, M. A., Solis, J. L., Mosqueda, E., & Rodriguez, A. (2011, April). *Effective science teaching for English language learners (ESTELL): Measuring preservice teacher practices*. Paper presented to the annual meeting of the American Educational Research Association, New Orleans.

PART I

SCIENCE FOR DIVERSE LEARNERS

CHAPTER 1

SUPERMOON! LITERACY INFUSED STEAM

Kevin M. Carr
Pacific University

Lena Baucum
Pacific University

Students of color leave the STEAM career pipeline at greater rates than white students (Radunzel, Mattern, & Westrick, 2016). Student access to STEAM education and careers is fostered by multiple, deeply interlinked factors, both in and out of school. Each student comes into our STEAM classroom having traveled an educational and institutional pathway that has served to either nurture, or deny, possibilities in STEAM. Our goal as teacher-educators is to help teachers transform K–12 STEAM classrooms into positive access points for students of color to pursue STEAM careers. To borrow a metaphor from Frank Smith, we seek to create classroom experiences that invite and induct novice students into the "STEAM club" (Smith, 1998). As STEAM teachers, we act as chief admissions officers to the STEAM club, responsible for integrating students into the cultural practices, knowledge, and specialized academic language of STEAM.

Culturally and Linguistically Diverse Learners and STEAM, pages 3–25
Copyright © 2019 by Information Age Publishing

3

Figure 1.1 Broadening participation in STEAM careers by supporting STEAM language literacy.

In this chapter, we focus on ways STEAM teachers can provide students supported access to STEAM academic language. The specialized vocabulary, syntax, and discourse styles of STEAM represent a particularly significant barrier to students of color, future bilingual students (English language learners), and first-generation college students. Therefore, supporting access to STEAM academic language represents a leverage point teachers can use to improve the experience of students in the STEAM classroom. First, we will discuss how supporting STEAM language literacy will broaden pathways into STEAM education and careers for all students, and then we will illustrate tools and routines for infusing language support into middle school STEAM curricula and instruction at the classroom level (see Figure 1.1).

BROADENING STEAM CAREER PARTICIPATION BY SUPPORTING STEAM LANGUAGE LITERACY

We work with schools educating Latino students who speak Spanish or an indigenous language at home and English elsewhere, are from low socio-economic backgrounds, and represent the first generation in their families to pursue an American education. Latino students, as a group, are less likely than their white peers to pursue and succeed in STEAM education and careers (Wang, 2013). The achievement gap in STEAM academic outcomes between White students and students of color is well-known, and frequently cited as the main driver of underrepresentation in STEAM (Chen, 2013). Rather than focus on the achievement gap directly, we find it more useful for STEAM teachers to think in terms of the many *opportunity gaps* experienced by students in the classroom (Carnegie Institute for Advanced Study, 2009). One opportunity gap affecting many students of color is the lack of support in school for acquiring STEAM academic language (Zacarian, 2013).

The process of acquiring the specialized language of a discipline is part of a wider sociocultural process of gaining identity and membership in a discourse community (Gee, 2004; Lemke, 2004; Snow, 2010; Zacarian, 2013; Zwiers, 2014). The vocabulary, symbols, syntax, and discourse used within STEAM hold the "deep structure" within which conceptual understanding is built and practice is carried out (Chomsky, 1965; Gee, 2004). STEAM conceptual understanding and practices are internalized as language, and carry what Norton (2013, pp. 25–26) refers to as *investment, imagined identity* and *imagined community.* The investment of novice students in STEAM identities and communities may be supported, invited, discouraged, or even forbidden, by classroom experiences.

We believe that the development of STEAM identity through language is a critical goal for equitable education, opening for students of color the possibility for membership in communities of power (Collier, Burston, & Rhodes, 2016). Lisa Delpit (1988) used the term *cultural codes* to name the specialized academic language used by members of a discourse community, making explicit the connection between knowing the code, identity, community membership, and power:

> If you are not already a participant in the culture of power, being told explicitly the rules of that culture makes acquiring power easier. In my work within and between diverse cultures, I have come to conclude that members of any culture transmit information implicitly to co-members. However, when implicit codes are attempted across cultures, communication frequently breaks down. Each cultural group is left saying, "Why don't those people say what they mean?" as well as, "What's wrong with them, why don't they understand?" (p. 283)

STEAM teachers, as fluent members of the STEAM club, often give little thought to the cultural codes (vocabulary, syntax, and discourse) used in their disciplines, how they serve to shape conceptual understanding and practice, and the role of codes in establishing students' STEAM identity and achievement. Much as a native English speaker is unaware of the implicit cultural codes involved in being fluent in English, STEAM teachers are unaware of the implicit language demands inherent in being a member of the STEAM club. We too often assume that students will simply absorb the cultural codes of STEAM without planned support. We conduct instruction as though students are already co-members in the STEAM club, when in fact our students are outsiders to STEAM, attempting to cross cultural boundaries (Aitkenhead, 2001). As a result, many STEAM students are left saying (as imagined by Delpit, 1988), "Why don't teachers say what they mean?"; while their teachers are left saying, "What's wrong with them? Why don't they understand?"

In the second section of this chapter, we illustrate how to plan STEAM instruction using a backward design process in which the desired cultural code (STEAM academic language) is made explicit at the outset. Inquiry learning activities are then designed to support academic language development and practice, building increased complexity and a gradual release to independent language use, so that cultural boundaries into STEAM are more smoothly crossed (Routman, 2012).

PART II: PLANNING AND IMPLEMENTING
LITERACY-INFUSED

A failure to support the development of STEAM academic language literacy in classrooms is an exclusionary practice that denies students equal access to opportunity and cultural capital. To share the cultural code of STEAM, Zacarian (2013) suggests a four-pronged framework in which academic language learning consists of

- a sociocultural process that must be grounded in our students' and their families' personal, social, cultural, and world experiences;
- a developmental process that calls for understanding the literacy levels of each of our students and targeting instruction a little bit beyond that level so that it is obtainable and reachable;
- an academic process that is built on our students' prior learning experiences and where the learning goals are understandable; and
- a cognitive process in which thinking skills are intentionally taught and practiced.

In order to successfully infuse literacy support into STEAM, we must first frame instruction as a sociocultural process grounded in experience. We must then uncover and decode the language demands inherent in the specific concepts, practices, and tasks students are asked to understand and do. To teach students the STEAM code, we must intentionally structure and scaffold practice in the concepts and language we want students to learn, and gradually move from more, to less, guided instruction. We first make students comfortable by providing them with the language at a basic level around a simple task prior to supporting them in more complex academic language. In this way, the cultural code is explicitly infused into accessible STEAM content.

Uncovering and Decoding SUPERMOON!: Determining What to Teach

The starting point for planning literacy-infused STEAM instruction is to determine what content is to be taught through which task, and then determine the language demands of that content and task. Given the core ideas within a STEAM topic, we must first create a summative performance task through which students will demonstrate understanding. The task could be as simple as to a writing prompt or as complex as an extended project. Then, we must uncover and decode the concepts and language students will need in order to complete the task successfully. Determining the language demands can be readily accomplished as the teacher completes the planning for the performance task and then analyzes the plan to evaluate the language required to complete the finished product.

Here, we use the common science topic of "moon phases" to illustrate this process with our STEAM teaching candidates and veteran teachers. The Next Generation Science Standards suggest a middle school-level (Grades 6–8) performance expectation (MS-ESS1-1) in which students who demonstrate understanding can "develop and use a model of the Earth-sun-moon system to describe the cyclic patterns of lunar phases, eclipses of the sun and moon, and seasons" (National Research Council, 2013, p. 234). There are many possible tasks by which students could meet the performance expectation. As an example, consider the following task, SUPERMOON!, designed to assess the ability of students to use a model to describe and explain the cyclical patterns of lunar phases (see Figure 1.2).

Once the performance task demanded of the students has been defined, the conceptual and language demands can be uncovered and decoded. The next step for the teacher is to define the desired ideas and language a proficient student (fluent in the concepts and code) might use to successfully demonstrate understanding. There are many ways to answer the prompts posed by SUPERMOON!; we invite the reader to develop their own responses applicable to the context of their own teaching. We present here our imagined "target" responses to the prompts, in the context of a middle school science class with a high enrollment of future bilingual students (see Figure 1.3).

Demystifying the Code: Analyzing Language Demands

SUPERMOON! demands that students integrate STEAM vocabulary, syntax, and symbols while describing observations and models, explaining phenomena, and justifying claims. After drafting possible responses to the task, it is possible to determine what concepts and language elements need to be targeted during instruction.

The most cognitively demanding task needed to understand the moon phases may be that of *shifting perspectives.* As the model moon revolves around the earth, students are asked to consider the changing appearance of the moon from both the earthbound and external, "God's eye" perspectives. To effectively describe and explain the changing alignment of the sun-earth-moon system as observed from two different perspectives, students must learn and use specialized language and vocabulary. For example, a proficient student might say, "From the earth's perspective, we observe that [describe the phase seen], which is called the [name the phase]." Both academic vocabulary (perspective, observe, names of moon phases) and syntax

SUPERMOON!

Late one afternoon a strange notification comes up on your phone. It shows a picture of a full moon and says, "Beware of the SUPERMOON!" You share it with your friends, saying, "We have to see this!" But everyone asks, "What night will it be on?" That evening you go outside to check for the SUPERMOON and instead the moon is a thin, crescent shape. The next evening, you check again and notice that the moon is still a crescent, but has grown just a little larger.

Q1: On this model of the sun, earth, and moon, draw the position of the moon the first night you observed.

SUN'S RAYS

EARTH

Q2: Use the model to explain why you saw a thin, crescent moon the first night.

Q3: Draw the position of the moon the second night. Explain why the appearance of the moon changed, using the scientific name of this moon phase.

Q4: Draw the movement of the moon over the next few nights, until it arrives at the position of the SUPERMOON.

Q5: Describe how the appearance of the moon will change during this time. Name the phases that moon goes through.

Q6: Explain how you predicted the date of the SUPERMOON.

Figure 1.2 SUPERMOON! performance task for assessing understanding of moon phases.

(From _____ perspective, one observes that _____) are needed to communicate conceptual understanding using STEAM discourse.

Another demanding aspect of the sun-earth-moon task is describing and explaining moon phases in relation to the source of light (the sun). Here we introduce the term *self shadow* to provide students specialized, descriptive

Q1: On this model of the sun, earth, and moon, draw the position of the moon the first night you observed.

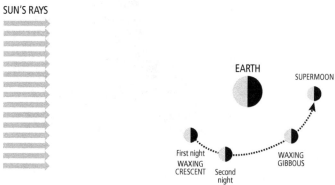

Q2: Use the model to explain why you saw a thin, crescent moon the first night.

"When you observe a thin crescent moon, you are seeing mostly the moon's self shadow, and a little of the lit side. When we modeled this in class, we observed that from the earth's perspective the moon appeared as a thin crescent when it was a little to the side on the sun."

Q3: On the model, draw the position of the moon the second night. Explain why the appearance of the moon changed, using the scientific name of this moon phase.

"From the earth's perspective, the moon's self shadow appeared smaller the second night, and the lit side appeared bigger, which means it is a waxing crescent phase.

Q4: Describe how the appearance of the moon would change over the next few nights, until it arrives at the position of the SUPERMOON. Name the phases that moon goes through. Explain how you predicted the date of the SUPERMOON.

"From the earth's perspective, over the next few nights the lit side of the moon will continue to grow and the self-shadow will shrink. This means that it will change phases from a waxing crescent to a waxing gibbous, and finally a full moon. This is the position when the SUPERMOON happens. From our data and models we observed that the moon takes about 14 days to revolve around the earth from new moon to full moon. Therefore, I estimate that it would take about 10 days to move from the first night of my observation to the SUPERMOON."

Figure 1.3 Target Responses to SUPERMOON!

language to use when explaining observations of the moon (Young & Guy, 2008). The term self shadow is used in art to describe the darkened side of an illuminated object, such as an apple placed in a scene with a lamp illuminating it from one side. To realistically sketch or paint the scene, the artist must not only depict the shadow cast by the apple on other objects (the apple's cast shadow), but also depict the dark side of the apple—the apple's self shadow (see Figure 1.4). Students use the self shadow concept when they say or write, "When I look at the moon, I see some of its lit side and some of its self shadow."

Figure 1.4   Cast shadow and self-shadow.

Planning and Implementing a Learning Segment

Next we plan a learning segment—a series of developmental inquiry activities—building on our students' prior learning experiences, in which thinking skills are intentionally taught and practiced. Our implementation of language-infused STEAM follows the pedagogical footsteps of the inquiry-based best practices originally set forth by Atkin and Karplus (1962) and Piaget (1970). We often plan using steps of *engagement, exploration, explanation,* and *elaboration* (4-E's). The conceptual and linguistic demands imposed on students increase as the instructional sequence progresses, roughly corresponding to the four levels of inquiry originally outlined by Herron (1971)—exploration, direct inquiry, guided inquiry, and open-ended inquiry (Lederman, 2010). What is most important for planning is that complex, multi-layered STEAM learning is scaffolded through a learning sequence leading to *independent forms of inquiry* (Routman, 2012). Throughout the learning sequence, vocabulary and syntax are carefully considered and language activities are planned to provide sufficient practice for students to acquire the scientific language required to engage in scientific practices and understanding.

Engagement

During *engagement,* the students are presented with an unfamiliar phenomena, objects, events, or questions. To support language, the teacher provides students with the basic vocabulary necessary to discuss what they are seeing and/or experiencing (*Note:* the teacher does not provide students with all of the key vocabulary for the unit). This would be overwhelming and ultimately not useful. Rather, needed vocabulary is introduced only as it becomes relevant to label what students have seen or experienced tangibly. Vocabulary introduction is done in a way that is analogous to how parent teaches their young child new words. For example, a parent first directs the child to look at a full moon in the sky, and once the child has seen it, names it, saying, "What an amazing, full moon!" A parent would not teach vocabulary removed from the presence of, or at least a picture of, the moon.

The student, during the engagement stage, is expected to focus on the new language and to be aware of their own understanding and use of new vocabulary. To support this process, students are explicitly prompted to use the new vocabulary, in context, with peers or the teacher. Students are not yet held accountable for using academic syntax. Instead the teacher holds students accountable for attempting to use the new words and supports students with scientifically accurate usage (meaning that we are using the appropriate STEAM club language for the object or concept). Again, this models how parents help young children extend their vocabulary. In terms of the imaginary conversations between parent and child, if a child states that the full moon is, say, a star, the parent simply repeats the vocabulary word and helps the child to correctly label the moon as the moon, and the star as a star.

The SUPERMOON! learning segment begins with an introduction of two key vocabulary terms and concepts for understanding the moon phases: *cast shadow* and *self shadow*. We show students a Styrofoam sphere illuminated by a nearby lamp, and we point out that the sphere both projects a shadow on nearby objects (its cast shadow), and is itself darkened on one side by its self shadow. We then engage students in an activity commonly done in an art class: sketching. Specifically, they sketch, with pencil and paper a white, Styrofoam sphere illuminated by a light source (see Figure 1.4). By viewing the sphere from different perspectives, students observe and sketch the appearance of different "sphere phases," analogous to moon phases. During the activity students are guided to speak and write with peers about the moon's self shadow as it appears from different *perspectives*, learning core language and concepts needed to construct a full explanation of the sun-earth-moon system (see Table 1.1). It is critical at this phase that student speaking and

TABLE 1.1 Engagement Stage of SUPERMOON!		
	Language Demands and Moves	
Engagement	**Vocabulary**	**Syntax**
Students practice sketching a white Styrofoam sphere that represents the moon. The sphere is illuminated by a light source (or the sun if done outside). Students sketch the illuminated sphere from different perspectives, shading the sphere's self-shadow, and observing the resulting illuminated shapes (Young & Guy, 2008).	Model Sphere Moon Self-shadow Perspective Angles Earth Styrofoam ball Skewer	From this perspective, the moon appears as a _____.

writing are framed by the teacher as *supported practice*, in which accurate language use is modeled, scaffolded, and informally evaluated.

Exploration

During *exploration*, students are provided with a common base of experience with which to enhance their thinking about the scientific concepts. The goal in the exploration phase is to provide students with ample opportunity to practice the use of the language and learn its flexibility. They actively examine and manipulate objects and phenomena through direct investigations organized by the teacher. It is essential during the exploration phase that the teacher introduce students to the specific scientific vocabulary they will require to sound like scientists. The teacher must also set students up to interact with the scientific learning in a way that requires student verbal and/or written interaction. Teachers support language during exploration by using tools and routines to orchestrate scientific conversation. It is at this point that the teacher begins to hold students accountable for applying the academic vocabulary and syntax that is needed to proficiently carry out exploration activities and informal writing in lab journals or worksheets.

We implement in SUPERMOON! an exploration activity in which students are provided with a set of 24 randomly ordered "moon phase cards," depicting the appearance of the moon on 24 consecutive days (see Figure 1.5), along with a Styrofoam sphere on a skewer representing the moon, and a light source. The teacher demonstrates holding the skewer in one hand, modeling the revolution and orbit of the moon around her head. Students are then directed to observe the self shadow and lit portion of the Styrofoam moon as they make the sphere orbit *their* head, and use their observations to arrange the moon phase cards in order.

Students are asked to justify their ordered cards in terms of the model, correctly using academic language (see Table 1.2). Students require significant practice in this stage to begin to internalize the language. Exploration is critical as it is the longest period of time where students are able to practice the language in a less formal situation. At this point, teachers must provide feedback to students regarding both content, and language usage and syntax. This can be done using sentence frames posted around the room or on cards, and word walls or other techniques for making new vocabulary visible and accessible.

Explanation

During *explanation*, students are asked to formalize their thinking both in verbal means through conversations with the teacher, and through written discourse in the form of lab reports or other formal scientific writing. During explanation, students are given tasks which prompt them to explain their understanding of the concepts and processes they have been

Figure 1.5   Moon phase cards.

exploring. Students rely on previously taught vocabulary and examples of language syntax and discourse to develop scientifically sound explanations. Students are also given opportunities after every investigation or activity to verbally explain new concepts and/or demonstrate new skills and abilities. Students are prompted to justify *why* (explain "how they know") their interpretations and predictions make sense, and to anticipate what they would do differently "next time." We have found that *evidence-based justification*, a central attribute of STEAM discourse, carries with it very high cognitive and linguistic demands. Moving students from describing and explaining to making evidence-based arguments demands careful attention from teachers. It is critical that the teacher press students for both correct academic language and accuracy of scientific concepts,

TABLE 1.2 Exploration Stage of Moon Learning Segment

Exploration	Language Demands and Moves	
	Vocabulary	**Syntax**
Provide students with pictures of the moon taken daily for a month. Student uses the sphere on a stick (moon) and a light source (sun) to model the phases of the moon. Students seek to arrange the moon pictures in the correct order and justify their choices.	Teacher holds students accountable for using the academic language that has been introduced.	Students, while engaged in experiences, use previously taught academic language with peers and teacher.
	Vocabulary is made central to the activity through the teacher making the vocabulary tangible to the students (e.g., vocabulary cards to be placed on moon pictures).	Science journals are initiated at this point so that students begin to attend to the formal aspects of the syntax.
	• Waxing Crescent • 1st Quarter moon • Waxing Gibbous • Full Moon • Waning Gibbous • Waning Crescent • New Moon • Phase • Alignment • Inclination • Solar Eclipse • Lunar Eclipse • Orbit • Revolve • Axis	From the perspective of the _____, the _____ appears as a _____. I ordered the moon phases _____, because, _____. I ordered the _____ before/after the _____ because as the…, it can be seen as _____ from the _____. As the moon _____, your perspective _____.

requiring re-speaking and rewriting as needed. The teacher gradually removes speaking and writing supports to move students towards independent communication of complete scientific explanations (Routman, 2012).

Consider the following illustration of how the moon-on-a-stick model can be used along with the sun outdoors (or lamp) to explain the sun-earth-moon system in motion. The teacher pauses to carefully model for students how to use the moon-on-a-stick to explain moon phases, and pauses to coach academic language use:

Teacher: "Everybody align your moon-on-a-stick with the sun like this. Remember, don't look at the sun." (Holds moon-on-a-stick about 45 degrees to the left of the sun.) Students: (Align their moons as directed)

Teacher: "Make sure you see a crescent lit side, and a gibbous self shadow in this alignment. In the astronomy club we call this the moon's crescent phase. Now, slowly make your moon orbit the right, and watch the lit side grow, and the self shadow shrink. In the astronomy club we call this change *waxing*. So the moon in this alignment is a waxing crescent."

(Students follow the teacher's modeling)

Teacher: "Next, partner with the person next to you. Decide who is A and who is B. We're going to do a little dialogue. First, person A explains using the moon on a stick how the moon phase changes as it orbits from a thin waxing crescent to a full moon. Then, you'll switch and B will explain how it changes from full moon to waning crescent. Get started."

Student A: "Okay, when the moon moves this way, it grows until it is full over here."

Teacher: "Good. Now let's use 'club language.' Go through that explanation that again using the 'club words' *waxing, crescent, gibbous,* and *self shadow*."

Student A: "When the crescent moon orbits this way, the self shadow shrinks and the moon grows, I mean, waxes. Then it turns to gibbous, and then full."

Teacher: "Better! I also noticed that you moved the moon so that is wasn't aligned with the earth's shadow. Why did you do that?"

Student A: "Because there isn't an eclipse every month."

Teacher: "Good. You might also explain that the moon's orbit is inclined, or tilted, so that the full moon isn't affected by earth's shadow."

Student A: "Got it."

Teacher: "So say that in the your own words."

Students A: "The moon's orbit is, uh, tilted, I mean, inclined so it misses the earth's shadow most of the time."

Teacher: "...which helps us understand..."

Students A: "...why there isn't an eclipse every month."

Teacher: "Good!"

As students practice explaining, the teacher circulates, and helps student restate their explanations in more scientifically correct way using academic language. Afterward, students are given a set of questions to pose to their colleague, who uses the "moon-on-a-stick" model to verbally respond using scientific vocabulary and syntax (see Table 1.3). After the "moon interview" is complete, students write out their own complete responses to the questions, using correct syntax and expected vocabulary. The teacher evaluates these responses and uses them as a formative assessment to inform further instructional moves prior to the summative activity.

TABLE 1.3 Explanation Stage of Moon Learning Segment		
	Language Demands and Moves	
Explanation	**Vocabulary**	**Syntax**
Model the system in motion. Demonstrate how a full moon isn't a lunar eclipse; demonstrate how a new moon isn't a solar eclipse. **Q1:** How are the sun, earth, and moon aligned at [pick a phase]? **Q2:** How does the moon move from new moon to full moon? What phases does it go through? How many days does this take? Why do we see the shapes the way we do? **Q3:** How does the moon move from full moon to new moon? What phases does it go through? Why do we see the shapes the way we do? **Q4:** Some people think the phases of the moon are caused by the shadow of the earth being cast on the moon. Is this true or false? Justify your answer using your model.	Vocabulary stays consistent at this point. Students are asked to continue to use the vocabulary • Waxing Crescent • 1st Quarter moon • Waxing Gibbous • Full Moon • Waning Gibbous • Waning Crescent • New Moon • Phase • Alignment • Inclination • Solar Eclipse • Lunar Eclipse • Orbit • Revolve • Axis	Students use the previously learned syntax during explanation but are also required to manipulate the language by using parts of the question in their answers. "The full moon isn't a lunar eclipse because the orbit is inclined." Students need to be asked to engage in the writing of explanations after using the language orally. This forces students to engage fully with the intricacies of academic register.

Elaboration

During *elaboration*, the teacher provides students opportunities to apply concepts in new contexts or situations. Students take part in activities that extend conceptual understanding and that allow them to practice new skills. They become involved in more open-ended inquiry, problem-solving, and decision-making. During elaboration, students may design and carry out their own investigations. The teacher works to orchestrate scientific discourse by requiring students to support claims with data and/or evidence. The teacher continues to support the development of both scientific language and content. During elaboration, student language should be moving toward full independence, with some flexibility in use of language structures (Routman, 2012).

The elaboration phase may be used as a space to introduce intentionally ill-defined or confounding material for discussion. For example, students

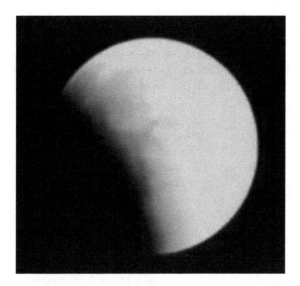

Figure 1.6 Lunar eclipse.

often remain confused by new/full moons and lunar/solar eclipses, convoluting prior conceptions of moon phases with the newly learned understanding of the moon's self shadow. Simple textbook diagrams of the earth-sun-moon system often exacerbate the issue, through inaccurate scale of sizes and distances, and omission of the inclination of the moon's orbit (e.g., Figure 1.2). Such diagrams tend to reinforce the common misconception that the moon phases are possibly caused by the earth's cast shadow rather than moon's self shadow. To prompt a discussion of these issues, students are shown a photograph of a lunar eclipse (see Figure 1.6), and given a small piece of paper that says either "I propose that a lunar eclipse is caused by the *earth's cast shadow during the full moon*" or "I propose that a lunar eclipse is caused by the *moon's self-shadow during the new moon*" (see Table 1.4).

TABLE 1.4 Elaboration Stage of Moon Learning Segment		
	Language Demands and Moves	
Elaboration	**Vocabulary**	**Syntax**
Lunar Eclipse Debate: "I propose that a lunar eclipse is caused by the earth's cast shadow during the full moon." "I propose that a lunar eclipse is caused by the moon's self-shadow during the new moon."	Full Moon New Moon Alignment Inclination Lunar Eclipse Self-Shadow Orbit	The moon phases are caused by _____. We saw this is in [activity].

Groups are formed (this can be arranged a variety of ways) in which students engage in a staged debate to argue both for and against the above propositions, using evidence from their prior observations, models, diagrams, and discourse. Consider this exchange between a teacher and two students working on placing the moon in the correct alignment for full moon using a two-dimensional diagram drawn on paper (see Figure 1.2).

Student A: (Looking at a two-dimensional diagram similar to Figure 1.2.) "I'm still not sure how the full moon works. If I put the moon here on the other side of the earth won't the earth's shadow go onto the moon and make a waxing crescent and then a new moon?"

Teacher: "I agree, this diagram is confusing. Why don't you think about the self shadow and what you worked out with the moon-on-a-stick model?"

Student B: "When we did it using the moon-on-a-stick the moon missed the earth's shadow. It was actually the moon's self shadow that made the crescents, and then the gibbous, moon."

Student A: "I get it."

Teacher: "So how would you explain that in club language?"

Student A: "When the moon changes alignment with the sun, our view of the self shadow changes."

Teacher: "What activity supports that idea?"

Student B: "It's like the moon sketching activity we did."

Teacher: "Good."

Evaluating Language Production

Evaluation of conceptual understanding and precision of language use is essential to ensuring that all students become proficient and are able to participate fully in STEAM discourse. During evaluation, students are asked to be metacognitive as they assess their own knowledge, skills, and abilities. Formal and informal evaluation should occur in every phase and level of inquiry (Lederman, 2010).

To support SUPERMOON!, we developed a rubric (see Table 1.5) to guide assessment and evaluation of student responses to the summative performance task (see Figure 1.1). Students complete the performance task independently and without explicit language support. We find that ELLs generally produce language ranging between nearly proficient and proficient, with the greatest challenge in accurately linking evidence to explanations.

TABLE 1.5 SUPERMOON! Evaluation Rubric

Criteria	Emergent	Nearly Proficient	Proficient	Exceeds Target
Develop a model of the earth–moon–sun system....	moon depicted in inaccurate locations in orbit *or* motion depicted inaccurately *or* moons labeled with incorrect phases	moon depicted in inaccurate locations in orbit *and* motion depicted accurately *and* moons labeled with correct phases	moon depicted in accurate locations in orbit *and* motion depicted accurately *and* moons labeled with correct phases	moon depicted in accurate locations in orbit *and* motion depicted accurately *and* moons labeled with correct phases *and* moons sketched as they appear from earth's perspective
...to describe lunar phases...	phases described in terms of nonacademic vocabulary (e.g., "dark side") *and* syntax of description incorrectly constructed	phases described in terms nonacademic vocabulary (e.g., "dark side") *or* syntax of description incorrectly constructed	phases described, using correct syntax, in terms of self-shadow	phases described, using correct syntax, in terms of self-shadow, and supported with explicit reference to the sketching activity
...explain cyclic pattern of phases...	phases explained in incorrect terms (e.g., shadow of the earth) *and* syntax of explanation incorrectly constructed	phases explained in terms of changing perspective or alignment over time *or* syntax of explanation incorrectly constructed	phases explained using correct syntax and in terms of changing perspective or alignment over time	phases explained, using correct syntax, in terms of changing perspective or alignment over time, with correct estimate and reasoning of days elapsed to supermoon

SUMMARY

We intentionally choose the metaphor of *infusion* to describe the relationship between the language of STEAM, and STEAM's core concepts and practices. There is no STEAM without STEAM language, and to learn STEAM language is to learn STEAM concepts, and vice versa. Furthermore, we consider STEAM to constitute a full-fledged discourse community (the "STEAM club") sharing the following characteristics (Swales, 1990; Swales, 2016):

1. Has a broadly agreed set of common public goals.
2. Has mechanisms of intercommunication among its members.
3. Uses its participatory mechanisms primarily to provide information and feedback.
4. Utilizes and hence possesses one or more genres in the communicative furtherance of its aims.
5. In addition to owning genres, it has acquired some specific lexis.
6. Has a threshold level of members with a suitable degree of relevant content and discoursal expertise.
7. Develops a sense of "silential relations," that is, "...things that do not need to be said or to be spelt out in detail in either words or writing" (Swales, 2016, p. 29).
8. Develops horizons of expectation.

In terms of supporting academic language, discourse community Characteristics 6 and 7 are of particular interest to STEAM teachers committed to equity and broadening participation in STEAM. The STEAM discourse community has criteria for membership based on fluency in both STEAM content and discourse (characteristic 6), and possesses an unspoken, unwritten code of "inside" understanding that identifies members to one another (characteristic 7). STEAM instruction must be infused with explicit support of both content and discourse, spoken and unspoken. We attempt in this chapter to illustrate what such support might sound and look like in the classroom. Planning literacy-infused STEAM requires that teachers first uncover, and then make visible the practices of the STEAM discourse community content, and then teach it to students in ways that engage them (Lave & Wenger, 1991). We use the 4-E framework to plan inquiry and language moves that scaffold novice students from emerging stages of concept and language acquisition to independent inquiry and communication (Collier, Burston, & Rhodes, 2016; see Table 1.6 for an overview). By gaining early membership in the STEAM club, we believe novice students will be more likely to remain in the STEAM pipeline.

To further this work, we end the chapter with inquiry questions for researchers and action research possibilities for practitioners.

TABLE 1.6 Overview of Language Moves, Tools, Routines, and Assessments for 4-E Inquiry Learning Segment

4-E Stage	Tools, Routines, and Assessments	Language Moves	
		Teacher	Student
Engagement	*Tools* • TPR • Re-vocalization of vocabulary • Drawings • Picture/word match • Word/definition match • Pictorial input charts • Gallery walks	Introduces essential vocabulary for elements of phenomenon.	Focus on new language and ensure accurate understanding
Exploration	*Tools* Checklist for holding students accountable for new vocabulary use. *Routines* Teacher corrects students who are not using language and encourages new language use.	Teacher holds students accountable for using the academic language that has been taught.	Students, while engaged in experiences, use previously taught academic language with peers and teacher. Journaling in this phase.
Explanation	*Routines* • Modeled writing • Shared writing • Interactive writing • Guided writing if necessary • Sentence patterning charts • Sentence frames created from language goal	Teacher holds students accountable for academic language and accuracy of scientific concepts. Teacher uses gradual release of responsibility for writing to move students towards independence in this area(Routman, 2012).	Students rely on previously taught vocabulary and examples of language syntax and register to develop scientifically sound explanations. Writing occurs at this phase.

(continued)

TABLE 1.6 Overview of Language Moves, Tools, Routines, and Assessments for 4-E Inquiry Learning Segment

4-E Stage	Tools, Routines, and Assessments	Language Moves
Explanation (cont.)	*Assessments* • Directs students back to language supports, models, pattern charts, etc. • Teacher holds students accountable for new language use (Students must attempt the new language). • Teacher corrects incorrect usage and syntax so that students can soon use language independently.	
Elaboration	*Tools* • Guided writing when necessary • Assessments • Academic vocabulary usage • Syntactic accuracy • Register	Orchestrating scientific discourse through supporting claims with data/evidence. Teacher continues to support errors in both language and content.	At this point student language should be starting to become independent. Students should have some flexibility of language structures.

Inquiry Questions

1. How might the development of STEAM language and discourse by students drive conceptual understanding, and vice versa?
2. How might interest and persistence in STEAM be related to the support of academic language in STEAM classrooms?
3. What tools might aid new and veteran teachers to a strong implementation of literacy infused STEAM in classrooms?

Action Research Possibilities

1. What practices and discourse in my teaching context (grade level, content area, and local community) signify "STEAM club membership"? It may be useful to review the Next Generation Science Standards Scientific and Engineering Practices for ideas (National Research Council, 2013).
2. What language demands (vocabulary, syntax, and discourse) are posed by a given STEAM lesson, activity, or lab? To analyze a lesson for academic language, we have found it very useful to write out "target" responses to the prompts given in your lesson (e.g., Figure 1.2). As an exercise, write target responses for a favorite lesson, activity, or lab. What vocabulary and syntax is required?
3. Develop a set of scaffolds to support language learning in a given STEAM lesson, activity, or lab (see Inquiry Question #4). Plan, teach, and analyze the results of the lesson. In what ways was student use of academic language supported? What are next steps for your students?
4. How might students be moved during an extended time frame school from highly-supported STEAM writing (e.g., sentence frames) to more independent writing?

AUTHOR NOTE

This material is based upon work supported by the National Science Foundation under Grant No. 1439628, & Oregon Department of Education Math Science Partnership Grant OR150507.

REFERENCES

Aitkenhead, G. S. (2001). Students' ease in crossing cultural borders into school science. *Science Education, 85*(2), 180–188.

Atkin, J. M., & Karplus, R. (1962). Discovery or invention? *The Science Teacher, 29*(5), 45–51.

Carnegie Institute for Advanced Study. (2009). *The opportunity equation.* New York, NY: Author.

Chen, X. (2013). *STEM attrition: College students' paths into and out of STEM fields* (NCES 2014-001). Washington, DC: National Center for Education Statistics, Institute of Education Sciences, U.S. Department of Education.

Chomsky, N. (1965). *Aspects of the theory of syntax.* Cambridge, MA: MIT Press.

Collier, S., Burston, B., & Rhodes, A. (2016) Teaching STEM as a second language. *Journal for Multicultural Education, 10*(3), 257–273.

Delpit, L. D. (1988). The silenced dialogue: Power and pedagogy in educating other people's children. *Harvard Educational Review, 58*(3), 280–298.

Gee, J. P. (2004). Language in the science classroom: Academic social languages as the heart of school-based literacy. In E. W. Saul (Ed.), *Crossing borders in literacy and science instruction: Perspectives on theory and practice* (pp. 13–32). Arlington, VA: NSTA Press.

Herron, M. D. (1971). The nature of scientific inquiry. *School Review, 79,* 171–212.

Lave, J., & Wenger, E. (1991). *Situated learning: Legitimate peripheral participation.* Cambridge, MA: Cambridge University Press.

Lederman, J. S. (2010). *Levels of inquiry and the 5 E's learning cycle model.* Retrieved from http://www.ngspscience.com/profdev/monographs/SCL22-0407A_SCI_AM_Lederman_FP.pdf

Lemke, J. L. (2004). The literacies of science. In E.W. Saul (Ed.), *Crossing borders in literacy and science instruction: Perspectives on theory and practice* (pp. 33–47). Arlington, VA: NSTA Press.

National Research Council. (2013). *Next Generation Science Standards: For States, By States.* Washington, DC: The National Academies Press. https://doi.org/10.17226/18290.

Norton, B. (2013). *Identity and language learning: Extending the conversation.* Bristol, England: Multilingual Matters.

Piaget, J. (1970). *Structuralism* (Chaninah Maschler, Trans.). New York, NY: Harper and Row.

Radunzel, J., Mattern, K., & Westrick, P. (2016). *The role of academic preparation and interest on STEM success.* ACT Research Report Series, *2016*(8). Retrieved from http://www.act.org/content/dam/act/unsecured/documents/5940-Research-Report-2016-8-Role-of-Academic-Preparation-and-Interest-on-STEM-Success.pdf

Routman, R. (2012). Mapping a pathway to schoolwide highly effective teaching. *Kappan, 95*(3), 56–61.

Smith, F. (1998). *The book of learning and forgetting.* New York, NY: Teachers College Press.

Snow, C. E. (2010). Academic language and the challenge of reading for learning about science. *Science, 328*(5977), 450–452.

Swales, J. M. (1990). *Genre analysis: English in academic and research settings.* Cambridge, MA: Cambridge University Press.

Swales, J. M. (2016). Reflections on the concept of discourse community. *ASp. la revue du GERAS, 69,* 7–19.

Wang, X. (2013). Why students choose STEM majors: Motivation, high school learning, and postsecondary context of support. *American Educational Research Journal, 50*(5), 1081–1121.

Young, T., & Guy, M. (2008). The moon phases and the self-shadow. *Science and Children, 46*(1), 30–35.

Zacarian, D. (2013). *Mastering academic language: A framework for supporting student achievement.* Thousand Oaks, CA: Corwin.

Zwiers, J. (2014). *Building academic Language: Meeting common core standards across disciplines, grades 5–12 (2nd ed.).* San Francisco, CA: Jossey-Bass.

CHAPTER 2

FOSTERING ENGLISH LEARNERS' ACADEMIC LANGUAGE IN A SCIENCE-THEMED SUMMER SCHOOL PROGRAM

Lauren Artzi
American Institutes for Research

Diane August
American Institutes for Research

Jennifer Letcher Gray
Marymount University

Rigorous English language proficiency standards, English language arts college and career readiness standards, and Next Generation Science Standards all put a premium on academic language. A recent U.S. Department of Education Practice Guide (Baker et al., 2014) asserts that "the rigors posed by

Culturally and Linguistically Diverse Learners and STEAM, pages 27–44

new standards provide an important window of opportunity for teachers to help English learners build English language skills while learning challenging new content" (p. 20). Recent reviews (Baker et al., 2015; National Academies of Sciences, Engineering, and Medicine, 2017) emphasize the important role that academic language plays in content-area learning and the need to teach domain-specific and general academic vocabulary explicitly. This chapter reports on the language development component of a science-themed summer school program called Science-Aligned Academic Language Instruction (SALI). The program served third- and fourth-grade English learners (ELs) who needed additional support in English language development.

In this chapter, we first describe the program goals, then turn to a description of the SALI program. We conclude with examples of evidence-based pedagogical practices used in SALI to develop ELs' academic language and link those examples to SALI program teacher reflections.

SALI PROGRAM GOALS

The SALI program goals were to prevent the loss of knowledge and skills during the summer months, adhere to rigorous grade-level academic standards, and attend to the features of language likely to be challenging for ELs.

Prevention of Academic Language and Content Loss During the Summer Months

The SALI program took place during a 5-week summer school program. Summer learning loss is a significant reason some students may fall behind in school (see Zvoch & Stevens, 2015). Some research indicates that students from lower-income households might be differentially impacted by summer learning loss related to reading because students from lower-income households declined in reading over the summer while their peers from higher-income households showed slight gains in reading during the summer months (Alexander, Entwisle, & Olson, 2007). However, high-quality summer school programs in elementary school can help prevent summer learning loss by reinforcing the academic and language skills learned during the previous school year and introducing new skills that students will encounter the following academic year (Beach et al., 2018; Cooper, Charlton, Valentine, & Muhlenbruck, 2000).

Alignment to Grade-Level Standards

Concepts and language targeted in the SALI program were informed by grade-level language proficiency, language arts, and science standards.

For example, widely used English language proficiency standards call for ELs to "construct grade-appropriate oral and written claims and support them with reasoning and evidence" (Council of Chief State School Officers, 2014, p. 4). Widely used English language arts standards, specifically, the Common Core State Standards in English language arts, require students to "interpret words and phrases as they are used in text, including determining technical, connotative, and figurative meanings, and analyze how specific word meanings shape meaning or tone" (National Governors' Association & Council of Chief State School Officers, 2010, p. 10.) The practices associated with Next Generation Science Standards require high levels of receptive and productive language skills. These practices include asking questions; developing and using models; planning and carrying out investigations; analyzing and interpreting data; using math and computational thinking; constructing explanations; engaging in argumentation from evidence; and obtaining, evaluating, and communicating evidence (NGSS Lead States, 2013).

Attention to the Features of Science Likely to be Challenging for ELs

SALI attended to the features of science texts and talk that make science challenging to comprehend (Quinn, Lee, & Valdes, 2012). One challenge students face contending with science language relates to vocabulary. Science includes dense levels of general academic vocabulary (e.g., *evaluate* and *analyze*) as well as technical vocabulary (e.g., *electricity*). As another challenge, students must master not only science vocabulary, but also nonlinguistic forms of representation used in science, such as pictures, diagrams, graphs, charts, tables, maps, and equations. Furthermore, students must learn to integrate verbal and visual information into a coherent whole. Other factors that make science difficult to understand include the frequent use of the passive voice and generalized or virtual actors, nominalization of verbs and adjectives, and abundance of compound and complex sentences in science texts.

SALI PROGRAM DESCRIPTION

The SALI program used evidence-based instructional practices that included (a) explicitly teaching discipline-specific academic vocabulary, as well as the general academic vocabulary that supports it, during content-area instruction; (b) using instructional tools to clarify and anchor course content; and (c) providing daily opportunities for students to talk about science in pairs or small groups. These practices are supported by research described in Baker et al. (2014). Each practice is described more fully in the last section of this chapter. Here, we briefly provide background information about the program, describe the SALI program components, and discuss the reflections on student learning from teachers who implemented the SALI program.

Program Background

The SALI program took place during a summer school program put in place by the district for EL students at risk for academic difficulty because they had not met language proficiency targets the prior academic year. Thirty certified teachers who had taught in the district during the school year taught in the summer school program. The program was full-day and included a 1-hour language arts block as well as a 1-hour science block. SALI was implemented daily, during the language arts block.

SALI was designed to support learning during the science block by enhancing students' understanding of science concepts and the academic language associated with these concepts during the language arts block. The district implemented Full Option Science System (FOSS, 2013) as the core science curriculum during the science block. It was also used in the district during the school year. FOSS is a research-based science curriculum, aligned to Next Generation Science Standards and developed for students in Grades K–8. FOSS puts a premium on inquiry and analysis and on language development within science. FOSS materials consist of experiments and investigations with equipment kits, assessments, experiment notebooks, and science readers. The science readers include stories related to the FOSS unit topics and are designed to enhance students' language development within science learning. In the summer school program where SALI took place, students studied magnetism and electricity during the science block; therefore, SALI units were aligned to the topics of magnetism and electricity.

SALI Components and Format

Teacher Preparation and Professional Development

There was a half-day professional development workshop prior to SALI implementation, during which teachers learned about the rationale and the theory behind the SALI program, watched as program developers modeled components, and then practiced implementing a lesson in pairs. Teachers also practiced responding to students in ways that developed students' oral language proficiency. During SALI program implementation, teachers were mentored weekly by district staff in the summer school program who had participated in the professional development sessions along with the teachers.

SALI Program Materials

SALI program materials consisted of a student reader that drew from the FOSS reader, glossaries, concept maps, assessments, and reinforcement games. Teacher materials included a teacher guide with detailed instructions for each 60-minute SALI lesson; answer keys for student materials; picture cards with routines for teaching target vocabulary; and listings of short, captioned United Streaming video clips aligned with the daily science topics.

SALI Lesson Format

Each SALI lesson included activities to be used before, during, and after students read the daily FOSS story. Teachers prepared for the lesson by reviewing the teacher guide and other materials, selecting the daily United Streaming video clips, and posting key vocabulary picture cards and sentence frames that helped students use the words when speaking or writing.

Before reading. Each hour-long SALI lesson began with a discussion of the daily content and lesson objectives, which were aligned to the language and science standards. Figure 2.1 displays language and science objectives for Unit 4 of SALI.

Teachers then pre-taught the meanings of three to five words using picture cards. To introduce the daily reading, teachers used a *hook question* to focus students on the main idea of the passage. Students answered the hook question after they had read the text. After the teacher posed the hook question to the class, he or she conducted a picture walk with the students, pointing out the pictures and other visuals in the FOSS reader associated

---

Students will...

1. Read, write, and define vocabulary from the 3-day lesson: assistant, technology, reveal, nervous, drafting, perception.

2. Explain who the Edison Pioneers were and describe some of their important inventions.

3. Describe how the Edison Pioneers worked together to create a better light bulb.

4. Explain who Lewis Latimer was and describe how he became an important inventor.

Figure 2.1 Science and language objectives.

Picture Walk
Using an overhead projector, display the illustrations included in the Student Reader for today's interctive reading lesson (these pictures are found at the end of the interactive reading selection). Discuss the pictures with students.

Hook Questions
Pose the hook questions and ask students to keep these in mind as they read.

Hook Question: Why do you think such a large crowd came to see the light bulb? [Anticipated response: They came because very few people had ever seen an electric light before at that time.]

Figure 2.2 Picture walk and hook question.

with the daily lesson. Figure 2.2 shows an example of the hook question for SALI Unit 4 and the picture walk.

During reading. After the pre-reading activities, the teacher engaged the students in interactive shared reading of the passage. The teacher read aloud while students followed along in their student readers.

The teacher stopped every few paragraphs so that the students could have peer conversations related to comprehension questions that had been inserted in the text. For example, in the passage shown in Figure 2.3, students discussed, in pairs, why a large crowd came to see the light bulb revealed. The teacher also stopped at points to briefly explain the meanings of difficult words in the passage that had not been pre-taught but were defined in context (see also Figure 2.3).

After reading. After the interactive reading session, students worked together, in pairs or small groups, on activities that reinforced vocabulary and science concepts. The activities incorporated glossaries, games, and assessments to reinforce vocabulary. Students completed concept maps to reinforce science concepts. Teachers also used mini lessons to promote students' awareness of cognates, or words that sound and look alike across Spanish and English and have similar meanings.

Results

SALI methods were validated in a study that included 509 third- and fourth-grade Spanish-speaking ELs in 18 schools. Student outcomes are reported in August, Artzi, and Barr (2016). Findings show that the methods

I'll never forget the day Mr. Edison and the team <u>revealed, or showed,</u> the new light bulb to the world. It was New Year's Eve, 1879. They let me stay up until after midnight, even though I was still a kid. We strung lights from the lab to the train station. <u>An enormous, or really large,</u> crowd came to see what would happen. They say over 3,000 people were there! It was a very dark night, and the gaslights were turned off. We were all a little worried or scared. I remember Mr. Edison stepped up to the platform. Then he turned on the light.

Discussion Questions:

1. What did Mr. Edison reveal or show to the world?
   [Anticipated response: the new light bulb]

2. Who came to see what happened?
   [Anticipated response: an enormous or large crowd]

3. What kind of night was it?
   [Anticipated response: a very, dark night].
   How did the people feel?
   [Anticipated response: worried or scared].

4. What did Mr. Edison do when he stepped up to the platform?
   [He threw the switch or turned on the light.]

Figure 2.3   Interactive reading.

used to support student learning were effective in enhancing ELs' knowledge of discipline-specific and general academic vocabulary. Although the extended instruction (with the picture card and reinforcement activities) was the more effective approach, embedded instruction (words explained parenthetically in the interactive reading) also helped promote EL word learning.

In addition to assessing student vocabulary outcomes, we administered a teacher reflection survey after the completion of the program and report some of those reflections in this chapter. In general, teachers rated the program very highly (an average score of 6.6 out of 7 on a Likert scale) and noted that integrating science and language was very beneficial for both science and language learning, and that the enrichment motivated students in science and reading. Teacher reflections related to the evidence-based instructional practices used in SALI appear in the following section.

SALI PEDAGOGICAL PRACTICES TO SUPPORT AND PROMOTE EL ACADEMIC LANGUAGE

In this section, we describe more fully the three evidence-based instructional practices used to support EL learning in the SALI program: (a) explicitly teaching discipline-specific and academic vocabulary during content-area instruction, (b) using instructional tools strategically to clarify and anchor the content, and (c) providing daily opportunities for students to talk about content in pairs or small groups (practices supported by Baker et al., 2014). We also show examples from the SALI curriculum and discuss teacher reflections related to each of these practices.

Pedagogical Practice 1: Explicitly Teaching Academic Vocabulary Important for Content Understanding

Bailey (2007, pp. 10–11) defines being academically proficient as "knowing and being able to use general and academic vocabulary, specialized or complex grammatical structures, and multifarious language functions and discourse structures—all for the purpose of acquiring new knowledge and skills, interacting about a topic, and imparting information to others." Because science content knowledge is acquired through language, it is essential that teachers ensure that their EL students are able to understand and use the language of science (Quinn, Lee, & Valdés, 2012).

In school text, discipline-specific words, or technical words (e.g., *photosynthesis, germination, prokaryote*) tend to be used with lower frequency; yet, often, these words are key to content-area learning. General academic words (e.g., *identify, analyze*) are found across subject areas and are equally important for students to learn.

Word Selection in the SALI Program

Eighty vocabulary words were selected for the 5-week program. Half of the words were discipline specific (e.g., *magnetism, electricity*), and the other half were general academic words (e.g., *efficiency, consider*). All the words were extracted from the FOSS science readers that focused on magnetism and electricity because these topics were taught during the science block. The general academic words were also selected from the science readers. An additional criterion for selecting those general academic words was their frequency in text as determined by the Academic Word List (Coxhead, 2000). The Academic Word List comprises the 570 most frequent general academic word families found in academic texts.

Vocabulary Instruction

Teachers taught vocabulary using two instructional approaches that differed in intensity. The more intensive approach used teaching routines that were more elaborate, took more time, and included visuals. The more intensive vocabulary instructional approach was referred to as *extended instruction*, and the less intensive method was referred to as *embedded instruction*.

According to Graves and colleagues (2014), vocabulary instruction should take the "least intensive, most efficient form necessary to provide students with the knowledge they need to understand word meanings and comprehend the texts containing the words" (p. 337). As such, words that were less conceptually complex were taught through embedded instruction. Previous research has shown this technique to be effective with English-proficient students (Biemiller & Boote, 2006; Coyne et al., 2007; Graves et al., 2014). In both kinds of vocabulary instruction (extended and embedded), words were defined with child-friendly definitions, there were multiple exposures to words across lessons using the four modalities of language (listening, speaking, reading, and writing), and there were opportunities for students to talk about the words through structured discussions.

In SALI, about half the targeted vocabulary words were taught using extended vocabulary instruction. Words taught through extended instruction were taught before the interactive reading using picture cards. In the picture card activity (see Figure 2.4), the teacher held up two pictures that illustrated the target word, provided a definition of the word in Spanish and English, and discussed how the pictures depicted the word meaning. Students then answered, in pairs, a question about the word. For Spanish/English cognates, the teacher explained to students that the words were cognates and reminded students what cognates were.

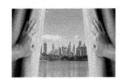	1. *A word in the text is reveal. Reveal means to show something that was hidden.* 2. *En español "reveal" quiere decir revelar.* 3. *Reveal in English and revelar in Spanish are cognates.* 4. *Now, let's look at a picture that demonstrates the word reveal. If we open this curtain [point to the curtain in the picture], the city is revealed. You can see it now.*
	5. *Here is another picture of reveal.* *Partner talk: Turn to your partner and talk about why this picture demonstrates the word reveal.* [Anticipated possible response: the coconut was opened and now the inside of the coconut is revealed; you can see the inside of the coconut now.] 6. *Say reveal with me three times: reveal, reveal, reveal.*

Figure 2.4   Vocabulary picture card (General Academic Vocabulary).

Reveal	*Reveal means to make something known or to show or bring something into view.* In this picture a town and countryside are revealed. **Your sentence:** You cannot reveal a test answer to your friend because _____.	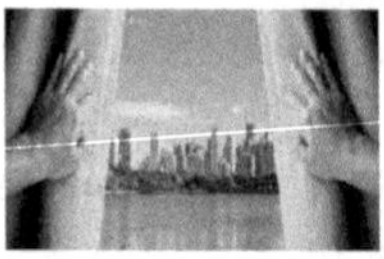
Technology	*Technology is using science and engineering to help solve common problems of life.* The workers use technology such as computers to help find and keep track of items in their warehouse. **Your sentence:** An example of technology in the classroom is _____.	

Figure 2.5   Glossary.

The other half of the words were taught through embedded instruction—definitions were inserted in the text immediately after each target word. SALI reinforced these words through a number of different activities. Students completed glossaries after each day's interactive reading (see Figure 2.5 for glossary entries for a general academic and a domain-specific word) and took weekly quizzes, for which they matched the unit words to definitions.

At the end of each unit, all words were reinforced through games that students played in pairs or small groups for about 10 minutes. One game was Memory, in which students matched picture cards with their corresponding definitions. Another reinforcement game was a modified form of Chutes and Ladders. In this activity, a student selected a number card, moved the number of spaces indicated, and had to answer a question that used the target word. If the student then defined the target word, the student was eligible to select another card.

Word-Learning Strategies

Word-learning strategies help students become more independent word learners. Teaching students about roots and affixes and to use context clues, cognate knowledge, and reference tools supports their word learning (Carlo et al., 2009; Graves, August, & Mancilla-Martinez, 2013).

Instructions: Rate the words "Y" if they sound the same, if they look the same, and if they mean the same thing.			
Sanish Word	**English Word**	**Different Letters in Spanish**	**Do These Words Sound the Same, Look the Same, and Have the Same Meaning?**
pie	pie	no	YYN
investigar	investigate	missing "t" and "e"	YYY
region	region	has an accent	YYY
magnetismo			

Figure 2.6 Cognate activity.

SALI taught students to use their cognate knowledge to figure out meanings for words they did not know in English. Cognates are words that are shared across two languages, or words that look and sound similar across two languages and share similar meanings. Students learned about cognates and false cognates, words that look the same across two languages but mean different things (e.g., the English word *pie* that means *foot* in Spanish). Students practiced identifying cognates and false cognates in their reading passages by assessing similarities and differences in spelling, sound, and meaning between words in English and Spanish (see Figure 2.6).

Teacher Feedback for Pedagogical Practice 1

According to two teachers who implemented the program, pre-teaching vocabulary was an important step because "students would understand the meaning when a picture was shown," and that "reviewing vocabulary before reading made students understand what they were reading." Another program teacher said, "Students were able to identify cognates very easily at the end of the program."

The SALI program teachers saw that the vocabulary reinforcement activities aided in review of the words and language. According to one teacher, "The students' glossary was very helpful because they [students] had to create their own sentences." Another teacher noted, "Reviewing and using vocabulary was great practice for students. The students loved to go back and review the definitions. It was so helpful to students' understanding and [helped them with] visualizing the meanings."

Teachers also found that the students engaged well with the games. One program teacher explained, "Students enjoyed them [the games] very much because they were able to remember vocabulary and apply it [that knowledge] to the games." Another program teacher explained that the games "helped students review and memorize new words," and the students "drew knowledge from each other through interacting."

With respect to the weekly assessment, one teacher mentioned that it was a "very effective way of finding out if students understood the vocabulary." Another teacher mentioned that the assessment "let us know if students understood and knew what the words meant, on a weekly basis."

Pedagogical Practice 2: Using Instructional Tools to Clarify and Anchor the Content

Recent reviews recommend that teachers strategically use instructional tools—such as short videos, visuals, and graphic organizers—to anchor instruction and help students make sense of content (Baker et al., 2014; National Academies of Science, Engineering, and Medicine, 2017).

Videos

Videos support ELs by integrating oral language with visual support. In one study, middle-grade ELs acquired vocabulary from captioned content-based TV programs better than did a comparison group that read a text on the same topic (Neuman & Koskinen, 1992). Other studies found similar results for younger learners (Uchikoshi, 2005).

In SALI, very short (less than 3 minutes) United Streaming video clips aligned to the content in the SALI program were used to support ELs' understanding of complex concepts. Teachers could show the video clips prior to the shared interactive reading. For example, when introducing the concept, teachers were given the option to share a short video clip that explained static electricity, using child-friendly examples (e.g., children sliding down a slide) in 2 minutes. Teachers were encouraged to turn on the closed captioning features so that students could read the captions while they were listening and watching the videos that demonstrated science concepts. Showing short video clips with the addition of closed captioning is helpful for EL students because students can reread the text at the bottom of the page, and the captions reinforce visual and auditory information.

Visuals and graphic organizers

Other visual supports discussed in the research include gestures, pictures, diagrams, timelines, and graphic organizers, such as tables and graphs (see Baker et al., 2014; National Academies of Sciences, Engineering, and Medicine, 2017). Real-life objects, such as models of animate and inanimate objects, can provide concrete examples to students as an additional instructional scaffold (Silverman & Hines, 2009; Vaughn, et al., 2009).

Prior to reading in the SALI program, teachers used picture cards as well as video clips to illustrate key vocabulary words and science concepts. Pictures and diagrams were used during the SALI shared interactive to illustrate key concepts. Following the interactive reading, students worked in pairs to complete graphic organizers, called concept maps. The concept maps used in the SALI program displayed the key science concepts and associated vocabulary taught each week. In the student version of the concept maps, students worked in pairs to fill in blanks that indexed missing concepts. Students were provided with a word bank to assist them. See Figure 2.7 for a student version of a concept map.

Verbal supports

Baker et al. (2014) point out that, because ELs are learning science in the language they are also acquiring, scaffolds can help them access the key content concepts from text and discourse. Language scaffolds that have been shown to be effective in prior research include techniques such as sentence starters and frames, comprehensible input, and graphic organizers (August et al., 2016; August et al., 2009; Silverman et al., 2017).

The SALI program provided sentence frames for the peer-to-peer discussion activities in the teacher materials on sentence strips. The teacher modeled use of the sentence frame and then posted the frames around the classroom so that students could see the frames during the classroom conversations.

Teacher Feedback for Pedagogical Practice 2

With respect to the visual aids in the program, one teacher explained, "Students learn better seeing the pictures. Students recall pictures when testing the vocabulary words. Students would associate the pictures with the reading." For concept mapping, one program teacher noted that the "concept mapping was helpful for students because it would give them a visual concept for understanding the activity." Another teacher wrote that the concept map was "a good way to review the investigation [unit]."

Pedagogical Practice 3: Providing Daily Opportunities for Students to Talk About Content in Pairs or Small Groups

Research highlights the importance of providing opportunities for students to work in pairs or small groups (Baker et al., 2014; National Academies of Sciences, Engineering, and Medicine, 2017). Active student engagement and classroom discussions have been shown to be particularly supportive for ELs because these peer-mediated activities provide authentic

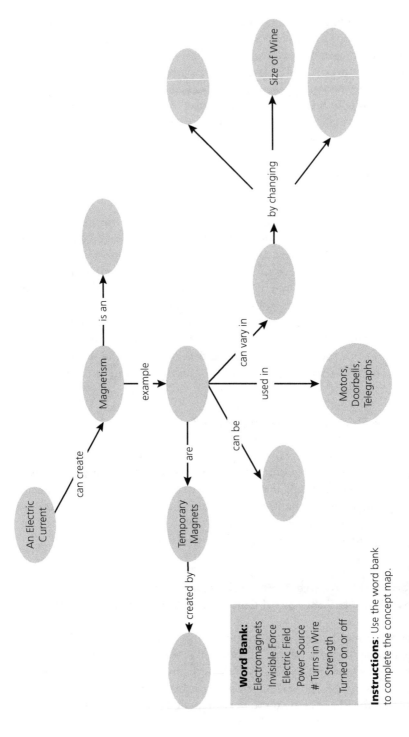

Word Bank:
Electromagnets
Invisible Force
Electric Field
Power Source
Turns in Wire
Strength
Turned on or off

Instructions: Use the word bank to complete the concept map.

Figure 2.7   Concept map for electromagnetism.

opportunities for students to actively engage with English (Gersten et al., 2007; Silverman et al., 2017).

In the SALI program, students participated in peer and partner work before, during, and after interactive reading. For example, prior to reading, students answered, with partners, questions about the target vocabulary. During the shared interactive reading, the teacher stopped reading after every few paragraphs for students to work together to answer questions about the text. Students also worked together to complete post-reading activities, such as completing glossaries and concept maps and playing vocabulary reinforcement games.

Teacher Feedback for Pedagogical Practice 3

A teacher noted a high level of engagement by the students, especially during the interactive reading. According to one teacher, "Students were very engaged during the interactive reading." Another teacher explained, "Students enjoyed answering the questions during the reading. They were very eager to learn." A third teacher mentioned that the interactive reading "allowed students to interact and share ideas." Another teacher said that "students had a lot of interest using the hook questions and [there was] lots of participation by most students." Another program teacher explained, "[The] picture walk was excellent because it gave students the opportunity to interact and share experiences and their perspectives."

CONCLUSION

Aligning English language development with science instruction supported the acquisition of English academic language and science knowledge in the elementary-age ELs participating in the SALI program. Theory and research guided the development of the SALI instructional components, namely the importance of explicitly teaching academic vocabulary that is important for students' understanding and acquisition of the course content, using instructional tools strategically to clarify and anchor the course content, and providing structured opportunities for engaging students in academic discussions about the content.

This project demonstrated that combining effective evidence-based science teaching practices used with all students, in this case the FOSS program, with additional evidence-based practices to scaffold the language demand of science as well as promote academic language skills, helped support the learning of the EL students who took part in the program. These practices included attention to vocabulary important to understanding science concepts, visual and verbal supports, and opportunities for peer collaboration. The methods discussed in this chapter can be applied in many different classroom contexts to support ELs in meeting standards in English language proficiency, English language arts, and science. We provide some suggestions below, followed by inquiry questions for further research.

Action Research Suggestions

1. Investigate ways to mitigate summer learning loss in struggling learners, including ELs.
2. Continue to explore methods to promote the learning and acquisition of the academic language often encountered in science and math course content by ELs.
3. Explore the use of scaffolded shared interactive reading and visual and verbal aids to enhance language instruction for ELs in science classrooms.
4. Assess current content and English language development instruction in your classroom/district to determine how well the instruction uses evidence-based instructional methods described in this chapter and reported in Baker et al., (2014): explicitly teaching the content-specific academic vocabulary, as well as the general academic vocabulary that supports it, during content-area instruction; providing daily opportunities for students to talk about content in pairs or small groups; and using instructional tools strategically to clarify and anchor the content.

Inquiry Questions

1. What additional methods can schools or districts implement to prevent summer learning loss in students who are ELs?
2. What are instructional practices that promote learning by EL students in STEM subjects?
3. The techniques described in this chapter were used in a designated English language development block. How might they be used in an integrated science and English language development block?

ACKNOWLEDGMENTS

The research reported in this chapter was carried out through the Center for Research on the Educational Achievement and Teaching of English Language Learners (CREATE Center; http://www.cal.org/create/) with funding from the U.S. Department of Education, Institute of Education Sciences, under Contract No. EDR305A05056. The opinions expressed herein do not necessarily reflect the positions or policies of the U.S. Department of Education. The authors would like to acknowledge the Center for Applied Linguistics as the institution where the research was carried out and thank the Center for Applied Linguistics for supporting this work. Figures used in this chapter were adapted from the CREATE Center and used with permission from the Center for Applied Linguistics.

REFERENCES

Alexander, K. L., Entwisle, D. R., & Olson, L. S. (2007). Summer learning and its implications: Insights from the beginning school study. *New Directions for Student Leadership, 2007*(114), 11–32.

August, D., Artzi, L., & Barr, C. (2016). Helping ELLs meet standards in English language arts and science: An intervention focused on academic vocabulary. *Reading & Writing Quarterly, 32*(4), 373–396.

August, D., Branum-Martin, L., Cardenas-Hagan, E., & Francis, D. J. (2009). The impact of an instructional intervention on the science and language learning of middle grade English language learners. *Journal of Research on Educational Effectiveness, 2*(4), 345–376.

Bailey, A. L. (Ed.). (2007). *The language demands of school: Putting academic English to the test.* Mahwah, NJ: Yale University Press.

Baker, S., Lesaux, N., Jayanthi, M., Dimino, J., Proctor, C. P., Morris, J., . . . Newman-Gonchar, R. (2014). *Teaching academic content and literacy to English learners in elementary and middle school* (NCEE 2014-4012). Washington, DC: National Center for Education Evaluation and Regional Assistance.

Beach, K. D., McIntyre, E., Philippakos, Z. A., Mraz, M., Pilonieta, P., & Vintinner, J. P. (2018). Effects of a summer reading intervention on reading skills for low-income Black and Hispanic students in elementary school. *Reading & Writing Quarterly, 34*(3), 263–280.

Biemiller, A., & Boote, C. (2006). An effective method for building meaning vocabulary in primary grades. *Journal of Educational Psychology, 98*(1), 44–62.

Carlo, M. S., August, D., McLaughlin, B., Snow, C., Dressler, C., Lippman, D., . . . White, C. E. (2009). Closing the gap: Addressing the vocabulary needs of English-language learners in bilingual and mainstream classrooms. *Journal of Education, 189*(1–2), 57–76.

Cooper, H., Charlton, K., Valentine, J. C., Muhlenbruck, L., & Borman, G. D. (2000). Making the most of summer school: A meta-analytic and narrative review. *Monographs of the society for research in child development, 65*(1), 1–118. (EJ630022)

Council of Chief State School Officers. (2014). *English language proficiency standards.* Washington, DC: Council of Chief State School Officers.

Coxhead, A. (2000). A new academic word list. *TESOL quarterly, 34*(2), 213–238.

Coyne, M. D., McCoach, D. B., & Kapp, S. (2007). Vocabulary intervention for kindergarten students: Comparing extended instruction to embedded instruction and incidental exposure. *Learning Disability Quarterly, 30*(2), 74–88.

Gersten, R., Baker, S. K., Shanahan, T., Linan-Thompson, S., Collins, P., & Scarcella, R. (2007). *Effective literacy and English language instruction for English learners in the elementary grades: A practice guide* (NCEE 2007-4011). Washington, DC: National Center for Education Evaluation and Regional Assistance, Institute of Education Sciences, U.S. Department of Education. Retrieved from http:// ies.ed.gov/ncee.

Graves, M., August, D., & Mancilla Martinez, J. (2013). *Teaching vocabulary to English-language learners*. New York, NY: Teachers College Press.

Graves, M. F., Baumann, J. F., Blachowicz, C. L. Z., Manyak, P., Bates, A., Cieply, C., . . . Von Gunten, H. (2014). Words, words everywhere, but which ones do we teach? *The Reading Teacher, 67*(5), 333–346.

National Academies of Sciences, Engineering, and Medicine. (2017). *Promoting the educational success of children and youth learning English: Promising futures*. Washington, DC: National Academies Press.

National Governors Association Center for Best Practices, Council of Chief State School Officers (2010). *Common Core State Standards*. Washington, DC: National Governors Association Center for Best Practices, Council of Chief State School Officers.

Neuman, S. B., & Koskinen, P. (1992). Captioned television as comprehensible input: Effects of incidental word learning from context for language minority students. *Reading research quarterly, 27*(1), 94–106.

NGSS Lead States. (2013). *Next Generation Science Standards: For states, by states*. Washington, DC: The National Academies Press.

Quinn, H., Lee, O., & Valdés, G. (2012). Language demands and opportunities in relation to Next Generation Science Standards for English language learners: What teachers need to know. In *Commissioned Papers on Language and Literacy Issues in the Common Core State Standards and Next Generation Science Standards, 94*, 32.

Silverman, R., & Hines, S. (2009). The effects of multimedia-enhanced instruction on the vocabulary of English-language learners and non-English-language learners in pre-kindergarten through second grade. *Journal of educational psychology, 101*(2), 305–314.

Silverman, R. D., Martin-Beltran, M., Peercy, M. M., Hartranft, A. M., McNeish, D. M., Artzi, L., & Nunn, S. (2017). Effects of a cross-age peer learning program on the vocabulary and comprehension of English learners and non-English learners in elementary school. *The Elementary School Journal, 117*(3), 485–512.

Uchikoshi, Y. (2005). Narrative development in bilingual kindergarteners: Can Arthur help?. *Developmental psychology, 41*(3), 464–478.

Vaughn, S., Martinez, L. R., Linan-Thompson, S., Reutebuch, C. K., Carlson, C. D., & Francis, D. J. (2009). Enhancing social studies vocabulary and comprehension for seventh-grade English language learners: Findings from two experimental studies. *Journal of Research on Educational Effectiveness, 2*(4), 297–324.

Zvoch, K., & Stevens, J. J. (2015). Identification of summer school effects by comparing the in-and out-of-school growth rates of struggling early readers. *The Elementary School Journal, 115*(3), 433–456.

CHAPTER 3

CONCEPT-BASED TEACHING IN DUAL LANGUAGE SCIENCE CLASSROOMS

Using Oral Language Routines to Develop Scientific Descriptions and Arguments

Zenaida Aguirre-Muñoz
University of Houston

Maria O. Gregory
Harwell Elementary School

Ms. O., why do we learn the same thing in science every year? . . . We've been taught the exact same thing since like second grade. Will we ever learn anything different than the stages of the water cycle, animal adaptations, and states of matter?

—Juan, Grade 5

In the opening quote, Juan (a fifth-grade bilingual learner in a Spanish-English dual language immersion program) expresses his frustration with the repeated surface-level coverage of the same content over several

Culturally and Linguistically Diverse Learners and STEAM, pages 45–75

years. His teacher attempted to explain that while the topics may overlap each year, the content is covered more in depth. Juan did not agree with this assessment of the coverage. He was adamant that he had not learned about these science topics any differently since second grade. Unfortunately, his recollection is closer to what many underserved student populations (e.g., poor, urban, non-White, English learners [ELs]), experience. Although the standards-based reform in the 1990s and early 2000s was intended to close persistent achievement gaps and lead towards greater educational equity, the continued use of high stakes testing has resulted in a trend toward standardization of "standards-based" curricula which may grossly limit ELs learning opportunities (Lee & Luykx, 2008). ELs are students who constitute a substantial and growing demographic in United States schools (McFarland et al., 2017), but receive inadequate instruction in STEM (Feldman & Malagon, 2017) and are struggling to meet the requirements for academic success.

In addition to this narrowing of content, standardized curricula can be limiting because they are not developed with the intent to develop ELs' content and language understanding simultaneously. Although curricula aligned to best practices are needed and important, they are generally insufficient for developing ELs' reasoning skills because they do not provide the full spectrum of language scaffolding and differentiation necessary for developing ELs' deep understanding or cultivating higher-order thinking skills (Aguirre-Muñoz & Pando, 2017). While state and national content standards are designed to cover science topics more in depth as students matriculate through elementary grades, teachers (who are not adequately trained) may feel compelled to start with more basic concepts if they believe that is how to address students' language learning needs. Consequently, diversifying instruction to meet ELs' varied content and language learning needs continues to be a central educational concern.

We report on an ongoing collaborative action research effort among three bilingual elementary teachers and a university professor (first author) examining the interplay between disciplinary language (oral and written) and deep content learning. We describe how knowledge about language use in science inquiry empowers teachers to deepen the coverage of science topics in ways that also address ELs' language learning needs and their desire to do more with science as communicated by Juan above. The approach is accomplished by contextualizing language learning in science instruction with a focus on making explicit conceptual links. The results show that this instructional approach supports conceptual learning and disciplinary literacy for ELs with beginning and intermediate levels of English proficiency.

BACKGROUND: LANGUAGE FOCUSED SCIENCE TEACHING AND LEARNING

Although there has been a steady increase in research that directly targets ELs' language and content learning needs, until very recently, the majority of education research for this student population has not been grounded in approaches that meaningfully integrate contemporary theories of content learning and language development and use. We contend that meaningful contributions to the achievement of ELs requires instructional practices grounded in research that targets the intersection of cognition, learning, language, and culture. How is it that the advantages bilingual students possess in acquiring skills in mathematics (e.g., Golash-Boza, 2005), logic (e.g., Bacolod and Rangel, 2017), and cognitive processes (e.g., Bialystok & Majumder, 1998) are elusive for so many ELs the longer they engage in U.S. public schools? For example, although modest gains in science achievement of ELs have been made in fourth grade, these gains begin to dissipate in eighth grade and disappear in 12th grade (U.S. Department of Education, 2015). We argue that these negative achievement trends of ELs are due in part to the lack of theory-driven research about how to simultaneously develop ELs' conceptual understanding and academic discourse, or how to use both language and practice to produce knowledge (Hall, 2001).

A focus on academic discourse is necessary because past research has found that academic language skills (a subset of academic discourse) mediate content knowledge (Greenleaf et al., 2011; Kieffer, Lesaux, Rivera, & Francis, 2009). Problems in achieving content standards could be mitigated through exposure to oral and written literacy activities that build familiarity with science vocabulary and concepts and establish connections through real-world, meaningful applications and family funds of knowledge. The assumption this perspective takes is that scientific discourse is a requisite to developing science knowledge and science habits of mind (focused observation, recording of observed data, reporting results, healthy skepticism, etc).

Scientific Discourse: A Specialized Disciplinary Language

Current conceptions of science teaching and learning emphasize the importance of gaining command of reading and communicating in ways consistent with the discipline (National Research Council [NRC], 2012). Indeed, the NRC guidelines make clear that language development should be a goal of science lessons. For ELs, engaging in science instruction requires using and producing language in new ways, specifically in communicating scientific observations, reasoning about relationships, explaining abstract concepts and ideas, and making scientific arguments (Zwiers, 2014).

There is growing consensus, particularly among those who work with EL populations, that science entails language that includes not only specialized literacy components and skills, such as academic vocabulary and scientific language (Fang, 2005; Gee, 2005; Norris & Phillips, 2003; Wellington & Osborne, 2001), but also dispositions, behaviors, critical language arts skills, higher order thinking, and metalinguistic knowledge needed to understand scientific concepts (Merino & Scarcella, 2005).

From this perspective, scientific vocabulary and the discourse patterns of science (e.g., forming a hypothesis, making an evidence-based argument) are viewed as different from everyday language (Schleppegrell, 2004). Linguistic theorists have suggested that even students who are native speakers of English must recognize scientific discourse as a different type of English language (Halliday & Martin, 1993). Past research demonstrates that in order to be engaged in scientific discourse, students, whether their first language is English or not, must be taught and learn the discourse of science (e.g., Fang & Schleppegrell, 2008; Fang & Wei, 2010). A recent randomized trial involving underserved middle school students (e.g., poor African-American, Hispanics, and ELs) found that a modest amount of literacy integration in inquiry-based science instruction can promote students' science and reading achievement as measured by district and standardized content and literacy assessments (Tong et al., 2014). These findings are encouraging, but these efforts have approached literacy simply by integrating reading and writing from a generic literacy approach and science learning focused on achievement, without information about the impact on conceptual understanding. That is, these authors engaged students in strategies, such as anticipation guides, that were developed for monolingual students and there was no attempt to evaluate the impact of these strategies on content understanding of ELs with different proficiency levels. The problem with these generic literacy strategies is that they do not make the language of science explicit. We contend that scientific discourse should be foregrounded in science teaching if the results are to be replicated with ELs.

Another relevant research effort was conducted by Lee and her colleagues (Lee & Buxton, 2013; Lee et al., 2016; Llosa et al., 2016; Maerten-Rivera, Ahn, Lanier, Diaz, & Lee, 2016), who designed science units for elementary ELs that approached reading texts similar to Tong et al. (2014). Although the writing approach included in the Lee et al. (2016) randomized trial involved more extended writing opportunities than the Tong et al. (2014) study (e.g., summaries of observations, and procedures taken), there was no explicit instruction on relevant science literacy genres (scientific description and/or explanation) in ways that scaffolded conceptual understanding or reasoning. Not surprisingly, the groups that most benefited from science instruction in the Llosa et al. (2016) study were students who had been redesignated as English proficient and monolingual English students.

Llosa et al. (2016) suggest that this differential effect may have been attributed to the teachers needing more time to become proficient in implementing the curricula they developed. We hypothesize that these results were also attributable to the need for more targeted scaffolding of science disciplinary discourse; general language accommodation and literacy integration are not sufficient to developing students' academic language and deep content understanding (i.e., science disciplinary literacy). To test this notion, we investigated the impact of language focused and conceptually organized science teaching on ELs' science conceptual learning.

CONCEPTUAL FRAMEWORK

Our approach to teaching science to ELs targets: (a) explicit planning foregrounding science discourse and literacy practices, and (b) incorporating conceptual and linguistic supports or scaffolds that enable students to take advantage of learning opportunities that science inquiry brings to the learning context. To be effective, scaffolding should be different from simply helping students complete tasks they cannot do independently. Thus, our framework integrates innovations in: (a) cognitive science (e.g., Chi, Feltovich, & Glasser, 1994; Novak, 1998), (b) culturally congruent science instruction (Lee & Buxton, 2010), (c) disciplinary literacy (e.g., Shanahan & Shanahan, 2012), and (d) systemic functional linguistics (e.g., Fang & Schleppegrell, 2008). As depicted in Figure 3.1, this integration occurs in three phases of instruction: lesson preparation, building the field, and making conceptual connections.

Lesson Preparation

A key goal of instruction in the approach we describe here is to develop conceptual understanding. Our working definition of conceptual understanding is as follows: an understanding of concepts and principles within a domain and how they are interrelated (Perkins, 2006). Thus, the focus of lesson preparation is the identification of a "big idea" based on key concepts identified in content standards and other relevant curriculum documents (e.g., scope and sequence documents).

To be clear, these conceptual items are not overarching concepts or strands (e.g., change and constancy) often mislabeled as big ideas. Concepts have sufficient scope (e.g., energy transfer, force) to tie smaller concepts and facts (e.g., hours in the day, seasonal changes, orbit) in coherent ways. They are not so overarching that they become less useful in organizing information, particularly for young learners. Most importantly, concepts are important for understanding and generating the scientific

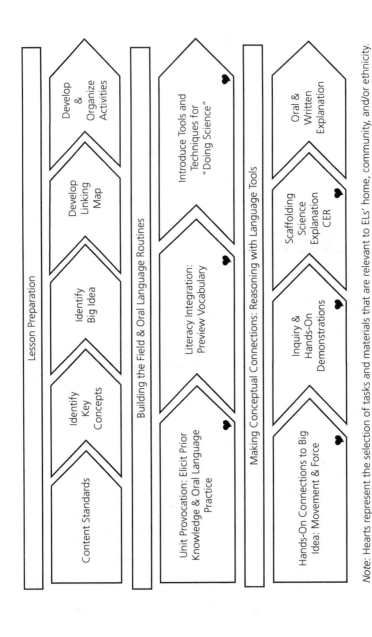

Figure 3.1 Conceptual frame of instructional approach: Language focused science teaching. *Note:* Hearts represent the selection of tasks and materials that are relevant to ELs' home, community, and/or ethnicity.

explanations, arguments, and reasoning that undergird scientific phenomena. If phenomena are the most visible aspects of an observation, a big idea is a hidden aspect related to the phenomenon. To organize lessons around a big idea, it is helpful to create a concept map that shows how the concepts and facts are interrelated. (See Appendix A for an example of a concept map for a unit on "objects in the sky" generated by the teachers involved in this action research project.) Organizing instruction around big ideas helps ensure that activities direct attention to relationships among concepts to support development of conceptual knowledge (see Kame'enui, Carnine, Dixon, Simmons, & Coyne, 2001; Schmidt & Houang, 2012).

Building the Field

What makes our approach distinct is the equal attention to "building the field" and setting up the expectation for principled oral language practice that serves as critical scaffolds for scientific descriptions and arguments. Given the variations in interactional styles of culturally diverse students and the need to develop foundational knowledge that many ELs may not have, teachers need to activate students' prior knowledge as well as "build" the contextual experiences hidden in Western science. Oral language routines and a focus on the content are necessary to build up background information necessary for recognizing and understanding conceptual relationships. Since we are also interested in developing ELs' science written discourse, knowledge of the general topic is essential for writing factual texts common in science discourse (Brisk, 2015).

Thus, it is important to dedicate time to building the field for the targeted phenomena and associated big ideas involved in "knowing science." This process includes eliciting prior knowledge, integrating factual and narrative texts, and explicitly focusing on the tools and methods for "doing science." Further, selection of culturally relevant materials for these experiences increases productive engagement (Lee & Buxton, 2008). The hearts in Figure 3.1 represent the selection of tasks and materials that are relevant to ELs' home, community, and/or ethnicity. These aspects could be broad themes in the literature that are used to build vocabulary, culturally-based contexts where the scientific principles are applied, or measurement-based comparisons where differences can be found between cultures.

For example, in the unit utilized for this study, tools used in ancient Mayan civilizations were compared to modern tools used by astronomers. Students compared ancient Mayan tools with modern technological tools to appreciate how ancient tools were able to accomplish difficult tasks, as well as to understand the need for the increased precision of modern tools to aid in observations for testing hypotheses and developing more robust understandings of the universe.

Given the scope of phenomena occurring in space, simulation was necessary to make phenomena more concrete for students. Thus, in this unit, an internet-based interactive astronomical tool was used to build the field, called Interactive Sky Chart (available at http://www.skyandtelescope. com/observing/interactive-sky-watching-tools/). This free interactive sky chart provided observations of the night sky from any point on Earth at any point in time (past or future), allowing teachers to create customized naked-eye sky maps that students used to find sky objects when making observations from their own neighborhoods. Students also compared what they observed from their neighborhood with what their relatives saw in their home countries and/or what the night sky looked like when they were born. These activities provide students with meaningful experiences to learn relevant vocabulary and foundational knowledge needed in the Making Conceptual Connections phase of the unit. Thus, the online maps provided the students with visual representations of abstract content vocabulary (star movement, orbit, constellation, etc.), which are pivotal to describing changes in their own observations of the night sky, which in turn builds the field for making sense of the big ideas that explain such changes. During discussions of these observations, students were given the intellectual space to articulate alternative explanations and/or interpretations of the night sky that might compete with Western models.

Building Oral Language Routines

An additional crucial aspect of building the field is that the teacher is aware of interactional styles that may be different than those encouraged in the western science classroom; the oral language routines introduced and practiced in this phase make explicit the interactional styles that are expected and necessary in western science when making claims, building on evidence posed by group partners, or presenting counter arguments to reason about observed phenomena. As students develop understanding and cognitive capacity to engage in academic structures more germane to the language of a given discipline, teachers engage students in academic conversations with techniques adapted from those developed by Zwiers and Crawford (2011). These instructional techniques build on extensive past research in classroom discourse and cooperative learning (e.g., Cazden, 2001; Goldenberg, 1991; Mercer, 1995; Rogoff, 1990; Schleppegrell, 2004; Tharp & Gallimore, 1991; Vygotsky, 1978). Instructional conversations that focus on academic content, in particular have been linked to increased achievement (Goldenberg, 1991; Tharp & Gallimore, 1989) and prolonged engagement (Aguirre-Muñoz & Pantoya, 2016). The goal of these academic conversations is to improve productive conversations with students that promote students' authentic and repeated use of content vocabulary and understanding as well as develop scientific thinking and reasoning. Academic conversations are ideal for young ELs since their first and second language literacy skills are still emerging. Authentic and repeated practice is most effective for younger age groups. Academic conversations are also ideal when the content is highly abstract or is difficult to concretize because language in context has been shown to be an effective tool in developing understanding (Gee, 2005; Mercer, 2000).

Making Conceptual Connections

Current national science standards recognize that students must understand that science is a process of thinking and reasoning rather than a set of technical terms to define or steps to go through in an inquiry lesson. Once ELs have the necessary background, have some oral language practice in thinking about the phenomenon and in using key ideas and terms, students engage in inductive hands-on experiences directly connected to the big idea. If the ELs have sufficient English proficiency, these experiences can be integrated into the inquiry experience. However, for ELs who have lower English proficiency or have lower literacy skills in their home language, it is usually beneficial to engage them in hands-on experiences that reinforce the big idea.

In our unit, we aimed to develop students' understanding of different types of forces and movement so that they can eventually understand that force (specifically gravity) plays a role in the orbital movement of objects in the solar system (e.g., Earth and Moon). Once students were excited about objects in the sky and noticed changes in their position (from online observations) and noticed changes in the appearance of the Moon (from hands-on models of the phases of the Moon), a second simulation was used to connect students' observations with concepts (e.g., orbit, gravity, force) that could explain the patterns they observed. This free internet-based simulation tool, the Gravity and Orbits Simulation Tool (©PhET-Interactive Simulations) allowed students to adjust the mass of the Sun, Moon, and Earth to test hypotheses about the relationship between mass and gravitational pull among other relationships. Thus, teachers were able to engage students in "what if" scenarios to base claims about the role of gravity in orbital movement of objects in the solar system. Again, extended oral language opportunities facilitated activation of experiences, vocabulary, and principles needed to complete the inquiry experience successfully.

Linguistic Scaffolding

It should be evident from the previous discussion that we believe ELs need explicit instruction in *articulating concepts and principles*, not just focusing on the description, sequence, and choice that are the more practical aspects of science knowledge (Huang, Normandia, & Greer, 2006). Making reasoning language transparent to students is a complex process and is especially complex for teachers who work with ELs, because it involves making complex language features transparent to ELs who may not have the literacy skills in the target language to make sense of them without careful and skillful scaffolding. To develop instructional activities for making language transparent to ELs, we draw on systemic functional linguistics (Halliday, 1975). From the systemic functional linguistics perspective, language is conceptualized as a whole text actualized within specific situations rather than as isolated words or sentences. From this perspective, writing practices (or genres) are recurrent forms of texts used for specific purposes with specific organization and linguistic features (Martin & Rose, 2008). Genre structure refers to the overall structure of the text that marks macro level differences among genres. A genre structure commonly taught for expository texts, including scientific texts, is the five-paragraph essay. From a systemic functional linguistics perspective, this organizational pattern does little to illuminate the relationship between text organization and purpose. Many of the difficulties elementary students have in writing in general, and scientific writing in particular, is understanding the purpose of distinct genres (e.g., description versus explanation).

Given the complexity in making language transparent to ELs, language modeling is planned for and utilized in each delivery phase of instruction. Language modeling enables ELs to adopt ways of "talking" science that are valued by and important to the science and scientific community (Herbel-Eisenmann & Schleppegrell, 2008). Strategies that make language of science reasoning transparent to students enables teachers to develop and reinforce norms for talking science in valued ways. Over time, students appropriate these ways of doing and talking science, thereby affecting students' science beliefs and self-efficacy (Cobb, Yackel, & McClain, 2000). Table 3.1 presents three important ways teachers can begin to model science language in ways that direct their attention to valued ways of talking and thinking about principles and relationships between concepts: (a) stepping out, (b) revoicing, and (c) text deconstruction.

Thus, the goal of the language modeling is to support students as they bring to bear key ideas and concepts to: (a) make a claim about the phenomenon they observed, (b) summarize relevant evidence, and (c) reason about the evidence based on the key concepts and big ideas. The claims-evidence-reasoning (CER; Zembal-Saul, McNeill, & Hershberger, 2013) approach coupled with the systemic functional linguistics metalanguage allows the teacher to provide linguistic scaffolding of the science reasoning (genre) structure and associated linguistic features. For example, the claim is a declarative statement about the phenomenon. Declarative statements help produce the authoritative tone characteristic of scientific texts. Table 3.2 presents possible targets for text deconstruction during CER lessons to model structures and associated linguistic features.

TABLE 3.1   Types of Language Modeling for Conceptual Understanding

Strategy	Description
Stepping Out	Explicit language moves such as reflection on science actions and talking about science. The teacher momentarily "steps out" of the discussion to explicitly state thought processes and questions s/he would ask while examining evidence or identifying aspects of an appropriate scientific explanation.
Revoicing	Less explicit language moves that allow the teacher to reformulate a student's response by either clarifying or extending what a student has said. Revoicing is a way for the teacher to clarify students' statements, make connections, or fill in missing elements of an explanation, thereby helping other students to understand the significance of the contribution.
Text Deconstruction	Use of mentor texts to call attention to how authors accomplish the purpose of the genre by making the linguistic resources used by the author explicit to students. The teacher calls attention to text features students are expected to reproduce to make generalizations about the observations they are making during inquiry tasks and to reason about those generalizations.

TABLE 3.2   Targets for Language Text Deconstruction Modeling During CER Lessons

Linguistic Feature	Description	Example
Claim	1. Declarative statement to produce the authoritative tone characteristic of scientific texts.	The sun's gravity is the force that causes the Earth to orbit the sun.
Evidence	1. Verbal groups that describe directly observable actions.	traveled
	2. Verbal groups that mark qualitative features of the phenomenon.	appeared brighter
	3. Adverbials that present the circumstantial information about important aspects of the phenomenon; expressions of how, where, and when something happened.	Three days later, the location of the northern star traveled right by 3 degrees.
Reasoning	1. causal verbs	caused, produced, resulted in
	2. causal conjunctions	because, as, since, so
	3. clause complexes to present logico-semantic relationships (cause and effect)	if, then statements as in: If the moon's gravitational force did not act on Earth's rotation, [then] Earth would spin faster on its axis

Classroom activities that make language expectations explicit is a unique way of giving all students opportunities to observe scientific reasoning in action and to develop their own abilities with reasoning. When teachers make language moves a regular feature of their teaching and interactions, it sends the message that science is flexible, has meaning, and requires particular kinds of language use (Herbel-Eisenmann & Schleppegrell, 2008).

RESEARCH QUESTIONS

Given the research background and the conceptual frame presented above, we investigated the degree to which a conceptually-based unit that foregrounds science language use facilitated second grade ELs' science discourse. Our specific research questions are as follows:

1. Does language-focused science conceptual teaching improve ELs' conceptual understanding and written discourse of science phenomena? Does the impact vary by EL status or gender?
2. Does engagement in academic conversations predict science understanding, written descriptions, or written arguments?

METHODOLOGY

Study Design and Analysis

To answer the research questions a mixed-methods study was conducted that included a pretest, posttest design to answer the first research question, and correlational analyses and linear regression analyses to answer the second research question. We also presented some qualitative data to illustrate the key findings. The study was implemented over the course of three weeks. Students were engaged in the science unit for four days on each of these three weeks. The first day of the unit was dedicated to administering the pretest and engaging students in an academic conversation designed to introduce the activities and expected behaviors.

Participants

Three teachers and 50 students from three schools participated in this pre-posttest action research study. All three teachers, Alfonso, Maribel, and Yesenia (all names are pseudonyms) were enrolled in a masters' degree program in bilingual education at a research university in the southwest.

They were also part of an intensive program aimed at deepening their science and mathematics content and pedagogical knowledge. At the time of the study, Alfonso and Maribel had 5 years of teaching experience and Yesenia had 3 years of experience. All three teachers had had 2 years of experience teaching second grade science in dual language enrichment programs.

However, the teachers' school settings and student demographics were somewhat different. Maribel taught in a 90–10 dual language program where 53% of students were designated as ELs by their school district criteria (i.e., responses to home language survey and performance on English oral proficiency test in prekindergarten or kindergarten) and 98% were designated as economically disadvantaged (based on parent income reports). Alfonso also taught in a 90–10 dual language program, but it was also part of an international baccalaureate school which emphasized inquiry-based learning in all content areas. Only 38% of Alfonso's students were designated as ELs and 85% were identified as economically disadvantaged. Yesenia taught in a 50–50 dual language program where 100% were designated as ELs; in fact, they are newcomers or recent arrivals. One hundred percent of her students were identified as economically disadvantaged.

Students' Language Profiles

Maribel's and Alfonso's ELs' language backgrounds were more diverse than Yesenia's in that they had students who were classified as initially bilingual; the students met district standards for school readiness in both languages. Their students were also more proficient in English than Yesenia's students, as indicated by their proficiency classifications. Table 3.3 presents language profiles by classroom. Classifications for Maribel and Alfonso's students were based on the previous year's State English Language Proficiency Assessment System. Since Yesenia's students were newcomers, their classifications were more recent, occurring within three months prior to the start of the action research project.

TABLE 3.3 Language Background Profiles by Classroom					
	No. ELs (*n* = 32)			No. ELs (*n* = 18)	
Class	Beginner	Intermediate	Early Advanced	Bilingual	Monolingual
Maribel (17)	0	5	4	4	4
Alfonso (16)	0	5	1	4	6
Yesenia (17)	12	5	0	0	0

Note: Number in parentheses refers to total class size.

Instruments

Multiple-Choice Unit Tests

Prior to the start of the unit, students were administered a 16-item test consisting of 10 multiple-choice items with three response options (A, B, or C), three open-response items (i.e., they drew an object's location, circled items representative of a set, or excluded items not representative of a set), and three true-false items. Five items targeted conceptual connections, five targeted observations of sky objects (star, Moon, Sun), three targeted object movement that did not involve conceptual connections, and three items targeted science methods relevant to astronomy. At the end of the unit, a parallel version of the test was administered. Like district assessments, the teachers read the items to students to reduce confounding effects of students' low English reading levels. Teachers translated words and phrases of the test whenever students requested a translation.

Academic Conversation Prompts and Observation Protocol

To facilitate student uptake of astronomy discourse patterns, teachers engaged students in academic conversations every day of the unit. In addition to providing opportunities for using technical terms in context, every academic conversation was designed to build student understanding of the interactional styles of Western science (e.g., challenge ideas) and science habits of mind (e.g., use evidence to support claims, build on others' ideas, reason with data). Teachers began with conversations that taught and reinforced Western conversation behaviors (e.g., attentive body posture, eye contact, staying on topic) as well as taught at least two core academic conversation skills (see Figure 3.2).

Our past work and that of Zwiers and Crawford (2011) have demonstrated that academic conversation skills do not come naturally when addressing academic topics. As students gained practice and content understanding, the academic conversations targeted more complex discourse skills. To start academic conversations, students were provided with a contextual prompt and were given conversation mats to facilitate turn taking. At the start of the unit, a student began their turn by paraphrasing their partner's response before responding to the prompt themselves. This moved to paraphrasing, followed by building on the other student's turn with evidence, then challenging an idea. The unit ended with developing students' language for reasoning. For example, a student reported a change in the Moon's appearance by saying, "The Moon look bigger on fourth day of my observation." The partner paraphrased by using information from their data recording sheet to add on more precise language in the following: So I see in your chart, your fourth day is when the Moon orbits around the Earth to this point here…it looks bigger because we saw more of the Moon's

Language & Discourse Skills

Day	Nonverbal cues	Paraphrase	Building On with Evidence	Challenge Ideas	Reason with Data	Content Targets♥
1 (2)	████████████					BV
2 (2)	████████████					KV & MP♥
3 (3)	████████████████					Link DC♥ to KV
4 (3)	████████████████					Link G to OS
5 (4)	█████████████████					Link OS to OP
6 (4)	█████████████████					Links to Cycles
7 (4)	█████████████████					Misconceptions♥
8 (5)	██████████████████████					Evidence
9 (5)	██████████████████████					Explanations♥
10 (5)	██████████████████████					Explanations

Note: Numbers in parentheses represent the length of the academic conversation; Symbols and abbreviations: ♥Cultural connections explicitly made on days marked with the heart symbol; BV = background vocabulary; KV = key vocabulary; MP = moon phases; DC = data collection; G = gravity; OS = orbit simulations; OP = object position.

Figure 3.2 Academic conversation targets and content links by day of instruction.

face, no seface, s-suurface light up. It changed from a quarter Moon to a half-Moon . . . (sic).

Teachers monitored the quality of student participation by using short checklists during academic conversations. The checklist measured three characteristics of academic conversations: (a) use of nonverbal cues demonstrate active listening; (b) accurate use of science terms to paraphrase/build on, challenge, or reason; and (c) use of science linguistic features to communicate ideas/reasoning. All three teachers were trained on linguistic features of scientific description and reasoning during a master's degree level course in which they were enrolled. To make it feasible for teachers to monitor each students' contribution during academic conversations, these features were recorded dichotomously for each student (behavior present or not present). Thus, each student had a daily score of up to three points (one potential point per characteristic).

Writing Prompts and Rubric

Students were also asked to complete three quick writes based on structured prompts targeting the unit topics. One was administered on the first day of the unit, another on the fifth day of the unit, and a post-writing prompt at the end of the unit. Students were given 20 minutes to write on each prompt. Students were encouraged to draw pictures to augment their written responses. Teachers recorded the length of time most students completed the responses. Table 3.4 displays the writing prompts and teacher

TABLE 3.4 Writing Prompt Administration and Length of Completion Time by Classroom

Prompt Wording	Admin. Time	Duration Range*		
		M	A	Y
1. Do objects in the sky (sun, moon, and stars) change their location? Explain why or why not. Be sure to use what you know about objects in the sky, movement, and gravity/forces in your response.	Prior to Day 1	8–10	8–10	8–10
2. Look at the picture below. [Picture shows the light from the sun projected onto the moon.] What do you see? Use what you know about the movement of the sun and the moon to describe what is happening in this picture.	Day 5	10–12	10–12	8–10
3. Explain why the appearance of the moon changes every month. Be sure to include: (a) evidence from your night sky observations, (b) evidence from the interactive chart, and (c) a description of the moon phases.	End of Day 10	13–15	12–15	10–12

Note: M = Maribel; A = Alfonso; Y = Yesenia
* Duration ranges are reported in minutes.

reports of the length of time students took to complete the writing task. Each written response was scored on a four-point focused holistic rubric comprised of six dimensions of writing: (a) genre structure, (b) idea expression, (c) cohesion and elaboration, (d) scientific tone, (e) grammatical accuracy, and (f) spelling and punctuation conventions. The first four dimensions were operationalized based on systemic functional linguistics organizing concepts (see Appendix B). An overall score was computed by calculating the average of all six dimensions of writing.

Classroom Observations

Given the focus on oral language as a scaffold for content understanding and written discourse, classroom observations were conducted during planned academic conversations. Transcripts of student exchanges were used to examine the nature of student's use of oral science discourse as evidence of conceptual knowledge. Table 3.5 presents the targets for observations of student exchanges. Classrooms observations were only conducted in Maribel's classroom as she had the most experience in the language approach taken here.

TABLE 3.5 Targets of Observations of Students Exchanges	
Category	Description
Expression of Ideas	1. Extent to which verb and noun groups are linked to the intended function (i.e., identifying phenomenon, presenting evidence and reasons, presenting/referring to cause and effect, or generalizing). 2. Extent to which embedded phrases/clauses provide specific details about the phenomenon.
Cohesion and Elaboration	1. Extent of elaboration by using accurate causal connections such as text connectives, collocation, and some forms of clause complexes.

RESULTS

Impact of Instructional Approach on Student Outcomes

Conceptual Understanding

To determine the impact of language-focused science teaching on science conceptual knowledge, a repeated measures analysis of variance (ANOVA) was conducted, with the pretest and posttest scores as the within-subject factor and EL status and gender as between subject factors. Since there were only five students designated as early advanced in English proficiency, they were grouped with intermediate students for the analysis. The main effect for test scores was significant, $F(1, 44) = 1930.13.$, $p < .000$, $n^2 = 0.98$, indicating that regardless of EL status or gender, student mean scores were significantly higher at posttest ($M = 13.53$, $SD = 1.28$) than pretest ($M = 3.82$, $SD = 0.94$). The high effect size (0.98) indicates that this is a meaningful increase in mean scores. Mean scores across levels of EL status (beginning, intermediate, and non-EL) were not significantly different from each other, $F(2, 44) = 0.6$, $p > 0.05$. Further, increases in boys and girls pre- to posttest scores were comparable, $F(1, 44) = 0.26$, $p > 0.05$. Finally, the EL status by gender interaction was not significant, $F(1, 44) = 1.02$, $p > 0.05$. These findings suggest that there was no differential impact of the approach based on language proficiency or gender. Thus, a focus on conceptual connections with language scaffolding benefitted ELs of varying levels of English proficiency and equally benefited boys and girls.

Quality of Extended Oral Language

Classroom observations provide qualitative evidence of a progression in the appropriation of science oral language discourse patterns. For beginning ELs, students progressed from a heavy reliance on sentence stems, word banks, and code switching to a gradual tendency toward less reliance on sentence stems and more risk taking in the use of text connectives when making causal connections between observations and content concepts. The following example illustrates a typical exchange that relied on sentence stems, a word bank, and first language resources (code switching) to respond to the prompt.

> **Maria:** I see the Sun, panets [planets] and stars in the picture. What you see?
> **Yara:** (Rephrase) You see the Sun, planets and the stars. (Adding on) I see [them] too. I see the Sun, planets and stars. Maybe the Moon too. I think the Sun and planets *se mueven* [they move], pero [but] I no think stars *mueven* [move].
> **Maira:** (Rephrase) You say Sun and planets *se mueven*. I agrrr, agrr, aaagreeees [agree]. *¿Pero, por que no se moverían las estrellas?* [But why don't the stars move?] They move too, *¿qué no? Tenemos que decir como sabemos.* [We have to say how we know.] How we know. I aagree [agree] because they move in *el cielo* [the sky].
> **Yara:** Si, Yes, I agree because they move *alrededor del* [around the] ... the Moon ... *¿Cómo se dice alrededor?* [How do you say around?]—
> **Maira:** *Aquí esta.* [Here it is. (Maira points to the word bank)]
> **Yara:** Around. I agree because Moon move around the Earth and the Earth around Sun.

The academic conversation exchange above occurred early on in the unit. Maira and Yara demonstrate that although they make syntactical errors typical of beginning ELs (e.g., omission and substitution), they can rephrase each other's contributions with the support of the sentence stems (*I see the... , I think... I agree because...*) provided by their teacher, Maribel. Yara is able to "add on" to the conversation by identifying additional objects observed in the visual and Maira adds on by addressing the second part of the conversation prompt ("How do you know?"). Both use the word bank to use unit vocabulary. Also evident is the lack of elaboration and causal verbs or connectives that would indicate explanation or argument. This result is not surprising given Maribel had not introduced these skills at this point in the unit.

Later in the unit (after hands-on activities), academic conversations targeted oral explanations with the use of concept maps as linguistic supports. The concept maps illustrated relationships among concepts and facts related to the phenomenon. Pairs of concepts or terms were linked with a verbal link such that it provided a proposition students could make during academic conversations. For example, "Sun" and "light" were linked by the verb "projects" as in "Sun→*projects*→light." Thus, a student could verbalize the following proposition, "The Sun projects light on the Moon." The following student exchange was observed in response to the prompt: "What is happening when we observe a change in the Moon's appearance?"

> **Yara:** Ok, Ok. Sunlight is projects on the Moon. In different parts of month we see different phase because there is different amount of sunlights projects on the Moon.
>
> **Maira:** *Si. Espera.* [Yes. Wait.] So you say, The sunlight is projects on the Moon surface. Because the Moon is orbits the Earth we see different—
>
> **Yara:** —we observe different amount of light on surface. Start with lunar cycle, like the *párrafo que vimos ayer* [paragraph we saw yesterday].
>
> **Maira:** Ok, The Moon is part of lunar cycle. No, The phases of the Moon is part of lunar cycle. The Moon appearance changes in lunar cycle.... (pause)
>
> **Yara:** ...because it orbits the...around the Earth.
>
> **Maira:** *movimiento* [movement]....because it changes the location when it orbits...orbits around the Earth. When Moon orbits, we see different parts of the light on surface. The light comes from the Sun.
>
> **Yara:** So the phases of Moon are different amounts of light on the face of the Moon that we see from the Earth.
>
> **Maira:** The different locations causes the Moon phases.
>
> **Yara:** *Mejor* [better], The orbit around the Earth causes the Moon phases, like new Moon, half Moon, and, and...
>
> **Maira:** and full Moon.

In the excerpt above, the students relied less on sentence stems. With the linguistic scaffolding made possible by the use of the concept map, these students used verbs and nouns that corresponded with the topic (e.g., projects, orbit, location, surface), including causal verbs (causes) and extended noun phrases (e.g., different parts of the light, different amount of light). The causal conjunction, because, and text connective, so (used to mean "therefore"), signal this dyad's appropriation of science discourse to explain a scientific phenomenon.

Similar appropriation progressions in oral language were observed with intermediate level EL dyads. The main difference found between the beginning dyads and intermediate dyads was in the nature of syntactical errors produced. Fewer omission and substitution errors were observed among intermediate dyads.

Appropriation of Science Written Discourse

We found similar trends of impact on written explanations of science phenomenon. A second repeated measures ANOVA was conducted with the writing scores at Time 1 (prior to the start of the unit) and Time 3 (at the conclusion of the unit) as the within-subject factor and EL status and gender as between subject factors. Students designated as early advanced in English proficiency were grouped with intermediate students for the analysis as in the pre- posttest analysis. The main effect for writing scores was significant, $F(1, 44) = 119.21$, $p < 0.000$, $n^2 = 0.73$, indicating that regardless of EL status and gender, student mean writing scores were significantly higher at Time 3 ($M = 2.38$, $SD = 0.42$) than Time 1 ($M = 1.22$, $SD = 0.78$). The moderate effect size (0.73) indicates that this is a meaningful increase in mean scores. Mean score increases across levels of EL status (beginning, intermediate, and non-EL) were not significantly different from each other, $F(2, 44) = 0.15$, $p > 0.05$. Further, increases in boys' and girls' scores from Time 1 to Time 3 were comparable, $F(1, 44) = 0.71$, $p > 0.05$. Like the conceptual knowledge measure, the EL status by gender interaction was also not significant, $F(1, 44) = 2.27$, $p > 0.05$. Thus, no differential impact of the approach based on language proficiency or gender was evident, and our approach to the unit appeared to have supported all students in these three classrooms similarly.

Student writing. Table 3.6 presents a writing progression of the beginning EL, Maira, from her Day 1 writing sample. We see that although Maira is a beginning EL, she has a command of key syntactical structures of basic English (subject, verb, object) and is capable of generating a compound sentence with the use of the conjunction "because." In addition, Maira uses generalized observations (I se dem evy dai) to form the basis of her claim

TABLE 3.6 Writing Progression of Maira, a Low English Proficiency EL Female

Day	Writing Excerpt Verbatim	Writing Excerpt "Translation"
1	Ojts no muv dicos I se dem evy dai.	Objects no move because I see them every day.
5	Sun lit projects to moon fas. Dats what we see from Erth. Da moon faz chegis bicos it obits da Erth.	Sunlight projects to moon's face. That is what we see from Earth. The moon phases change because it orbits the Earth.
10	Changes in the moon fases are part of the lunar cicle. The moons aparanc changes becuz it changis locton bcuz it obits the Earth. As resut, the moons orbit causes difrent amunts of light to show on face and that changes in the lunar cicle.	Changes in the moon phases are part of the lunar cycle. The moon's appearance changes because it changes location because it orbits the Earth. As a result, the moon's orbit causes different amounts of light to show on [its] face and that changes in the lunar cycle.

that "Ojts no muv..." instead of using scientifically based evidence. It is also evident that Maira does not use science principles to reason about evidence. Not providing more precise evidence makes reasoning about the evidence difficult. On Day 5 of the unit, the writing sample demonstrates Maira's attempts at using more content vocabulary (sunlight, Moon, Earth, Moon phases, orbit) to both describe the observation (Moon phase change) and reason about that observation (... because it orbits the Earth). Although this explanation is far from complete, it is clear that Maira is gaining command of a linguistic feature of science explanation, the use of technical terms (nouns and verbs). On Day 10 of the unit, we see a significant developmental shift in her writing. Maira starts by introducing the topic, "Changes in the Moon fases are part of the lunar cicle." This is followed by an accurate explanatory sequence that uses long noun phrases to condense information. This is an important feature of science written text because it is a resource that facilitates the structuring of arguments (Schleppegrell, 2004). Also evident in the writing is the use of clause complexes that support articulation of causal connections between observations and concepts. Thus, despite the fact that Maira makes some syntactical and spelling errors, her linguistic choices point to clear evidence of conceptual understanding. That is, the linguistic resources she uses are needed to articulate linkages between concepts and facts. Thus, after 2 weeks of instruction, Maira meets the minimum requirement for conceptual understanding.

Impact of Academic Conversations on Science Content and Discourse Learning

To address the second research question, two-tailed bivariate correlations were first computed to determine the relationship among key variables. Table 3.7 reports the observed correlations among them.

As depicted in Table 3.7, moderate and significant positive correlations were observed between academic conversations (AC) and two other variables:

TABLE 3.7 Bivariate Correlations (*n* = 50)					
	AC	WD	PrT	L2RP	PsT
1. Academic Conversations (AC)	—	0.678*	0.121	0.043	0.439*
2. Written Discourse (WD)		—	0.095	0.021	0.623*
3. Pre-Test (PrT)			—	0.043	0.127
4. Second Language Reading Proficiency (L2RP)			—	0.197	
5. Post-Test (PsT					—

* $p < 0.000$

written discourse (WD), $r = 0.678$, $p < 0.000$, and posttest (PsT) scores, $r = 0.439$, $p < 0.000$. The lower correlation between academic conversations and posttest scores is expected as the posttest scores were generated by a different response format (multiple choice exam) and thus likely accounts for the lower correlation. In addition, written discourse was positively and significantly correlated with posttest scores, $r = 0.623$, $p < 0.000$. Thus, increases in the average participation in academic conversations were associated with increases in science written discourse and science conceptual understanding. The moderate association also indicates that written discourse and posttests capture similar skills. Since both measures were designed to capture conceptual knowledge, this result provides some evidence that this is the case.

To address the degree to which participation in academic conversations could predict written discourse as measured by the writing rubric, a linear regression was conducted for written discourse using the backward method. The results of the regression indicated that three predictors (academic conversations, EL status, and gender) explained 46.5% of the variance ($R^2 = 0.465$, $F(3, 46) = 13.09$, $p < 0.000$). However, only one predictor, participation in academic conversations, significantly predicted science written discourse $\beta = 1.67$, $p < 0.000$ and this predictor essentially accounted for nearly all of the variance (46.0%). That is, EL status and gender only accounted for 0.5% of the variance combined, which did not reach statistical significance ($\beta = -0.018$ and $\beta = 0.091$ respectively, $ps > 0.05$). For each 1.0 score point increase of academic conversation participation, students' written scores increased 1.67 points. The same pattern of results was found for predictors of posttest scores. The regression indicated the same three predictors as in the previous regression analysis explained 23.0% of the variance ($R^2 = 0.230$, $F(3, 46) = 4.58$, $p = 0.007$). However, only participation in academic conversations significantly predicted posttest scores, $\beta = 1.77$, $p = 0.001$, and accounted for almost all of the variance (19.2%). That is, EL status and gender only accounted for 3.8% of the variance combined, which did not reach statistical significance ($\beta = -0.133$ and $\beta = -0.233$ respectively, $ps > 0.05$). Students' posttest scores increased 1.77 points for each 1.0 score point increase of academic conversation participation.

Overall, these results indicate that participation in academic conversations supported conceptual learning and science disciplinary literacy for students with beginning and intermediate levels of English proficiency in this study.

LIMITATIONS OF STUDY

Two major limitations of the study deserve some discussion. First, this study did not utilize a control group. Therefore, the effect of external influences on student outcomes was not minimized. Given that that this study grew from the teachers' desires to improve their own practice in the context of action research, rather than make broad generalizations about the approach across a wide array of contexts, a control group was neither necessary for this purpose nor feasible. Still, we believe that the pre- posttest design allows some narrow conclusions to be drawn that can be useful to others. Differences across the students in different classrooms were tested and no differences in initial oral language proficiency or home language proficiency were detected. Recall that Yesenia's class was primarily comprised of students in the beginning level of English proficiency. Her students started with significantly lower writing proficiency than the other two classrooms prior to the unit as measured by the Time 1 writing response scores. Yet, no significant differences across classrooms were observed at Time 3. Thus, for Yesenia's students, the approach appeared to help them increase their science written discourse to the level of the other two classrooms. However, this result is not generalizable given the limitations of the design.

A second limitation is the small sample size. Sample size is important because it relates to the power of a study in detecting an effect. While the sample size appeared to have been sufficient for detecting large effects (as indicated by the large effect sizes reported above), it may not have been sufficient in detecting small effects of the approach. For example, the lack of a significant interaction between outcome measurers and EL status may be attributable to the sample size if the effect was small. That is, a larger sample size may have yielded a significant interaction. Further, larger sample sizes increase the power of a study, which would help to minimize Type II errors. A Type II error occurs when the results confirm the hypothesis on which the study was based when, in fact, an alternative hypothesis is true. A small sample size increases the likelihood of a Type II error skewing the results, which decreases the power of the study. Despite the sample size limitation, we found large effect sizes for posttest score and science written discourse increases. These findings suggest that the academic conversation approach was very powerful in supporting EL language and content learning needs in these three classrooms.

CONCLUSION AND DISCUSSION

This exploratory study sought to examine the impact of a language-focused approach to science teaching on student conceptual learning and to explore the interplay between written disciplinary discourse and content learning. The significant increase in posttest scores on a measure that targeted conceptual links among concepts suggests that integrating frequent academic conversations in lessons was an effective strategy for meeting ELs' content and language needs. Moreover, the finding that participation in academic language participation was positively and significantly related to science conceptual understanding and science written discourse indicates the potential for using language tools to develop deep understanding for students of varying levels of English proficiency. This pattern of results is significant in that there is growing attention to the need to contextualize language learning in content-based situations in order to sufficiently address the academic needs of ELs (Moschkovich, 2010). We attempted to provide this contextualization with the focus on making conceptual links explicit to students and the use of systemic functional linguistics to support language use in a manner that is consistent with science disciplinary discourse.

We started with everyday concepts, but used academic conversations and linguistic scaffolding to go beyond the use of everyday concepts while engaging in science inquiry and in activities designed to consolidate understanding. From a sociocultural perspective, everyday (spontaneous) concepts are the starting point of the development of scientific concepts (Panofsky et.al., 1990). Everyday concepts are not scientific concepts that can be used to generalize to fully internalize scientific principles because they are defined and conceptualized by perceptual or contextual features of its referent (Panofsky et al., 1990). Scientific concepts, on the other hand, are defined in terms of their relationship to other concepts (Vygotsky, 1962). The power of scientific concepts as the basis of instructional organization has been known for several decades, but only recently have researchers begun to examine the use of specific linguistic resources to develop conceptual understanding.

The predictive power of academic conversations found in this study is consistent with both the sociocultural and systemic functional linguistics perspectives. From both lenses, oral language is essential for the development of understanding. For Vygotsky, scientific concepts are developed through social exchange (Vygotsky, 1962). Systemic functional linguistics researchers remind us that genres are found in both oral and written forms and thus oral language can be used as a starting point for mastering genres in more formal written forms (Gibbons, 2002). In addition, systemic functional linguistics metalanguage provides a framework for targeting features that signal distinct features of various genres. This study indicates that the use of academic conversations, supported by systemic functional linguistics metalanguage, was a useful strategy for connecting oral language and scientific meaning as well as the construction of written approximations of science discourse. Unlike other approaches (e.g., Echevarria, Richards-Tutor, Canges, & Francis, 2011; Lara-Alecio et al., 2012; Lee et al., 2016; Llosa et al., 2016; Maerten-Rivera et al., 2016), the language development strategy utilized here was not limited to generic English language development strategies such as reduced rate of speech, use of visuals and graphs, and opportunities for unstructured oral discussion during the inquiry process. While these are important strategies for ELs, they may not be effective mediating tools for supporting the appropriation of science concepts or discourse patterns.

From a sociocultural perspective, it is the appropriation of the discourse patterns that leads to development of scientific knowledge. Qualitative evidence of ELs' appropriation of science discourse was found in observations of student academic conversations as well as their quick writes. We show how ELs with a beginning level of English proficiency used linguistic tools (systemic functional linguistics metalanguage and concept maps) to generate language structures that were initially beyond their developmental stage. Making science discourse features transparent with the use of systemic functional linguistics metalanguage during academic conversations served to provide students linguistic mediators that supported appropriation of science discourse. While more direct evidence of this hypothesis is necessary, this study lends some support for this assertion.

Overall, this study demonstrates that focused language interactions, specialized linguistic tools, and culturally responsive materials can support mastery of science discourse and by extension, the concepts used to communicate science phenomena. Approaching ELs' content and learning needs in this way may address more effectively the slow-moving national performance trends in science understanding and English development. We invite other research and teaching practitioners to further explore these issues with the following inquiry and action research questions.

Inquiry Questions

1. How would you systematically develop disciplinary lessons for ELs in ways that validate their cultural and linguistic backgrounds?
2. How can one create scaffolded and conceptually rich science lessons in linguistically diverse classrooms?

Action Research Questions

1. What happens to ELs' content understanding when I organize instruction around big ideas?
2. What happens to the quality of student writing when I plan carefully constructed oral language practice that targets key genre features?
3. How can I use focused language lessons during science lessons to improve ELs' reasoning about observations during science inquiry?

APPENDIX A

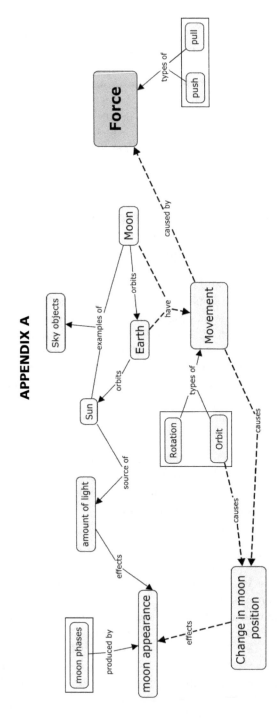

Teacher generated concept map for Objects in the Sky Unit. Force is a hidden big idea concept underlying observation of sky objects. The dotted line represents the conceptual links. The items in the boxes represents what is typically taught.

APPENDIX B

Writing Feature	Science Novice 1	Science Apprentice 2	Junior Scientist 3	Established Scientist 4
Genre Structure	Does not at all follow expected overall structure of genre	Somewhat follows expected overall structure of genre: no identification and/or major gaps in explanation sequence	Follows expected explanation structure; explanation sequence mostly complete	Follows expected explanation structure (e.g., identifies phenomenon, complete explanation/reason sequence)
Idea Expression	Verb and noun groups are not linked to intended function; little or no embedding and/or does not provide specificity	Verb and noun groups are insufficiently linked to intended function; embedding does not provide specificity in most of the text	Verb and noun groups are mostly linked to intended function with limited variation; embedding mostly provides specificity	Verb and noun groups are linked to intended function[1] with wide variation; embedded phrases/clauses provide specific details about the phenomenon throughout
Idea Cohesion & Elaboration	Cohesion & elaboration strategies are not evident; no causal connections are made; content may be consistently inaccurate	Clauses are loosely connected (listing of events, reasons or examples) and do not build causal connections; content somewhat inaccurate	Cohesion & elaboration strategies somewhat build causal connections; content mostly accurate	Cohesion & elaboration strategies[2] help build accurate causal connections; content consistently accurate
Scientific Tone	May include some use of declarative statements but relies on first person references to express opinion; no use of interpersonal metaphor	Declarative statements are the primary method for creating tone; may use a few first person references; no use of interpersonal metaphors	Appropriate use of declarative statements; little or no use of first person references, at least one use of interpersonal metaphor	Appropriate use of declarative statements: no use of first person references; use of interpersonal metaphors to express opinions
Grammatical Accuracy (Basic Syntax)	Grammar errors impede communication, such as incomplete sentences throughout the text; Only use simple sentences	Grammar errors somewhat impede communication: Most sentences are complete and very few complex sentences	Errors do not impede communication; Sentences are complete throughout the text; some use of complex sentences.	Little or no grammatical errors; Sentences are complete and complex;
Spelling & Punctuation Conventions	Spelling or punctuation errors consistently impede communication	Spelling or punctuation errors occasionally impede communication	Errors do not impede communication	Minor errors or none at all are present

Writing rubric. Function refers to (a) identifying phenomenon, (b) presenting evidence and reasons, (c) presenting/referring to cause and effect, and (d) generalizing. Strategies appropriate for this age group are text connectives, colloca-tion, and some forms of clause complexes.

REFERENCES

Aguirre-Muñoz, Z., & Pando, M. (2017). Knowing and teaching elementary math to bilingual students: Examining the role of teaching self efficacy on content knowledge. *Journal of Bilingual Education Research and Instruction (JBERI)*, *19*(1), 126–145.

Aguirre-Muñoz, Z., & Pantoya, M. (2016). Engineering literacy and engagement in kindergarten classrooms. *Journal of Engineering Education, 105*(4), 630–654.

Bacolod, M., & Rangel, M. A. (2017). Economic assimilation and skill acquisition: Evidence from the occupational sorting of childhood immigrants. *Demography, 54*(2), 571–602.

Bialystok, E., & Majumder, S. (1998). The relationship between bilingualism and the development of cognitive processes in problem-solving. *Applied Psycholinguistics, 19*(1), 69–85.

Brisk, M. E. (2015). *Engaging students in academic literacies: Genre-based pedagogy for K–5 classrooms*. New York, NY: Routledge.

Cazden, C. (2001). *Classroom discourse: The language of teaching and learning*. Portsmouth, NH: Heineman.

Chi, M. T. H., Feltovich, P., & Glaser, R. (1994). Categorization and representation of physics problems by experts and novices. *Cognitive Science, 5*(2), 121–152.

Cobb, P., Yackel, E., & McClain, K. (Eds.). (2000). *Communicating and symbolizing in mathematics: Perspectives on discourse, tools, and instructional design*. Mahwah, NJ: Erlbaum.

Echevarria, J., Richards-Tutor, C., Canges, R., & Francis, D. (2011). Using the SIOP model to promote the acquisition of language and science concepts with English learners. *Bilingual Research Journal, 34*(3), 334–351.

Fang, Z. (2005). Scientific literacy: A systematic functional linguistics perspective. *Science Education, 89*(2), 335–347.

Fang, Z., & Schleppegrell, M. J. (2008). *Reading in secondary content areas: A language-based pedagogy*. Ann Arbor, MI: University of Michigan Press.

Fang, Z., & Wei, Y. (2010) Improving middle school students' science literacy through reading infusion. *Journal of Educational Research, 103*(4), 262–273.

Feldman, S., & Malagon, V. F. (2017). *Unlocking learning: Science as a lever for English learner equity*. Oakland, CA: The Education Trust-West.

Gee, J. P. (2005). Language in the science classroom: Academic social languages as the heart of school-based literacy. In R. Yerrick & W. M. Roth (Eds.), *Establishing scientific classroom discourse communities: Multiple voices of teaching and learning research* (pp. 19–37). Mahwah, NJ: Erlbaum.

Gibbons, P., (2015). *Scaffolding language scaffolding learning: Teaching English language learners in the mainstream classroom* (2nd ed.). Portsmouth, NH: Heinemann.

Golash-Boza, T. (2005). Assessing the advantages of bilingualism for children of immigrants. *International Migration Review, 39*(3), 721–753.

Goldenberg, C. (1991). *Instructional conversations and their classroom applications. Educational Practice Report 2*. Santa Cruz, CA: The National Center for Research on Cultural Diversity and Second Language Learning, University of California.

Greenleaf, C., Litman, C., Hanson, T., Rosen, R., Herman, J., Schneider, S., & Schneider, S. A. (2011). Integrating literacy and science in biology: Teaching and learning impacts of reading apprenticeship professional development. *American Educational Research Journal, 48*(3), 647–717.

Hall, S. (2001). Foucault: Power, knowledge, and discourse. In M. Wetherell, S. Taylor, & S. J. Yates (Eds.), *Discourse theory and practice: A reader* (pp. 72–81). Thousand Oaks, CA: SAGE.

Halliday, M. A. K. (1975). *Learning how to mean: Explorations in the development of language.* London, England: Edward Arnold.

Halliday, M. A. K., & Martin, J. R. (1993). *Writing science: Literary and discursive power.* London, England: Falmer Press.

Herbel-Eisenmann, B., & Schleppegrell, M. (2008). 'What question would I be asking myself in my head?' Helping all students reason mathematically. In M. Ellis (Ed.), *Mathematics for every student: Responding to diversity, Grades 6–8* (pp. 23–38). Reston, VA: NCTM.

Huang, J., Normandia, B., & Greer, S. (2006). Communicating mathematically: Comparison of knowledge structures in teacher and student discourse in a secondary math classroom. *Communication Education, 54*(1), 34–51.

Kame'enui, E. J., Carnine, D. W., Dixon, R. C., Simmons, D. C., & Coyne, M. D. (2001). *Effective teaching strategies that accommodate diverse learners* (2nd ed.). Columbus: OH: Merrill, Prentice Hall.

Kieffer, M. J., Lesaux, N., Rivera, M., & Francis, D. J. (2009). Accommodations for English language learners taking large-scale assessments: A meta-analysis on effectiveness and validity. *Review of Educational Research, 29*(3), 1168–1201.

Lara-Alecio, R., Tong, F., Irby, B. J., Guerrero, C., Huerta, M., & Fan, Y. (2012). The effect of an instructional intervention on middle school English learners' science and English reading achievement. *Journal of Research in Science Teaching, 49*(8), 987–1011.

Lee, O., & Buxton, C. A., (2010). *Diversity and equity in science education: Research, policy and practice.* New York, NY: Teachers College Press.

Lee, O., & Buxton, C. A. (2013). Integrating science learning and English language development for English language learners. *Theory Into Practice, 52*(1), 36–42.

Lee, O., Llosa, L., Jiang, F., Haas, A., O'Connor, C., & Van Booven, C. D. (2016). Elementary teachers' science knowledge and instructional practices: Impact of an intervention focused on English language learners. *Journal of Research In Science Teaching, 53*(4), 579–597.

Lee, O., & Luykx, A. (2008). Science education and student diversity: Race/Ethnicity, language, culture, and socioeconomic status. In S. K. Abell & N. G. Lederman (Eds.), *Handbook of research on science education* (pp. 171–197). New York, NY: Routledge.

Llosa, L., Lee, O., Jian, F., Haas, A., O'Connor, C., Van Booven, C. D., & Kieffer, M. J. (2016). Impact of a large scale science intervention focused on English language learners. *American Educational Research Journal, 53*(2), 395–424.

Maerten-Rivera, J., Ahn, S., Lanier, K., Diaz, J., & Lee, O. (2016). Effect of a multiyear intervention on science achievement of all students including English language learners. *The Elementary School Journal, 116*(4), 600–624.

Martin, J. R., & Rose, D. (2008). *Genre relations: Mapping culture.* Oakville, CT: Equinox.

McFarland, J., Hussar, B., de Brey, C., Snyder, T., Wang, X., Wilkinson-Flicker, S., . . . Hinz, S. (2017). *The condition of education 2017* (NCES 2017-144). Washington, DC: U.S. Department of Education, National Center for Education Statistics. Retrieved from https://nces.ed.gov/pubsearch/pubsinfo. asp?pubid=2017144

Mercer, N. (1995). *The guided construction of knowledge: Talk amongst teachers and learners*. Clevedon, England: Multicultural Matters.

Mercer, N. (2000). *Words and minds: How we use language to think together*. New York, NY: Routledge.

Merino, H. J., & Scarcella, R. (2005). Teaching science to English learners. *UC LMRI Newsletter, 14*(4), 1–5.

Moschkovich, J. N. (2010). *Language and mathematics education: Multiple perspectives and directions for research*. Charlotte, NC: Information Age.

National Research Council. (2012). *A framework for K–12 science education: Practices, crosscutting concepts, and core ideas*. Committee on a Conceptual Framework for New K–12 Science Education Standards. Board on Science Education, Division of Behavioral and Social Sciences and Education. Washington, DC: The National Academies Press.

Novak, J. D. (1998). *Learning, creating, and using knowledge: Concept maps as facilitative tools in schools and corporations*. Mahwah, NJ: Erlbaum.

Norris, S. P., & Phillips, L. M. (2003). How literacy in its fundamental sense is central to scientific literacy. *Science Education, 87*(2), 224–240.

Panofsky, C. P., John-Steiner, V., & Blackwell, P. J. (1990). The development of scientific concepts and discourse. In L. C. Moll (Ed.), *Vygotsky and education: Instructional implications and applications of sociohistorical psychology* (pp. 251–267). Cambridge, England: Cambridge University Press.

Perkins, D. (2006). Constructivism and troublesome knowledge. In J. Meyer, & Ray Land, (Eds.), *Overcoming barriers to student understanding: Threshold concepts and troublesome knowledge* (pp. 33–47). New York, NY: Routledge.

Rogoff, B. (1990). *Apprenticeship in thinking: Cognitive development in social context*. New York, NY: Oxford University Press.

Schleppegrell, M. J. (2004). *The language of schooling: A functional linguistics perspective*. Mahwah, NJ: Erlbaum.

Schmidt, W. H., & Houang, R. T. (2012). Curricular coherence and the Common Core State Standards for Mathematics. *Educational Researcher, 41*(8), 294–308.

Shanahan, T., & Shanahan, C. (2012). What is disciplinary literacy and why does it matter? *Topics in Language Disorders, 32*(1), 7–18.

Tharp, R. G., & Gallimore, R. (1989). Rousing schools to life. *American Educator, 13*(2), 20–25, 46–52.

Tharp, R. G., & Gallimore, R. (1991). The instructional conversation: Teaching and learning in social activity (Learning Research Report No. 2.). *National Center for Research on Cultural Diversity and Second Language*. Berkeley, CA: University of California.

Tong, F., Irby, B. J., Lara-Alecio, R., Guerrero, C., Fan, Y., & Huerta, M. (2014). A randomized study of a literacy-integrated science intervention for low-socioeconomic status middle school students: Findings from first year implementation. *International Journal of Science Education, 36*(12), 2083–2109.

U.S. Department of Education, Institute of Education Sciences, National Center for Education Statistics, National Assessment of Educational Progress. (2015). *Science assessment.* Retrieved from https://www.nationsreportcard.gov/science _2015/#?grade=4

Vygotsky, L. S. (1962). *Thought and language.* Cambridge, MA: MIT Press.

Vygotsky, L. (1978). *Mind in society: The development of higher psychological processes.* Cambridge, MA: Harvard University Press.

Wellington J., & Osborne, J. (2001). *Language and literacy in science education.* Philadelphia, PA: Open University Press.

Zembal-Saul, C., McNeill, K. L., & Hershberger, K. (2013). *What's your evidence: Engaging K–5 children in constructing explanations.* San Francisco, CA: Pearson.

Zwiers, J. (2014). *Building academic language: Meeting common core standards across disciplines* (2nd ed.). San Francisco, CA: Jossey-Bass.

Zwiers, J., & Crawford, M. (2011). *Academic conversations: Classroom talk that fosters critical thinking and content understanding.* Portland, ME: Stenhouse.

CHAPTER 4

SUPPORTING LINGUISTICALLY DIVERSE STUDENTS IN SCIENTIFIC ARGUMENTATION ACROSS WRITING AND SPEAKING

María González-Howard
University of Texas at Austin

Katherine L. McNeill
Boston College

Ms. Williams has been a middle school science teacher for nearly ten years. Over the years, as her confidence in her teaching grew, she became more attentive to her students' needs, tailoring instruction to better support their learning. In particular, given the large number of linguistically diverse students in her school, Ms. Williams often incorporates language supports, like sentence starters and word walls, in her instruction. Recently, she learned

Culturally and Linguistically Diverse Learners and STEAM, pages 77–94
Copyright © 2019 by Information Age Publishing
All rights of reproduction in any form reserved.

about changes to her state's science standards and feels nervous about the goals described in these standards around science practices. Ms. Williams wonders what it means to include science practices in the classroom, especially in terms of their language demands. How will her students be expected to use language to engage in science practices? What kinds of language supports could she use to help her linguistically diverse students successfully participate in them? Could she modify any of her old strategies? Would the strategies that address speaking also work for writing?

Teachers might find themselves asking these questions, especially in light of recent reforms in science education, such as the development of the Next Generation Science Standards (Next Generation Science Standards Lead States, 2013). New standards describe students engaging in science practices as a means by which to make sense and develop understandings of natural phenomena with their peers (Osborne, 2014). However, science practices are linguistically demanding since they require students to use language in complex ways in order to communicate with others while generating knowledge (Lee, Quinn, & Valdez, 2013). Consequently, teachers will need to respond to the language demands in science practices, making the necessary instructional modifications to ensure that all students, including those from linguistically diverse backgrounds, are able to participate in them.

Our work has focused on the science practice of argumentation, which is also addressed in other STEAM subject areas, like mathematics. In this chapter, we describe a research study conducted with a middle school teacher of all English learning (EL) students as she taught an argumentation-focused curriculum. Specifically, we discuss the linguistic strategies this teacher used to help her EL students access and better engage in a variety of argumentation activities. We also share and describe other example activities that teachers could integrate into their science instruction to support linguistically diverse students in argumentation across writing and speaking. Our hope is that with this information, teachers like Ms. Williams,[1] can better help their linguistically diverse students engage in argumentation. Before jumping into the instructional strategies and activities, we offer a brief overview of recent changes in science instruction and describe the science practice of argumentation.

RECENT CHANGES IN SCIENCE INSTRUCTION

Students have traditionally held passive roles in the science classroom, memorizing facts about science and carrying out prescribed investigations, both of which are far from how the discipline is carried out in the real world (Pruitt,

2014). Recent reform efforts are striving to improve science education by encouraging that K–12 students actively participate in authentic experiences that enable them to develop their own understandings about the natural world (National Research Council, 2012). Students should engage with natural phenomena as they try to make sense of the world around them (Berland et al., 2016). For example, instead of just memorizing that a balanced force is when two forces (i.e., pushes or pulls) are acting on an object in opposite directions and in equal size, to develop understandings of this phenomena, 3rd graders should plan and conduct investigations in which they apply different forces to a ball and examine its resulting motion. Planning and conducting investigations is one of eight science practices highlighted in recent science standards (Next Generation Science Standards Lead States, 2013). Science practices mirror the different activities that scientists engage in, such as analyzing and interpreting data, constructing explanations, and developing and using models (Bybee, 2011). Creating a classroom culture that prioritizes science practices requires significant time as well as instructional strategies and activities that support students in this work.

Supporting Culturally and Linguistically Diverse Students in Science Practices

Science practices are language-intensive, requiring students to use various language modalities (e.g., writing, speaking, reading) to generate and revise scientific knowledge (Hakuta, Santos, & Fang, 2013). For example, students might orally develop and use models to predict when the next solar eclipse will occur or write scientific explanations about why the biodiversity of sea turtles has decreased. Argumentation can be particularly challenging in terms of language as it requires students to engage in various types of social interactions with peers all the while comparing and reconciling differing science ideas (González-Howard & McNeill, 2016). For instance, students ideally challenge or build on their peers' evidence when debating whether dinosaurs became extinct due to a large meteor crash or a chain of volcanic eruptions.

Science practices offer teachers opportunities to simultaneously support students' science and language learning (Lee, Miller, & Januszyk, 2014). However, because of the rigorous ways students will be expected to use language in the science classroom, teachers need different instructional strategies to support all of their students in meeting these demands. This will be especially important for students from linguistically diverse backgrounds who may be partaking in these practices in a language they are in the process of learning (Lee et al., 2013). Strategies like small group work that increases student interactions have been shown to help EL students better engage in discourse intensive science practices (Honeycutt Swanson, Bianchini, & Sook Lee, 2014). Yet, teachers should be thoughtful about when to incorporate these supports and for what purposes in order to help students meaningfully participate in science practices.

Additionally, it is critical that teachers' instruction around language and science be complementary and not send mixed messages. For example, second language pedagogy recommends that teachers make learning objectives explicit at the beginning of lessons, which is at tension with how recent science standards describe students coming to their own conclusions about scientific phenomena (Weinburgh, Silva, Horak Smith, Grouix, & Nettles, 2014).

Teachers will need to carefully consider all of these issues when planning for instruction that successfully addresses both areas, as we will demonstrate in this chapter through example strategies obtained from our work with middle school teachers. We will also share a website we developed which contains resources that can help teachers simultaneously attend to students' language and science learning. Specifically, in our work we have focused on one of the science practices, engaging in argument from evidence.

Engaging in Argument From Evidence

Argumentation is a social process in which students construct and critique claims about the natural world using scientific evidence. We consider both structural and social features of argumentation, which can often be challenging for students and teachers in K–12 science classrooms (McNeill, González-Howard, Katsh-Singer, & Loper, 2017). In terms of *structure*, an argument consists of three elements: claim, evidence, and reasoning (CER; McNeill & Krajcik, 2012). The claim is a conclusion about a question or problem. Evidence is scientific data, such as observations or measurements from the natural world, which are used to support a claim. Reasoning explains why the evidence supports the claim using appropriate disciplinary core ideas (e.g., science concepts, like weathering and friction). In terms of a *social* process, argumentation includes the consideration and critique of multiple competing claims. To engage in rich discourse, students need to consider and have support for more than one claim. If everyone in the class agrees on one claim, such as combining vinegar and baking soda causes a chemical reaction, there will be limited exchanges between students and questioning of science ideas (Berland, McNeill, Pelletier, & Krajcik, 2017). Thus, the process of argumentation requires that students consider and critique multiple science ideas using evidence. Figure 4.1 illustrates both

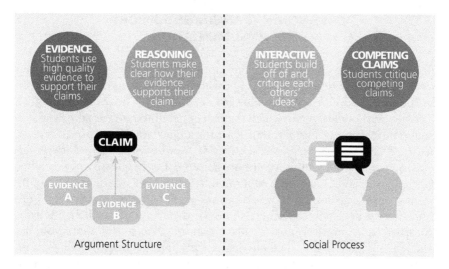

Figure 4.1 The structural and social features of argumentation. *Note:* This image is reprinted with permission from Innovations in Science Teacher Education. Original publication in *Innovations in Science Teacher Education* (Innovations) http:// innovations.theaste.org/designing-and-using-multimedia-modules-for-teacher -educators-supporting-teacher-learning-of-scientific-argumentation

features of this science practice; the structure of an argument is depicted on the left side, and the social process on the right side.

All students can engage in the structural and social features of argumentation across writing and speaking (González-Howard, McNeill, Marco-Bujosa, & Proctor, 2017). For example, ninth grade students might be tasked with writing persuasive arguments around whether the benefits of using pesticides outweigh their impact on the environment. To make their arguments persuasive, students would need to substantiate their claim with numerous pieces of relevant evidence. Additionally, students' arguments would become stronger if they justified their reasoning and incorporated scientific ideas. Writing arguments can also involve the social dimension of this science practice as students could address counterarguments for their claim or consider multiple competing claims. Students could also participate in both aspects of argumentation through talk. For instance, a class might carry out a debate about which natural element causes more erosion, wind or water. During the discussion students could critique the validity of peers' evidence and question how someone arrived at a particular claim. Therefore, it is necessary for teachers to consider the ways that students are expected to use written and spoken language to be successful in these argumentation activities.

CASE STUDY—LANGUAGE SUPPORTS
FOR ARGUMENTATION

In this section, we describe language supports from a case study that we carried out with a middle school teacher who taught in a sheltered English instruction classroom (González-Howard et al., 2017). The sheltered English instruction model is one in which the teacher simultaneously addresses language development and content learning objectives (Echevarria, Vogt, & Short, 2008). At this particular school, Ms. Newbury (all names are pseudonyms) was the only middle school sheltered English instruction science teacher, and as such taught a rotating curriculum with students remaining in her classroom for sixth, seventh, and eighth grade (unless they were transitioned to a mainstream class due to advancements in their English). We spent four months observing Ms. Newbury's class as she piloted two life science curricular units. The curriculum piloted was intentionally written to offer students multiple opportunities to participate in argumentation across writing and speaking as they engaged with life science content. For instance, in one lesson students' observations of an agar-plate streak test were used to orally debate whether there was evidence that penicillin kills bacteria. In another lesson, students wrote arguments explaining whether a fictitious patient had one of four medical conditions they had read about (e.g., diabetes). In this study, we were specifically interested in identifying and examining the language supports Ms. Newbury used to help her EL students access and better engage in various argumentation activities included in the curriculum. We will now share a few of these language supports.

Tables 4.1 and 4.2 in the subsequent section include the name and a description of each language support for argumentation that Ms. Newbury incorporated into her science instruction. Table 4.1 includes supports that target writing, while Table 4.2 has strategies to help EL students participate in argumentation through talk.

The instructional strategies in these tables are categorized by the way in which we observed Ms. Newbury using them in her classroom. However, a few could also be used to support students' argumentation in the other language mode. For example, Ms. Newbury offered her students conversational sentence starters when they carried out a whole class debate. This language support could also be given to students in the form of writing prompts when they write arguments (e.g., a writing prompt to help students articulate their reasoning might read, "This evidence supports my claim because _____").

Additionally, although these strategies were incorporated into a middle school life science curriculum, with the appropriate modifications they could help EL students in Grades K–12 successfully engage in argumentation around a variety of disciplinary core ideas. We now highlight one strategy for writing and one for speaking in order to illustrate how paying attention to the language demands in this science practice can result in EL students having successful argumentation experiences.

Example Writing Language Support

The first life science unit that Ms. Newbury piloted focused on the human microbiome (Regents of the University of California, 2013a). Throughout the unit, there were multiple lessons around the idea that at the cellular level, the human body systems work together to produce energy by getting matter to and from cells. Toward the end of the unit, students were tasked with writing arguments that answered the question, "How did a fecal transplant cure the patient who was infected with *C. difficile?*" Students had learned about this topic for a few weeks through readings and investigations, including the agar-plate streak test previously described, which they were expected to incorporate into their written arguments. Table 4.1 features the writing supports provided.

TABLE 4.1 Language Supports for Engaging in Scientific Argumentation Through Writing	
Language Support	**Description**
Writing scaffolds	Giving students instructional supports for writing arguments, such as a template or sentence starters that highlight the structural components of an argument (i.e., claim, evidence, reasoning) or the social process (e.g., What counter claims should be considered? What critique do you have of the evidence?).
Modeling language expectations for an activity*	Making explicit how students should use language to carry out an argumentation task (e.g., using a model written argument to highlight how to critique a counterargument). Doing so helps students develop an understanding of how language can be used to accomplish specific goals (e.g., make a persuasive argument).
Simplifying claims	Modifying the language of complex claims by identifying the key concepts or words in them. Simplifying the language can increase students' comprehension of the claims. (However, it is important that at some point the original language of the complex claim be provided and addressed with students as well.)
Working with peers	Offering students time to process and talk about ideas with peers before completing a writing task. Peer work gives students opportunities to jointly develop language and engage in sensemaking.
Providing extended time	Providing students with additional class time to develop ideas and/or finish an argumentation activity. Having additional time enables students to engage in this science practice more meaningfully.

* Language support described in the example.

After introducing the assignment, Ms. Newbury spent nearly twenty minutes modeling language expectations for the activity. Specifically, she facilitated a discussion in which she asked students to think about and share phrases associated with the structural aspects of argumentation that they could use in their written arguments. As students brainstormed ideas, the teacher typed and projected them onto the whiteboard at the front of the classroom (see Figure 4.2). Each phrase was written under the appropriate heading (e.g., "In the data from Experiment 1 it shows..." is beneath the section Evidence). However, before writing the brainstormed phrases to the projection, Ms. Newbury asked students whether it aligned with the claim, evidence, or reasoning of an argument. Having students make this distinction further helped them understand the role that each structural piece played in answering the guiding question. Moreover, this support made transparent how students were expected to use language to carry out this argumentation activity.

Students' written arguments reflected the use of this language support. As exemplified by the student argument presented in Figure 4.3, the student started the third sentence with the phrase, "This means...," which the class had brainstormed for articulating reasoning. The phrase is then

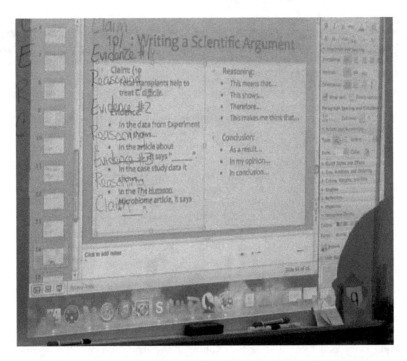

Figure 4.2   Phrases for an argument's structure. *Note:* This image is from an article published in the *International Journal of Science Education* in 2017, which is available online at http://dx.doi.org/10.1080/09500693.2017.1294785

Original Student Work	Transcription of Student Work

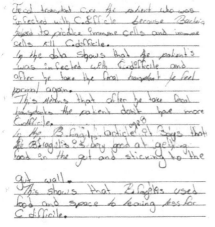

C Fecal transplant cure the patient who was infected with C. difficile because bacteria helped to produce immunecells and immune cells kill C. difficile.

E In the data shows that the patient's was infected with C. difficile and after he take the fecal transplant he feel normal again.

R This mean that after he take fecal transplants the patient don't have more C. difficile.

E In the B. gragilis article on p. 8 it says that the B. fragilis is very good at getting food in the gut and sticking to the gut wall.

R This shows that B. fragilis used food and space to leaving less for C. difficile.

Figure 4.3 Student written argument.

followed by the student's explanation of how their evidence supported the claim that they were making. Thus, the time this teacher spent working with students to make the language expectations for this argumentation activity clear helped students to participate meaningfully in the task.

Example Speaking Language Support

Ms. Newbury also incorporated many strategies in her instruction to help her EL students engage in argumentation through talk. Table 4.2 describes the language supports that we observed the teacher using with her students.

For example, one lesson involved students collecting, analyzing, and then orally debating evidence from a virtual simulation of a human's metabolism (Regents of the University of California, 2013b). Prior to running the simulation, Ms. Newbury presented students with the following scenario:

TABLE 4.2 Language Supports for Engaging in Scientific Argumentation Through Speaking

Language Support	Description
Conversational sentence starters	Providing students with phrases around an argument's structure or the processes of argumentation, which help them enter discussions (e.g., "How does that evidence support your claim?")
Allowing use of students' native language	Letting students use their first language to participate in an argumentation task. They might choose to use only their first language or work across multiple languages.
Offering students practice time*	Providing students with time to prepare and practice articulating their argument and other points they may want to make during a discussion (e.g., a question for a student). This practice may be done individually or with peers.
Checking for understanding	Monitoring student comprehension as they listen to others articulate an argument (e.g., "How does Fernando's claim compare to what Cecilia said earlier?").
Peer modeling	Having students demonstrate to peers how to carry out an argumentation task (e.g., a pair of students asking each other questions about the other person's argument).

* Language support described in the example.

"Cooper is sick but still wants to attend soccer practice. He wants to know whether he will be able to run as hard as he normally would." During the simulation, as Cooper's activity levels increased with him running faster, messages would appear indicating that his body was undergoing additional cellular growth and repair. Students then used this data to determine which of two claims was best supported: (a) Cooper's body could not maintain the same level of activity as it normally would, or (b) Cooper's body could maintain the same level of activity as it normally would when healthy. Before the class engaged in the oral argumentation aspect of the lesson, Ms. Newbury set aside time for students to prepare and practice articulating their ideas with peers. The following exchange was heard between a small group of students:

> **Daniela:** Qué piensas? Que él puede correr, o no, como antes? [What do you think? That he can run, or not, like before?]
>
> **Adrian:** I think he cannot correr tanto [run as much].
>
> **Daniela:** Why?
>
> **Adrian:** Porque había muchas, cómo se dice alertas? [Because there were many, how do you say alerts?]
>
> **Marina:** Alerts. So, you think he cannot run like before?
>
> **Adrian:** Yes. He cannot run like before because the alerts.

Giving students this time allowed them not only to engage in sense-making with peers around the simulation, but also to think collaboratively about the language they could use to express their argument in English. This practice time resulted in students' debates being much richer in terms of both the science ideas and academic language. Specifically, students expanded their initial understandings of how the human metabolism works by incorporating evidence from the simulation, all the while using new language to express their scientific thinking.

Ms. Newbury's EL students had multiple opportunities to engage in argumentation activities partly because of the curricular units that their teacher was piloting. However, it was the combination of these activities with Ms. Newbury's inclusion of language supports that enabled her students to meaningfully construct and refine their understanding of scientific phenomena with their peers through this science practice. Certain tasks are better than others at providing rich contexts for argumentation. In the following section, we describe argumentation activities that have shown to be productive in supporting students in this science practice across different language modalities (Marco-Bujosa, McNeill, González-Howard, & Loper, 2017).

ARGUMENTATION ACTIVITIES ACROSS WRITING AND SPEAKING

There are many reasons why teachers might experience difficulty incorporating argumentation in their science instruction. For one, successfully engaging in this science practice requires the teacher and students to take on new roles in the classroom, with students more actively driving the learning process (McNeill et al., 2017). Students may feel uncomfortable with this expectation, and could benefit from various supports that help them with this shift. Furthermore, few resources exist that offer ideas for argumentation across writing and speaking. Without this information, teachers might find it challenging to include argumentation in their instruction, and to address the language requirements embedded in this science practice.

In response to these issues, we teamed up with colleagues at the Lawrence Hall of Science to develop The Argumentation Toolkit (http://www.argumentationtoolkit.org), a website with many different resources for helping teachers learn about and integrate argumentation into their classrooms (e.g., rubrics for assessing written arguments and classroom videos). This free website also includes suggested activities and strategies for helping students learn to engage in this science practice across writing and speaking. For example, the Reasoning tool is a graphic organizer that serves as a writing scaffold to aid students in articulating how evidence supports a claim.

To help students participate in oral argumentation, an Evidence Gradient tool encourages students to discuss the quality of evidence.

The resources on this website are meant to help teachers with a range of knowledge and experiences pertaining to argumentation. For instance, novice teachers can use the suggested activities to try and include this science practice in their instruction. Meanwhile, teachers more familiar with argumentation might instead modify the activities found on this website to align with certain instructional goals. Additionally, the language strategies in Tables 4.1 and 4.2 could be incorporated into many of these activities to better support EL students in this science practice. Next, we describe two argumentation activities from this website, one that focuses on this science practice through writing and the other through speaking.

Anticipation Guide to Support Writing and Revising

An anticipation guide is a tool that can help students track their thinking as they engage in science. Specifically, it helps students think about how one's science ideas may change when considering new evidence. To carry out this argumentation activity, students are first presented with a set of claims that they read and then decide whether or not they agree with the claims. This process activates their background knowledge about the ideas expressed in the claims. Figure 4.4 includes a sample anticipation guide from the Argumentation Toolkit focused on fossils (http://www. argumentationtoolkit.org/session-33.html). Then, students examine and make sense of new evidence, by observing fossils (or photos of fossils), all the while keeping in mind the claims from the anticipation guide. While doing so, students can discuss with peers how their initial ideas remained the same or changed from reviewing the data. Afterwards, students return to the anticipation guide to revise the original claims in light of new understandings, incorporating evidence to justify their ideas.

Through this iterative process, this argumentation task mirrors the activities of scientists who consider multiple claims and refine their explanations of natural phenomena as new evidence is gathered or discovered. Moreover, an anticipation guide can help students in writing arguments because it naturally comprises a revision process.

Teachers can attend to the language demands embedded in this argumentation activity by including language supports. For instance, some EL students, particularly those who are newer to English, might benefit from having the claims in the anticipation guide simplified. Simplification can increase students' comprehension because it allows them to focus on the important aspects of the claim. For example, Claim 1 in Figure 4.4 could

Anticipation Guide—What Are Fossils?

Directions:
- Read the claims below. If you agree with a claim, write an *A* in the "Before" column. If you disagree with a claim, write a *D* in the "Before" column.
- You will return to these claims later in the session. At that time, you will think about whether you still agree or disagree with each claim (writing your decision in the "After" column). If you disagree with the claim, you will write a revised claim in the space provided. You will also include evidence that supports all of these claims.

Before	Claim	After
	1. While some fossils are the actual body of an organism, others are impressions left by the organism. Revised claim: Evidence:	
	2. Plants do not leave fossils. Revised claim: Evidence:	
	3. Fossils can only be made by organisms that lived on land. Revised claim: Evidence:	

Figure 4.4 Example anticipation guide—What are fossils?

be simplified from "While some fossils are of the actual body of an organism, others are impressions left by the organism" to "Fossils are bodies or impressions of organisms." We recommend making students part of this process. For instance, a teacher might ask their students, "If you had to say this claim in seven words, what seven words would you use?" This honing in helps students identify the key concepts or words in a claim. It is important to point out that this strategy is not meant to keep EL students from engaging with challenging language; instead, it is intended to help them unpack the meaning in complex claims.

A Card Sort to Debate Which Claim Is Best Supported by Evidence

A *card sort* is a versatile activity that can target many aspects of argumentation (e.g., whether evidence is relevant to supporting a particular claim). Regardless of its focus, this activity supports students in interacting with their peers and speaking about different aspects of an argument. One way this activity could be used is to prompt students to debate which of two competing claims is strongest. To carry out this activity, students are given an envelope with potential evidence cards. Then, they are tasked with sorting the cards as supporting Claim 1, Claim 2 or neither claim. The sample card sort in Figure 4.5, which is from the Argumentation Toolkit (http://www .argumentationtoolkit.org/session-21.html), involved students sorting evidence to decide whether a fossil tooth came from a prehistoric mountain lion or a prehistoric shark. While students sort the evidence cards, the teacher should encourage them to articulate why they categorize them as they do. Students can question one another during the sorting process, and even disagree with their peers. The important thing is that students' conversations and ideas be grounded in evidence. Additionally, having students discuss their sorting rationale with peers further supports them in expressing their reasoning. To help students understand that ideas about the natural world often change when new evidence is compared to existing evidence, a teacher could present students with a second set of evidence cards (see darker shaded cards labeled H–L in bottom right corner in

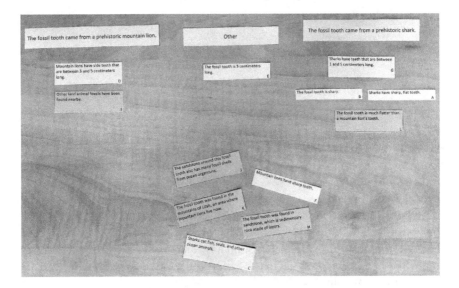

Figure 4.5 Example card sort—Where did the fossil tooth come from?

Figure 4.5). Students could then sort these new cards and reevaluate which claim they believe is best supported by the evidence.

This argumentation activity is linguistically demanding as it requires students to use language in complex ways to discuss which claim is best substantiated by evidence. Not only do students need to read and make sense of the evidence cards, but then they need to use language to question, critique, and persuade their peers. Additionally, all of these processes occur in real time. Without attention to these linguistic demands, EL students might not be able to access or engage in the task. The language supports in Table 4.2 offer ideas for ensuring that ELs have successful experiences with such a task. For example, a teacher might incorporate peer modeling into a lesson before students do this argumentation activity. The students modeling the activity could be strategically selected by the teacher (e.g., they are highly proficient in English, or have a strong understanding of argumentation). These students could then demonstrate to their peers how to carry out the card sort, modeling the various interactions students could engage in (e.g., challenging the other person over a particular way of sorting the evidence). Not only does the peer modeling offer example language for students, but it also highlights how the activity is about the process of making sense of evidence, and not about getting at the "right answer."

CONCLUSION

The science practices highlighted in recent reform efforts offer numerous opportunities and challenges for culturally and linguistically diverse students (Lee et al., 2013). By experiencing and making sense of phenomena with their peers, students have the opportunity to engage in rich science learning. However, teachers also need to consider appropriate instructional strategies and activities to support students in these linguistically demanding practices. In this chapter, we focus on ways to support all students in the science practice of argumentation. Specifically, we share language supports for writing (e.g., modeling language expectations) and speaking (e.g., offering students practice time) to modify existing curriculum and activities. Additionally, we provide example argumentation activities (e.g., anticipation guide, card sort) that can offer new opportunities for this science practice across language modalities. Supporting students in argumentation requires significant shifts in classroom instruction, but with sufficient time and support EL students can successfully engage in this science practice (González-Howard & McNeill, 2016; González-Howard et al., 2017).

We end this chapter with a few questions, that one can either consider individually or discuss with colleagues. The inquiry questions are intended for educational researchers, while the action research questions are meant for teachers. We hope that these questions prompt reflection and trigger new ideas, and that in doing so they help us all work towards developing better learning environments for linguistically diverse students.

Inquiry Questions

1. How do EL students' strengths and challenges as they engage in argumentation vary across grade level (i.e., preschool, elementary school, middle and high school)?
2. What variation exists in EL students' strengths and challenges when engaging in argumentation across disciplinary core ideas (e.g., bio-diversity, chemical reactions, or weather and climate)?
3. How do EL students' argumentation engagement levels vary for students with different English language proficiencies (i.e., beginning, intermediate, advanced)?
4. What language supports could be used to help EL students engage in other science practices, such as developing and using models or constructing explanations?

Action Research Questions

1. Examine your students' current argumentation writing to identify the strengths and challenges around the structural components (i.e., claim, evidence, reasoning) and social dimensions (e.g., consideration of competing claim, engagement in critique) of this science practice. In what areas do your students need more support in their writing?
2. Video record an argumentation discussion in your classroom (either small group or full class). Analyze the video to identify the strengths and challenges around the structural components (i.e., claim, evidence, reasoning) and social dimensions (e.g., consideration of competing claim, engagement in critique) of this science practice. In what areas do your students need more support in their talk?
3. Select one of the argumentation activities found in the Argumentation Toolkit (http://www.argumentationtoolkit.org) to integrate into your classroom instruction. Make sure to consider the language demands in the activity, and include language supports to address them (see Table 4.1 and Table 4.2 for ideas). After trying the new activity and language support, reflect on how similar and different the instruction was compared to how you previously taught that science idea. What went well? Did the language

support(s) help your students better engage in the argumentation activity? How would you further modify the lesson in the future?

ACKNOWLEDGMENTS

This research was conducted as part of the project "Constructing and Critiquing Arguments in Middle School Science Classrooms: Supporting Teachers with Multimedia Educative Curriculum Materials," which was supported by the National Science Foundation grant DRL-1119584. Any opinions expressed in this work are those of the authors and do not necessarily represent either those of the funding agency, University of Texas at Austin or Boston College. We would like to thank the teachers and advisors who provided valuable feedback. Also, we would like to thank our colleagues at the Lawrence Hall of Science, particularly Suzy Loper, and Boston College, especially Lisa Marco-Bujosa, for their invaluable collaboration in this work.

NOTES

1. Although Ms. Williams is fictional, her thoughts and experiences represent those of numerous middle school teachers with whom we have worked.

REFERENCES

Berland, L. K., McNeill, K. L., Pelletier, P., & Krajcik, J. (2017). Engaging in scientific argumentation. In C. Schwarz, C. Passmore, & B. J. Reiser (Eds.), *Helping students make sense of the world using next generation science and engineering practices* (pp. 229–258). Arlington, VA: National Science Teachers Association Press.

Berland, L. K., Schwarz, C. V., Krist, C., Kenyon, L., Lo, A. S., & Reiser, B. J. (2016). Epistemologies in practice: Making scientific practices meaningful for students. *Journal of Research in Science Teaching, 53*(7), 1082–1112.

Bybee, R. W. (2011). Scientific and engineering practices in K–12 classrooms: Understanding a framework for K–12 science education. *Science and Children, 49*(4), 10–16.

Echevarria, J., Vogt, M. E., & Short, D. J. (2008). *Making content comprehensible for English learners: The SIOP model (3rd ed.)*. Boston, MA: Allyn & Bacon.

González-Howard, M., & McNeill, K. L. (2016). Learning in a community of practice: Factors impacting English-learning students' engagement in scientific argumentation. *Journal of Research in Science Teaching, 53*(4), 527–553.

González-Howard, M., McNeill, K. L., Marco-Bujosa, L., & Proctor, C. P. (2017). 'Does it answer the question or is it French fries?': An exploration of language supports for scientific argumentation. *International Journal of Science Education, 39*(5), 528–547.

Hakuta, K., Santos, M., & Fang, Z. (2013). Challenges and opportunities for language learning in the context of the CCSS and the NGSS. *Journal of Adolescent & Adult Literacy, 56*(6), 451–454.

Honeycutt Swanson, L., Bianchini, J. A., & Sook Lee, J. (2014). Engaging in argument and communicating information: A case study of English language learners and their science teacher in an urban high school. *Journal of Research in Science Teaching, 51*(1), 31–64.

Lee, O., Miller, E. C., & Januszyk, R. (2014). Next generation science standards: All standards, all students. *Journal of Science Teacher Education, 25*(2), 223–233.

Lee, O., Quinn, H., & Valdés, G. (2013). Science and language for English language learners in relation to next generation Science standards and with implications for common core state standards for English language arts and mathematics. *Educational Researcher, 42*(4), 223–233.

Marco-Bujosa, L. M., McNeill, K. L., González-Howard, M., & Loper, S. (2017). An exploration of teacher learning from an educative reform-oriented curriculum: Case studies of teacher curriculum use. *Journal of Research in Science Teaching, 54*(2), 141–168.

McNeill, K. L., González-Howard, M., Katsh-Singer, R., & Loper, S. (2017). Moving beyond pseudoargumentation: Teachers' enactments of an educative science curriculum focused on argumentation. *Science Education, 101*(3), 426–457.

McNeill, K. L., & Krajcik, J. (2012). *Supporting grade 5–8 students in constructing explanations in science: The claim, evidence and reasoning framework for talk and writing.* New York, NY: Pearson Allyn & Bacon.

National Research Council (2012). *A framework for K–12 science education: Practices, crosscutting concepts and core ideas.* Washington, DC: The National Academies Press.

Next Generation Science Standards Lead States. (2013). *Next generation science standards: For states, by states (Appendix F).* Washington, DC: The National Academies Press.

Osborne, J. (2014). Teaching scientific practices: Meeting the challenge of change. *Journal of Science Teacher Education, 25*(2), 177–196.

Pruitt, S. L. (2014). The next generation science standards: The features and challenges. *Journal of Science Teacher Education, 25*(2), 145–156.

Regents of the University of California (2013a). *Microbiome. Field trial version of Middle School science unit developed by the Learning Design Group.* Berkeley, CA: Lawrence Hall of Science.

Regents of the University of California (2013b). *Metabolism. Field trial version of Middle School science unit developed by the Learning Design Group.* Berkeley, CA: Lawrence Hall of Science.

Weinburgh, M., Silva, C., Horak Smith K., Grouix, J., & Nettles, J. (2014). The intersection of inquiry-based science and language: Preparing teachers for ELL classrooms. *Journal of Science Teacher Education, 25*(5), 519–541.

CHAPTER 5

USING FUNCTIONAL GRAMMAR TO TALK AND WRITE ABOUT SCIENCE

Mary Schleppegrell
University of Michigan

Jason Moore
Oakland University

Catherine O'Hallaron
University of Michigan

Annemarie Palincsar
University of Michigan

This chapter describes how teachers and researchers, in partnership, introduced 4th grade children to writing arguments in science. They wanted to go beyond the typical "argument" where students take a position on something and support it with their experience and opinions. Instead, the goal was to support students in reading about an issue and identifying evidence

Culturally and Linguistically Diverse Learners and STEAM, pages 95–115
Copyright © 2019 by Information Age Publishing

from what they read that could be used to argue for a policy position. This kind of writing is challenging, but it offers opportunities for students to learn to read, talk, and write as they work over several days with an interesting and engaging issue. The instruction took place in a classroom where the children had varying levels of mother tongue literacy and English language proficiency. Many had first come to school without knowledge of English from their home contexts. In addition, a variety of experiences was represented in the classrooms: Some students were born in the United States to parents who had grown up in the community, while others were first- or second-generation immigrants. The teacher and researchers had been in a collaborative relationship for 2 years, working together in a project that explored how the tools of systemic functional linguistics (SFL) could be made useful to teachers of English language learners. The chapter illustrates some ways functional grammar from SFL supported teachers and students as they read challenging texts and shows how explicit naming and practice with the components of an argument supported children in their writing.

The larger collaborative context included seven researchers and 23 teachers and instructional coaches who interacted with each other over 3 years in a project called *Language and Meaning*. We used design-based research (DBR), an approach to inquiry that explores an issue in iterative waves of creating, piloting, refining, and then implementing and studying new approaches in authentic contexts. Our goal was to develop curriculum materials, drawing on SFL concepts, to support teachers in talking about language and meaning with their students who were English learners. Since SFL is a complex linguistic theory, we knew we needed to adapt the SFL concepts in ways that teachers could use to support children's language and literacy development in the context of grade-appropriate activities. Our goal was to offer teachers and children new ways of talking about language that would support their reading, speaking, and writing development.[1] For each approach and unit of study we developed, we first partnered with teachers to pilot the work in a classroom context that could inform its further development. In this chapter, we show how our work in that context enabled us to develop new perspectives on teaching the argument genre and on supporting students in identifying evidence from written texts and accomplishing the goals of argument in science.

Informed by previous research with English learners, we began this project with three key ideas in mind: (a) that our activities would *develop teachers' knowledge about language* so that they could (b) *support explicit, meaningful attention to language,* and (c) that this would always involve *meaningful interaction between students and teachers.* To develop teachers' knowledge about language, we drew on SFL research that suggested ways of making knowledge about language meaningful. To be explicit about the ways language works, we identified metalanguage (language about language) that

Figure 5.1 Phases of the lesson.

the teachers would find useful in accomplishing the goals of each unit of study. To engage learners in talk about language and meaning, we built plentiful opportunities for students to interact verbally with teachers and with one another into each lesson. The pedagogy we present here was also informed in part by the teaching–learning cycle prominent in SFL work, and its stages of *developing knowledge about the topic, deconstructing models of the text to be written, explicit attention to language in supporting joint writing,* and then *independent writing* (for more on the TLC see Spycher, 2017). We represented these stages to the teachers as a series of lesson phases to connect with the kinds of activities they typically engaged in across a unit of study, highlighting the new key role of talk about language in the texts students read and in analysis of the texts to be written (see Figure 5.1). Important as well was that the instruction was designed to be interactive, giving students the chance to share knowledge and offer ideas about the dilemmas driving the arguments in ways that in turn helped shape the instruction. In all of the units we developed, we endeavored to choose topics that students would find interesting, and we worked to make the central question for the unit relevant to the development of understanding about how to argue for change in the world.

THE UNIT OF STUDY

The lesson excerpts we present below come from a unit of study as it was enacted by a researcher–teacher pair in a fourth grade classroom over 6 days (60–100 minutes per day). Students had previously been learning about ecosystems, including about communities of organisms in different environments and the role of human impact on an ecosystem. In this unit, they learned about a South American toad, the *cane toad,* that was introduced into Australia to control a beetle that was attacking the sugar cane crop. Through video and reading materials, students learned how this invasive species has disrupted the balance of the ecosystem and is now proliferating in ways that have serious consequences for other species. They learned about some proposals that have been put forward to address the cane toad problem and thought about issues raised by those proposals. Then they focused in on a particular proposal, to use meat ants, a local species that was already known to be able to kill cane toads, to address the cane toad expansion. Students were asked to take a position on whether or not scientists should try the meat ant solution, and spent several lessons learning to draw evidence from what they read to support the position they were taking, as well as to address a counterargument to their own position. Table 5.1 offers a brief overview of the six lessons (each a little more than an hour) through which this unit unfolded.

THE CLASSROOM IN ACTION: METALANGUAGE OF *LIKELIHOOD* AND GENRE *STAGES*

Metalanguage is a key resource for being explicit about language and meaning, and for drawing children's attention to the language resources that enable them to express meanings of different kinds (Schleppegrell, 2013). We drew on two kinds of metalanguage in our work to support both reading for meaning and writing to argue from evidence. One type comes from functional grammar; the metalanguage Michael Halliday developed for his description of English from a meaning-based perspective.[2] In this unit, the focus in reading was on the language of *likelihood* as students considered the ways the authors of the texts they read presented the strength of the evidence for different potential solutions to the cane toad dilemma. Another kind of metalanguage comes from a focus on *genre* in SFL, where genres are described in terms of their purpose and *stages* (e.g., Christie & Derewianka, 2008). Using metalanguage to name purposes and features of

---

TABLE 5.1 Overview of the Unit With Key Activities

Lesson 1: Reading to Learn About the Issue

Students read "Stopping the Cane Toad Invasion" (O'Hallaron & Moore, unpublished curriculum materials) and discuss in pairs how intended and unintended consequences played out in the Australian situation. They make predictions, attending to "likelihood words" they had practiced using in a previous unit. They then generate potential solutions to the cane toad problem through pair or small group talk and teacher-facilitated discussion of likely benefits and drawbacks for each proposed solution. Next, they read "Using Parasites to Control the Cane Toad Invasion" (Moore & O'Hallaron, unpublished curriculum materials) and discuss the potential for lungworms to be used as a solution to the cane toad problem. Students again focus on likelihood to consider how sure scientists were that lungworms would be a viable solution.

(continued)

TABLE 5.1 Overview of the Unit With Key Activities (continued)
Lesson 2: Introducing the Argument Genre
Students view a video about the damage cane toads cause to an ecosystem, take notes, watch it again, and discuss it. They then read together and discuss a model argument that takes the position that lungworms would be a bad solution to the cane toad problem. The teacher briefly introduces the argument text type and some of its common stages, and the children then work together to deconstruct the lungworms model, focusing on its overall purpose, and then the different stages and their functions. They consider what makes an argument effective, such as anticipating what someone who does not agree with your argument might say.
Lesson 3: Exploring a Model Argument and Introducing the Issue to be Argued
Students explore another model argument, this one in favor of the lungworm solution. Students work in small groups to identify the different stages of the argument and report their findings. The teacher leads a discussion to refine students' understanding of stage boundaries, what function different sentences serve, and how the author used "likelihood words" in the Reason and Response stages to communicate how sure they were or how likely something was to happen. Students then read the "Meat Ants" text (Moore & O'Hallaron, unpublished curriculum materials), a one-page description of another potential solution to the cane toad problem. The argument task is presented, and students identify evidence for each position as they read and discuss the text in small groups. Students are introduced to a support for gathering evidence from the text that the teacher uses to guide discussion about how evidence can support a claim. Students identify likelihood expressions and judge the degree of likelihood the author communicates as they discuss the evidence.
Lesson 4: Developing a Claim Based on Evidence
Students review what they know about cane toads, lungworms, and meat ants. They continue to collaborate on the evidence chart they are developing to weigh the evidence for the three possible responses to the argument prompt they will address, adding the "why" or "how" of the evidence—and begin to formulate reasons. Students then decide on the positions they will take in discussion with others. They share their positions and the evidence they are using to support their claims. The teacher introduces the Evidence/Reason scaffolds and students decide which claim they will make and select the evidence they will use to support it.
Lesson 5: Consider a Counterargument
Teacher distributes the "Stages of an Argument" overview and the class reviews how all the stages fit together. Student volunteers share their Evidence/Reason scaffolds and all work to complete their Evidence/Reason pairs. The class discusses some students' examples, and the teacher helps students talk through and clarify their thinking: by adding detail, by using modality to "tone down" predictions or be more factually precise; or simply by orally rehearsing their reasoning. Then the Counterargument and scaffold for it are introduced and students practice an example Counterargument. Students work on their own to draft counterarguments; the class discusses the work of some students.
Lesson 6: The Description of Issue and Claim Stages; Bringing All the Stages Together and Writing the Argument
Students review what they know about cane toads, and students finish their Counterargument/Response scaffolds. The teacher introduces the Description of Issue and Claim stages, using the lungworms model. The class reviews the overall purpose and structure of the genre, and then students bring all of the stages together to build their final arguments (45 minutes of writing).

Note: All materials for the unit can be found at: https://sites.google.com/site/functionalgrammar/project-materials/scientific-argument/cane-toads—meat-ants. Materials needed to understand this chapter are included here.

the *stages* the children needed to include in their arguments was a means of being explicit about what was expected. Due to space limitations, we focus here on how the metalanguage of *likelihood* and genre *stages* supported the teachers in moving children from reading to writing, with lots of explicit talk about language and meaning.

Learning About the Purposes and Stages of an Argument

The stages of the argument genre that were supported in this unit included *Description of Issue and Claim, Evidence and Reason, Counterargument and Response,* and *Restatement of Claim*[3] (see Figure 5.2). To introduce the genre, on Day 2 the teacher briefly presented an overview of the overall purpose of argument, the stages, and their functions, and then asked students to think about whether any of the stages looked familiar. These 4th grade students immediately recognized *Claim* ("...when they give you a question, a prompt, and you have to answer it," one student explained) and *Evidence* ("...something to prove your claim," offered another). Students also made guesses about the purposes of stages they hadn't seen before, and were collectively able to come quite close to correctly describing several of

Stages of an Argument

- **Description of Issue**
  - *Tells the reader important information about the issue.*
- **Claim**
  - *Tells what you think should be done.*

- **Evidence**
  - *Information from the text that supports your claim.*
- **Reason**
  - *Why or how the evidence supports your claim about the issue.*

- **Counterargument**
  - *How someone might disagree with your claim.*
- **Response**
  - *Why that counterargument doesn't change your mind.*

- **Restatement of Claim**
  - *Says again what you think should be done.*

Figure 5.2 Stages of an argument, as presented in this unit.

them. This teacher-led part of the lesson was brief and dynamic, focused on sufficiently familiarizing students with the stages they would be exploring in the activities that followed.

The next step was to identify stages in the model argument against using lungworms to combat the cane toads (see Figure 5.3). First the class read the model and the teacher asked questions to get at the overall meaning ("What's their position?" "Did they use evidence?"). Students then chose to work by themselves or with a partner to identify each stage, and engaged in whole-class discussion of their findings with student volunteers projecting their marked-up models. Lively discussion ensued when there was disagreement about where one stage ended and another began, offering an opportunity to highlight the different kinds of meaning used to build the genre's stages. For example, Yasmin identified the first three sentences as the *Description of Issue,* and the last two as *Claim,* but several students immediately disagreed. Amir reported that he had also included the fourth sentence, *Scientists think that spreading the cane toad lungworm around could help solve the problem, but it is too dangerous,* as part of the *Description of Issue,* and marked only the last sentence, *They should not use it,* as the *Claim.* Yasmin's response reflected the research team's thinking in designing the materials, but the teacher took Amir's point and asked the class to think about it.

The *Description of Issue* stage had been characterized as including the factual information necessary to contextualize the argument for the reader; *Claim,* in contrast, was about the writer's opinion. The students looked

No, don't use the lungworm!

The cane toad invasion has been a disaster for the ecosystems in Australia. Cane toads were brought to Australia to solve a problem, but they have become an even bigger problem themselves. The huge toads eat anything that will fit in their mouths, and nothing can eat them because they are highly poisonous. Scientists thing that spreading the cane toad lungworm around could help solve the problem, but it is too dangerous. They should not use it.

First, using lungworms is a bad solution because it has never been tested in nature. When people brought the cane toad to Australia, they never thought it would cause such a big problem, and the same thing could happen with lungworms.

Another reason this is a bad solution is that the worms only kill about 30% of baby toads. That means 70% of toads would still survive. The impact is too small to place the ecosystem in such risk.

One reason to use lungworms is that they do make older toads smaller and slower. But smaller toads still eat a lot of food, and slower toads are still poisonous. In the end, it is highly unlikely that lungworms would make a real difference.

Australia needs a good solution to the cane toad problem, but using lungworm parasites is not the right one. Scientists should look for something better and safer.

Figure 5.3 Lungworms solution: Model argument against.

closely at the meaning and function of the language in the fourth sentence and saw that it does some work related to both stages: It contains factual information (*scientists think that spreading the cane toad lungworm around could help solve the problem*) as well as the writer's assessment of that approach (*but it is too dangerous*). On the projected model, the teacher marked this sentence as part of the Claim, but took an additional step toward acknowledging the ambiguity of the stage boundaries by underlining the last clause in the fourth sentence along with the fifth sentence, saying:

> I'm going to circle all of this as part of the Claim, but I'm going to underline in dark—... the heart of the Claim. *It is too dangerous, they should not use it.* That is really what the Claim is.... that first part of the sentence is... describing what scientists are considering.

In presenting the genre stages, we wanted to provide explicit guidance, but also show students where they had options for making choices.

Another productive student-initiated discussion came up as the class identified *Evidence* and *Reason* in the model, which was designed to illustrate different ways of presenting these genre stages. The students quickly found and labeled the first pair, but the second pair was challenging in that it used the word *reason* to introduce evidence:

> Another reason this is a bad solution is that the worms only kill about 30% of baby toads. That means 70% of toads would still survive. The impact is too small to place the ecosystem in such risk.

In this case the reasoning about evidence is in the last sentence, where the number of toads that would survive the lungworms is judged as too small to take the risks involved. Mohammad's group quickly labeled the number of toads killed by the worms as the *Reason*. The teacher acknowledged the challenge:

> **Teacher:** That word "reason" can be very tricky. Now, the *Reason* tells us why and how the *Evidence* supports [the *Claim*]. Does this tell us exactly why and how?
> **Students:** No.
> **Teacher:** ... What is it doing? It's introducing the evidence. The evidence is a fact that supports it, that only 30% are killed. Now, 70% would still survive—is that a fact?

The students concluded that the sentence beginning with *Another reason*... counts as *Evidence*. This discussion provided an opportunity to help students think about the meaning and function of these argument stages; as the teacher says "about what it's doing." The stages of an argument accomplish different purposes as the text unfolds, and consistently emphasizing meaning and function was a central goal for the teacher–researcher team in planning and implementing instruction. The *Description of Issue* and *Claim* example showed students that the stages are not always as distinct as the genre description may imply. The example raised by Mohammad's group reinforced the importance of going beyond the meaning of words themselves, because words can sometimes "mean" one thing but "do" another (e.g., the word "reason" can introduce evidence and not reasoning).

Focusing on *Likelihood* While Reading

Another focus throughout the unit was on the language of the texts the students read and on the language choices they would make as they wrote their arguments. This helped students continue to work with a concept that had already been introduced in the previous science unit; the notion of *likelihood*—how authors use language to show how *usual* or *likely* it is that something will happen or how *sure* they are about the evidence. In science, just understanding the meaning of the words in a text is not enough; students also have to consider the perspective of the author of the text. Although science is often talked about as if it is completely objective, in fact, scientists often indicate, by the language they use, that their conclusions or predictions are not certain. Meanings related to *likelihood* are an aspect of *modality* (*obligation, inclination,* and *ability* are other areas of modal meaning), and modality can be expressed in modal verbs (*could, might, will*), modal adjuncts (e.g., *probably, usually, certainly*), whole clauses (*it is likely that...; it's not possible for...*), nouns (*possibility*) and other language forms. These modal meanings are a challenging area of the grammar for second language learners, and learners need time and experience with the language to fully understand and express degrees of commitment and other modal meanings. Scientists choose their language carefully to be accurate about claims and predictions, and using meanings of *likelihood* enables them to carefully calibrate the ways they present evidence and make claims.

In the previous unit the students had worked with a pedagogical tool we developed called the *usuality/likelihood scale* (Figure 5.4). This support, posted on the classroom wall, enabled the teacher to make *likelihood* and *usuality* a focus of discussion and raise the children's awareness about how low, middle, and high degrees of *likelihood* and *usuality* are presented in language choices.

Students had already practiced identifying the language of *likelihood* and *usuality*, adding examples to the scale, and coming to recognize the range of language resources through which these meanings are made. So in the work of this unit, they were already poised to discuss whether the author

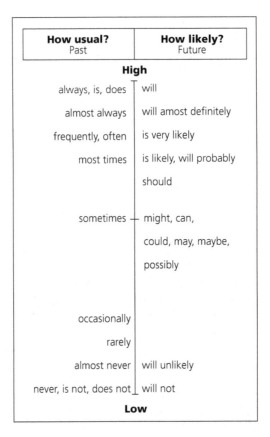

Figure 5.4 The Usuality/Likelihood Scale, with examples of low, mid, and high modality.

is presenting ideas as *definite* or just a *possibility*. Students paid attention to this language as they collected and evaluated evidence in the texts they read to develop understanding of the cane toad problem (see Palincsar & Schleppegrell, 2014; O'Halloran, Palincsar, & Schleppegrell, 2015). The prompt they were asked to respond to was:

> Scientists in Australia think using meat ants might be one effective way to stop cane toads from spreading and hurting more organisms. What do you think of this option? Is it a good option Australia should act on now, a good option they should study more, or not a good option? Why?

As students read the texts about the ways scientists have tried to control the spread of cane toads, they needed to consider the different solutions that had been proposed and think about the strength of the evidence used to present the problem and possible solutions. Looking for *likelihood* helped them recognize that some statements are definite, and others are more tentative or exploratory. The text on meat ants as a solution, for example, says

> the presence of meat ants across Australia *has not prevented* cane toads from invading that region, but meat ants *do kill* many toads. Increasing the numbers of ants where the toads breed *could slow their spread.*

As the class read this text, the teacher drew students' attention to the ways evidence was presented:

> **Teacher:** How likely is it that increasing the number of ants will stop cane toads?
> **Zeinab:** It's between *definite* and *sort of likely* because it says right here *The presence of meat ants across Australia has not prevented cane toads from invading that region.*

Zeinab points out that the text does not claim that meat ants will *definitely* slow the spread of the cane toads. In another instance, a student identified the phrase *will likely* in the sentence *Getting the ants to move to cane toads' ponds will likely lower the number of ants in other places,* suggesting that this meant the author thought the result was not just possible, but probable. Students were able to identify many places throughout the texts they read that showed that the proposed solutions were not presented as guaranteed.

Discussion also focused on *likelihood* when students were reading the lungworms model argument. A student commented on the words *highly unlikely* in the *Response* to the *Counterargument,* and the class talked about how sure the author was, whether credible writers would sound more sure about evidence, and whether it was possible to be entirely sure when reasoning about evidence.

Focusing on *Stages* and *Likelihood* While Writing an Argument

The metalanguage of *likelihood* continued to be in focus as students used the *stages* metalanguage to work with the model arguments, focusing both on the purpose and the language choices of the authors, as shown above. Then, as students prepared to write their own texts, the focus changed to exploring evidence from the readings that could be used to support the different possible claims. To accomplish this, the teacher led a discussion to develop a chart that listed each possible claim and evidence to support it (see Figure 5.5). This prepared the students to evaluate which claim(s) a

Collecting and Reasoning About Evidence: Meat Ants and Cane Toads			
Evidence: A piece of information from the text that supports...	**Good, act now**	**Good, study more**	**Bad, don't use**
Meat ants are able to kill live cane toads. The cane toads don't move when attacked. The cane toad's poison doesn't seem to hurt the meat ants. So the meat ants can attack the toad while it just sits there.	X	X	
Even though they're called meat ants, they mostly eat honeydew from certain caterpillars and butterflies. In return, the ants protect the caterpillars from predators.			X
In these experiments, damage to other living things appears to be low, but scientists don't know for sure. There will likely be fewer ants where they normally live... this could change the behavior of other organisms.		X	X
Female toads can lay 35,000 eggs at a time!	X		

Figure 5.5 Support for collecting and reasoning about evidence for different claims.

given piece of evidence could support, and helped the class work together to weigh the evidence as they considered the potential benefits and drawbacks of using meat ants to control the cane toad population.

After gathering and discussing several examples of evidence, the students practiced formulating *Reasons* that would link the *Evidence* back to the *Claim* it would support, as this example of dialogue illustrates:

> **Isa:** (reading from text) *Getting the ants to move to cane toads' ponds would likely lower the number of ants in other places. This could change the behavior of other organisms.*
>
> **Teacher:** Good. And that connects with an idea earlier in the text—
>
> **Isa:** —it's changing the behavior of the other organisms, that means it's changing the behavior of the whole ecosystem.
>
> **Teacher:** Okay, so... (writing on overhead) *There will likely be fewer ants where they normally live... This could change the behavior of other organisms.* Now, talk through your reasoning. Why might this support not using it or studying it more?
>
> **Isa:** I think it supports not using it... because if it changes the behavior of the organisms that means it's changing the behavior of the whole ecosystem, like let's say—
>
> **Teacher:** —Good, so give us an example of how changing the whole ecosystem could be bad.
>
> **Isa:** Like let's say there's a farmer and they're growing crops and there's meat ants, there's like small little animals the

meat ants could eat, like they usually eat them to protect the crops.

Teacher: And if you take them away?

Isa: There will be less meat ants, and the other animals, some of them will be eaten but mostly a *lot* of the crops will be eaten.

Teacher: (to class) So he's giving us an example, we don't know for sure, but it's possible—he's giving us our *Reason* for why changing an ecosystem could be bad . . . that's a very good example for a good *Reason* for that.

Isa's early comment—that changing the behavior of one organism would ultimately affect the entire ecosystem—reflected good understanding of the science content. The teacher's questions scaffolded the translation of this knowledge into an explanation that was explicit enough to make Isa's thinking accessible to others. The discussion of evidence helped students decide which claim they would adopt in their own writing. As the teacher filled in the projected chart with paraphrased evidence, the importance of presenting the degree of *likelihood* in the source text was emphasized. This practice remained important as children began to write their arguments and bring evidence to support their own claims.

As they gathered evidence for the possible claims, students thought about and discussed the evidence they thought was most important: that toxins from the toad are not likely to affect the ants, and meat ants can kill toads. Students talked about which of the pieces of evidence displayed on the chart would call for explanation and which were more self-evident. Anticipating just how much information the reader needs is an important writing skill that takes practice over time, and by returning several times to the issue of how much detail is needed, the teacher supported students in making this kind of judgment. Talk like this helped Isa and his classmates become more attuned to the process of building a *Reason* and served as oral rehearsal of reasoning in the ways students needed to in order to write *Reasons* that linked their *Evidence* back to their *Claims*.

Following this discussion, the students were ready to decide on the claim they wanted to support and develop their own *Evidence/Reason* pair. One issue that can emerge in teaching a genre is the danger that any graphic organizer that presents the stages of an argument has the potential to be seen as a template to fill in, treating the genre as if it must follow a given format, and not allowing flexibility. To reduce this possibility, we focused the work on genre stages not in the order that they would appear in the final written text, but instead in relation to the steps that need to be taken in an authentic process of developing a claim and supporting it with evidence. For example, it's important for students to read and think about what counts as evidence for a claim before deciding what claim they will support in their writing.

The students worked with separate scaffolds for each argument stage or pair of stages, beginning with the *Evidence/Reason* scaffolds (Figure 5.6), having their *Claim* in mind. (Their *Claim* was not fully articulated until the last day of the unit, when they wrote their final drafts. This gave them flexibility in continuing to consider the *Claim* that their *Evidence/Reason* would best support.) Later they transferred or modified the language they had written on these *stage* drafts as they wrote their final arguments.

The teacher asked students to think about which piece of evidence offered the strongest support for their position. In handing out the *Evidence/Reason* scaffolds, the teacher focused them on how much they would need to explain:

> You want to include enough information so that it makes sense. Some of these you really have to explain more than others. Which ones do you have to ex-

Name: _____

Circle your claim (your position on the issue) so far:

Good, act now!   Good, study more   Bad, don't use

Evidence: A piece of information from the text that supports your claim.

Reason: How or why does this evidence support your claim? How and why does the evidence help or hurt the cane toad problem?

Figure 5.6 Support for drafting the Evidence/Reason stage.

plain more than others? Which ones really require some talking through what actually happens?

As students worked on their *Evidence/Reason* scaffolds, the teachers interact-ed with them individually in supportive ways. For example, some students did not yet have a clear understanding of stage boundaries (for example, inserting their *Claim* into the *Evidence* or presenting new evidence in their *Reason*). After writing these genre stages, some students shared their drafts and discussed their reasoning with the whole class as further support for those still struggling.

As students wrote, the metalanguage of *likelihood* was also in focus. It helped them in two ways. First, it helped them use modality to calibrate their statements about the evidence and increase the credibility of their arguments, as they demonstrated their understanding of the history of the cane toad problem and the current state of scientific understanding (even scientists who study ways to eliminate cane toads are not entirely sure about the effects that proposed solutions might have on the ecosystem). Second, it helped them calibrate their claims to present the degree of confidence they had in them. As they analyzed *Claims* in the model texts, the students had also discussed how strong the authors felt about the positions they were taking. They recognized that one model used language choices that were more absolute (*They should not use it*) and the other left room for discussion (*It is worth trying*). The teacher asked students to be conscious of this in their own writing:

> As you're writing your *Evidence*..., you probably have an idea in your head about how strong you want to make your claim, right? So when you write your *Claim,* I want you to think about this too. Think about, are you going to make a really strong claim? Or are you going to make a claim that has room for *maybes* or *mights* or *probablys?* Think about, when somebody reads your *Claim,* how strong they're going to think that you feel.

After the children wrote, they analyzed the ways their peers had drawn on the evidence from the texts they read. For example, one student had written *The cane toads' toxins don't affect the meat ants.* The teacher asked, "Can we say the toxins won't affect the meat ants? Are there any *likelihood* words there?" The students recognized that the words *are not likely to* meant that this is not something that can be said definitely. Again, the metalan-guage enabled focus on precisely the language at stake in reading with good comprehension and writing with accuracy.

We have focused here on the pedagogy relevant to supporting students in bringing evidence and reasoning to support their claims. In writing the *Evidence, Reason,* and *Claim* stages, language choices are especially impor-tant. The *Counterargument* and *Response* stages were also carefully scaffolded, as described in O'Hallaron (2014b). On the last day of instruction, students prepared the *Description of Issue*, where the task was to decide how much the reader needs to know about the situation and paraphrase language from the source texts.

Summary

This unit models ways in which we can raise students' consciousness about social and political issues, while learning about both science and language. Additionally, the argument-writing focus positions students to be active investigators who evaluate information in order to formulate their own stances. Although in this example, students developed consciousness about a real-world problem that was half a world away, this approach to language and science learning could be directed at exploring local or regional environmental issues as well.

Some key features of the pedagogy we have described include:

- Providing source texts with information about the cane toad problem that students could use as evidence when they wrote their arguments, and incorporating expression of *likelihood* into the texts to support discussion about the author's degree of commitment to the evidence offered.

- Developing lesson phases that first built up information about the problem through close reading and then focused on stages of the argument genre through discussion of model arguments. Teacher and students collaborated in developing evidence and reasoning as well as counterarguments and responses to them, followed by students' independent writing. Throughout, the field of knowledge was further developed through discussion about the texts and the cane toad problem (students do not "finish" learning about the subject matter and then move on to learning about the genre; discussion of content and genre are integrated).

- Introducing the genre stages as both part of a whole text and as part of an inquiry process. Students were presented with an overview of the genre, its stages and their purposes, before they began this work. Then, through the analysis of model texts, as they began to write, the instruction focused on the development of the language and logic particular to each stage. These stages did not correspond to their linear ordering on the final argument text that was expected and were not laid out in a single organizer in fixed order. Instead, the stage scaffolds were presented and practiced in a way that followed the logic of inquiry in having students consider the ways evidence from the texts they read could support different possible claims. Scaffolds that helped them write the different stages of the argument were brought together only at the end of the process, as the *Description of Issue* and *Claim* were finalized. This follows the ways students need to think about the process of argumentation more generally. Focusing on the stages separately did not mean focusing on them in isolation: Discussion of the stages was recursive and aimed to locate their construction in the broader context of the overall purpose(s) for writing the argument and the interrelatedness of all its component parts.

- Introducing metalanguage naming the *stages* of the genre to be written and focusing on the *purposes* that need to be achieved in writing this stage. We have provided detailed description of our supports for developing the *Evidence* and *Reason* stages.
- Using the metalanguage of *likelihood* and *genre stages* to deconstruct mentor texts, making connections between language form and meaning and text structure explicit. This gave even those students still at lower English proficiency levels language to draw on as they wrote, and gave all students new language for referring to the ways language works in arguments.
- Allocating time for sustained attention to reading and interpreting text, and writing in response to text in a manner that was dialogic and that engaged students in interacting with the teacher and with one another.

DISCUSSION

We've shown here how language can become a point of focus when learning science when the activities *develop teachers' knowledge about language* so that they *support explicit, meaningful attention to language* in *meaningful interaction between students and teachers*. We provided frequent opportunities for meaningful interaction through the activities of the unit, and we enabled the teachers to learn about language and help their students learn about language through focus on meaningful aspects of the texts being used and by drawing on metalanguage from functional grammar to talk about the meaning. We also drew on SFL genre research to provide explicit, well-structured support to mentor learners into writing a new genre.

The metalanguage of functional grammar supported children who are learning English and science simultaneously, helping them focus on the ways language is used in science. And through activities built into the curriculum, teachers gained new understanding of language-meaning connections specific to the work they were preparing their students to do. For example, by exploring *likelihood*, teachers and children learned that authors are careful about the ways they make claims and offer evidence for their claims. Through focus on the purpose, stages, and language choices in arguments, teachers were able to support the children in writing that drew on evidence from the texts they read.

From the point of view of second language learning, the metalanguage supported interaction in the classroom focused on how the language means what it does, both in small group work and in whole-class interaction, providing opportunities for students to use language in ways that supported their science learning. Teachers saw that children learning English can work with grade-level texts and tasks when they are supported with a focus on meaning in context. This support is achieved through interaction with a teacher who is able to use meaningful metalanguage to guide students in developing understanding about language and meaning. Research tells us that high-quality conversation around reading and writing promotes academic language development, and that English learners in particular benefit greatly from meaningful interaction in the classroom. Modeling the pedagogy on the teaching-learning cycle meant that reading, writing, and discussion were concurrent throughout the unit, with focused discussion in each lesson both in partners or small groups, and with the whole class.

We learned through this project that the functional grammar metalanguage would work most powerfully in the classroom when it supported teachers in achieving the pedagogical goals they were already working toward, and when it did this in discipline-specific ways. We have shown how we worked toward goals teachers had in science, supporting analysis of text and conversations about meaning as well as students' writing development. The focus on author meaning and language choices helped us demonstrate that readers are in dialog with an author and can bring their own judgments to what they read. We used metalanguage to make links from language to meaning and reflection, and to stimulate talk about text in ways that supported reading and writing. What is most promising is that the children and teachers enjoyed the interactive activities and the talk about text that the functional grammar activities supported, and teachers reported that the class spontaneously used the metalanguage in other classroom activities. The teachers valued the more elaborated and focused writing that the children produced as they developed claims and presented evidence to support those claims.

This work raised children's consciousness about the ways language makes meaning, about the ways language works in science, and about the ways their peers and others interpret the same texts. It raised teachers' consciousness about supporting children learning English and school subjects at the same time, and about meaning in text and tools that can be used to explore language choices and reflect on meaning. And it enabled researchers who collaborated with teachers to develop new consciousness as well: about what is required to effect change in our context, about the need to connect with teachers and support their goals as we introduce new ideas, and about how to more effectively use the SFL theory and metalanguage to move toward those goals.

Inquiry Questions for Researchers and Professional Learning Facilitators

- What other language features are prominent in science discourse (texts and talk)? In what contexts would it be useful to study these and identify them?
- How can teachers be better supported to engage in the kind of exploratory talk needed to discuss issues with multiple potential perspectives?

Action Research Suggestions for Teachers

- Work with a colleague at your grade level to identify genres your students need to write. Set up a plan for strengthening your teaching of that genre.
  - Write your own versions of the genre. Analyze the language features.
  - Find some examples of student writing of that genre that you see as strong. Identify the stages they write and compare the ways your examples and the student examples realize the stages.
  - What do the students do well? What do they need further support for?
- Work with your grade level team to consider the key content for science at your grade level. In what ways does this content surface in real world (environmental) issues?
  - Search for newspaper articles that describe the issue or present research or perspectives about the topic. Distill these into readable texts for your students, but do not oversimplify. The talk about language and meaning helps students learn from challenging texts and better understand how English works to present knowledge in science.
  - Generate an accessible prompt that asks students to use evidence from reading to decide the best course of action.
  - Create a chart that organizes evidence on the topic.
  - Try out the sequence of activities described here to support students in reading, talking, and writing about the issue. What challenges do you encounter? What affordances for your students do you see in this work?

ACKNOWLEDGEMENT

We thank the teachers and students who participated in and contributed to this project, as well as Carrie Symons, who collaborated in the design of the unit. The research reported here was supported by the Institute of Education Sciences, U.S. Department of Education, through Grant R305A100482 to the University of Michigan. The opinions expressed are those of the authors and do not represent views of the Institute or the U.S. Department of Education.

NOTES

1. Here we focus on the ways we brought understandings from SFL into science lessons to support children's engagement in talk about language and meaning. For other reports on the project see O'Hallaron (2014a), Schleppegrell (2016), Schleppegrell & Moore (2018), Schleppegrell et al. (2014), Symons, Palincsar, and Schleppegrell (2017).
2. For an accessible introduction to functional grammar, see Humphrey, Droga, and Feez (2012).
3. Capital letters and italics are used to indicate when the terms refer to *stages* of the argument in contrast to other reference to claims, evidence, and reasoning.

REFERENCES

Christie, F., & Derewianka, B. (2008). *School discourse: Learning to write across the years of schooling.* London, England: Continuum.

Humphrey, S., Droga, L., & Feez, S. (2012). *Grammar and meaning.* Sydney, Australia: Primary English Teaching Association.

O'Hallaron, C. L. (2014a). Supporting fifth-grade ELLs' argumentative writing development. *Written Communication, 31*(3), 304–331. doi:10.1177/0741088314536524

O'Hallaron, C. L. (2014b). *Supporting elementary English language learners' argumentative writing through a functional grammar approach* (Unpublished doctoral dissertation). University of Michigan, Ann Arbor, MI.

O'Hallaron, C. L., Palincsar, A., & Schleppegrell, M. J. (2015). Reading science: Using systemic functional linguistics to support critical language awareness. *Linguistics and Education, 32,* 55–67.

Palincsar, A., & Schleppegrell, M. J. (2014). Focusing on language and meaning while learning with text. *TESOL Quarterly, 48*(3), 616–623.

Schleppegrell, M. J. (2013). The role of metalanguage in supporting academic language development. *Language Learning, 63*(S1), 153–170.

Schleppegrell, M. J. (2016). Content-based language teaching with functional grammar in the elementary school. *Language Teaching, 49*(1), 116–128. doi:10.1177/1362168818777519

Schleppegrell, M., & Moore, J. (2018). Linguistic tools for supporting emergent critical language awareness in the elementary school. In R. Harman (Ed.), *Bilingual learners and social equity: Critical approaches to Systemic Functional Linguistics* (pp. 23–43). New York, NY: Springer.

Schleppegrell, M., Moore, J., Al-Adeimi, S., O'Hallaron, C., Palincsar, A., & Symons, C. (2014). Tackling a genre: Situating SFL genre pedagogy in a new context. In L. de Oliveira & J. Iddings (Eds.), *Genre pedagogy across the Curriculum: Theory and application in US classrooms and contexts* (pp. 26–40). Sheffield, England: Equinox.

Spycher, P. (2017, September 26). *Scaffolding science learning and science writing with a little TLC* [Blog post]. Retrieved from https://leadingwithlearning.wested.org/blog/posts/scaffolding-science-learning-and-science-writing-with-a-little-tlc

Symons, C., Palincsar, A. S., & Schleppegrell, M. J. (2017). Fourth-grade emergent bilinguals' uses of functional grammar analysis to talk about text. *Learning and Instruction, 52,* 102–111. doi:10.1016/j.learninstruc.2017.05.003

CHAPTER 6

SCAFFOLDING YOUNG CHILDREN'S SCIENCE WRITING

Pamela Spycher
WestEd

Danielle Garegnani
Lemon Grove School District

Thea Fabian
Fresno Unified School District

In this chapter, we describe how preschool through first grade (PK–1) teachers scaffold young children's disciplinary writing in environmental science. The ideas we provide are informed by research, learning theories, and our work as teachers of young multilingual and multidialectal children and as teacher educators in culturally and linguistically diverse schools. First, we discuss the potential of integrating science with language and literacy learning and the importance of *linguistic pedagogical knowledge*. We then explain how teachers can weave into their existing practice the teaching and learning

Culturally and Linguistically Diverse Learners and STEAM, pages 117–143
Copyright © 2019 by Information Age Publishing

cycle (TLC), a supportive framework for scaffolding multilingual children's academic writing. Applied to science, the TLC provides abundant opportunities for children to think, talk, and write about science phenomena and to develop awareness of how the language of science works so that they are well prepared to communicate effectively through disciplinary writing.

Throughout the chapter, we offer illustrative examples of how the TLC looks in bilingual classrooms and in classrooms where English is the primary language of instruction. At the end of the chapter, we provide inquiry questions and action research suggestions so that teachers, teacher educators, and researchers can explore the full potential of the TLC so that all children have an equitable opportunity to learn and thrive in science.

INTEGRATING SCIENCE WITH LANGUAGE AND LITERACY LEARNING

The Next Generation Science Standards (NGSS Lead States, 2013) sets high expectations for all children's science learning, and the Framework for K–12 Science Education (National Research Council, 2012) guides teachers to engage all children in quality science learning. This new era of standards-based science education calls for dynamic and engaging science education, beginning in the earliest years of schooling, that is:

- *Inquiry focused:* Children pursue scientific questions they are curious about, engage in scientific inquiry, and come to their own understandings about science phenomena.
- *Collaborative:* Children interact in a learning community, explore their questions and reasoning with one another, and negotiate new meanings together.
- *Dialogic:* Children ask questions, explore phenomenon, explain their thinking, and offer their own interpretations in extended discussions with peers and teachers.
- *Inclusive:* Teachers—and children themselves—believe that all children are able to fully participate in science and have cultural and linguistic assets from their homes and communities that are valuable for classroom science learning; teachers promote children's use of their full linguistic repertoires, including multiple languages and dialects.

The National Research Council (2012) contrasts this new era of science education with more traditional approaches that overemphasize a focus on discrete facts and "breadth over depth," while de-emphasizing opportunities for students to engage in the real practices of science. In the Council's

1. Ask questions and define problems
2. Develop and use models
3. Plan and carry out investigations
4. Analyze and interpret data
5. Use mathematics and computational thinking
6. Construct explanations and design solutions
7. Engage in argument from evidence
8. Obtain, evaluate, and communicate information

Figure 6.1   Eight essential science and engineering practices (from National Research Council, 2012).

extensive framework to guide science education moving forward, they recommend three interrelated dimensions for science education: (a) scientific and engineering practices (Figure 6.1); (b) crosscutting concepts that unify the study of science and engineering through their common application across fields;[1] and (c) core ideas in four disciplinary areas—physical sciences; life sciences; earth and space sciences; and engineering, technology, and applications of science.

As illustrated in the scientific and engineering practices listed in Figure 6.1, science is a language-intensive discipline and a rich venue for science disciplinary language development. This dual challenge and opportunity requires teachers to develop new linguistic pedagogical knowledge, in other words, knowledge of how language works in the discipline and the relevant pedagogical practices to scaffold student learning and development of such language. *Science disciplinary language* refers to the specialized and often technical, grammatically dense language used in science that facilitates scientific thinking and communication. It differs from "everyday" language at the word, phrase, clause, sentence, and whole-text levels in terms of extent of precision, formality, and abstraction (Christie, 2012; Derewianka & Jones, 2016; Schleppegrell, 2004). It is characterized by sophisticated vocabulary, complex syntax and grammar, and highly structured and cohesive whole texts (e.g., an argument).

Beyond these generalities, each written genre in science (e.g., science information report, science explanation, science argument), uses language in different ways. The concept of *genre* that we use is from systemic functional linguistics, a theory of language first developed by Michael Halliday (1925–2018) and developed over the years by scholars and teachers around the world. The theory has been helpful to demystify language for students and support them to talk about how language works in the academic texts they read and write in school, thereby increasing educational equity. According to systemic functional linguistics, genres are goal-oriented and staged social processes (Rose, 2010). *Goal-oriented* means that there is always a social purpose for texts (e.g., to entertain, to persuade, to inform). *Staged* means that in the text, there are multiple "stages" toward achieving the goal. These stages are meaningful sections within the text that are recognizable because of where the stages are placed in the text (e.g., the "orientation" stage in a story that introduces the characters and setting) and the language resources used (e.g., the use of the word "suddenly" to indicate a shift in a story's plot). Teachers understand intuitively that genres have these meaningful stages, but they don't always discuss stages in texts with students. Teachers also recognize that genres within and between disciplines "feel" different (e.g., stories versus science information reports versus science arguments), but they don't always know why. When teachers develop their knowledge of how genres work and the linguistic pedagogical knowledge to support students' understanding of how genres work, this helps both teachers and students demystify the "why."

In order to teach students how the language of science works, teachers need to strengthen their own linguistic muscles by exploring the nuances of the various written genres of science. One example of how a science genre works is the case of an information report (e.g., "All About Honeybees"), the social purpose of which is to inform readers about a topic, or a class of things (e.g., honeybees). At the whole-text level, science information reports are organized logically, by category, because grouping important information about a topic is more readily understandable than a chaotic list of facts. The two main stages of science information reports are (a) general information about the topic (e.g., honeybees) to introduce it, and (b) coherent sets of key attributes about the topic to provide more detail. Within each stage, information is grouped together even further (e.g., characteristics and appearance, activities, and behavior) so the text "hangs together" cohesively, which makes it easier for readers to understand it. Specific language resources help with this cohesion. For example, text connectives (e.g., *in addition, however, finally*) connect large chunks of information across and within paragraphs and keep the information flowing (rather than just listing facts). At the sentence level, complex sentences often convey specialized science concepts, such as relationships between ideas (e.g., Bees are very important insects to humans *because they pollinate plants*). Complex grammar also provides a way to add more detail about an idea, for example by expanding a noun group with clause embedding[2] (e.g., Bees pollinate plants *that people need to survive*). At the word level, domain-specific vocabulary (e.g., pollinate, thorax, membrane) and general academic vocabulary (e.g., endangered, protect, contaminated) are used to communicate specialized and technical information with precision and clarity.

Here, we are presenting information about complex science texts that teachers need to understand in order to support children's disciplinary language development. These understandings about how science language works may seem too advanced for young children. But young children are much more capable of understanding how complex texts work than we often give them credit for. They already hear this complex language through their interactions with complex science texts during teacher read alouds and through science inquiry activities. Children also are frequently asked to use language to "ask questions and define problems," "obtain, evaluate, and communicate information," or engage in other science practices (National Research Council, 2012). When children learn to notice disciplinary language, discuss it with their peers and teachers, and try it out themselves, they stretch from what they can already say (e.g., "Bees are important") to a slightly higher level (e.g., "Bees are important *because* they *pollinate* plants"). With appropriate and strategic scaffolding, many children can stretch even higher (e.g., "Bees are *critical* to ecosystems *because* they *pollinate* plants *that* animals need to survive"). Beyond the sentence and vocabulary levels, instead of writing a set of disconnected facts, children can learn to organize their ideas cohesively and craft science informational reports, explanations, and arguments. This is not just aspirational. With scaffolding, daily exposure to science disciplinary language in complex texts, plentiful discussion about how texts work, and ample opportunities to write authentically, we've seen 5-year olds produce this type of language. Teachers can learn how to support their young multilingual students to meet these types of high science disciplinary writing expectations through the TLC, which we discuss in the next section.

THE TEACHING AND LEARNING CYCLE

We have found that many PK–1 teachers are quite skilled at providing content-rich activities for children, such as facilitating science inquiry tasks and experiments, using digital resources or photos to reinforce concepts, reading aloud science informational texts with children, or going outside the classroom to explore the natural world. Most teachers tell us that they are eager to support their students to develop as writers, as well, but they don't always know where to start or how to go beyond sentence frames and vocabulary. The TLC is an effective framework for scaffolding science learning, science disciplinary writing, and genre awareness, particularly for culturally and linguistically diverse students (Derewianka & Jones, 2016; Gibbons, 2015; Rothery & Stenglin, 1995; Spycher, 2017; Spycher, Austin, & Fabian, 2018; Spycher & Linn-Nieves, 2014).

Using the TLC to plan instruction (Figure 6.2), teachers guide their students through five stages of learning toward learning goals and a culminating writing task, such as a description of a local freshwater ecosystem or an explanation about why honeybees are a "keystone species."[3] These five stages are: (a) building the field, (b) exploring the language of text types,

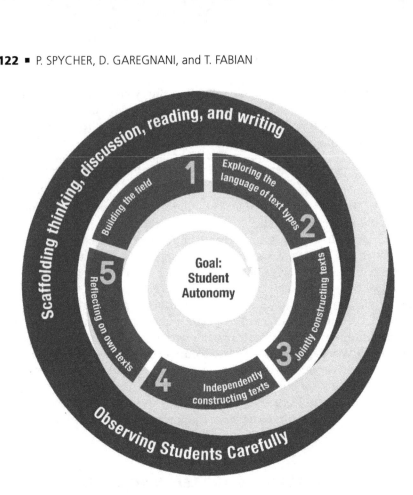

Figure 6.2 The teaching and learning cycle (TLC). *Source:* Spycher, 2017

(c) jointly constructing texts, (d) independently constructing texts, and (e) reflecting on one's own learning and writing.

In this section, we share suggestions for effective planning for a science TLC, including choosing worthy texts for teacher read alouds, establishing routines, crafting robust questions, and anticipating the language students will need to develop for a culminating writing task.

The Importance of Planning

Investing time in planning for strategic scaffolding and for a supportive classroom community are critical to a successful TLC science unit. The TLC is designed to support students to engage in science practices and meet the genre expectations for a culminating writing task. Therefore, one of the most important questions teachers ask themselves in the planning process is, "What will my students write about?" This decision is framed by the science learning goals for the unit and the unit's big ideas and inquiry questions, and is guided by standards for science, English language arts, and English language development. The complex texts teachers select also help to answer this question. Students can learn to emulate the complex science informational texts their teachers read to them and analyze with them, such as topic-based explanations (e.g., "How Honeybees Pollinate Plants"), as well as different types of arguments, including calls to action (e.g., "Save the Bees!"). Helping students write calls to action has the added benefit of promoting a sense of empowerment by instilling within young children the idea that their voices matter and they can make a positive difference in the world.

Being very clear early in the planning process about what students will write at the end of the unit and being familiar with the purpose, organizational structure, and language features of the culminating writing task help teachers to identify what content and language to focus on in each stage of the TLC. In our TLC planning process, we outline our big ideas, inquiry questions, and culminating tasks before beginning a unit, but as the unit progresses, students' questions and interests often shift or add to the focus.

Choosing Worthy Texts and Crafting Robust Questions

Text selection is key to creating rich science and disciplinary language learning opportunities using the TLC approach. Because higher order science concepts are communicated through rich and complex language, careful selection of complex science informational texts is critical. These are texts that are typically several grade levels above what most children in grades PK–1 are able to decode independently and that afford multiple peer-to-peer and children-with-teacher discussions about complex ideas. The texts need to be robust enough to pique students' curiosity about science knowledge and science language. Engaging with such texts interactively creates a special space for students to explore ideas through extended discussions. Texts also need to be relevant to students. For example, addressing topics related to environmental justice issues affecting students' communities, such as the prevalence of contaminated water in lower income neighborhoods, and affording them an opportunity to explore and communicate possible solutions (e.g., how communities can advocate for clean drinking water, ways of getting clean water) gives students a voice in something that is personally meaningful to them and a vision for the future.

Determining what young learners will talk about as they explore these texts is guided by science standards and learning goals, along with listening to what children themselves are interested in learning about. To support quality peer-to-peer interactions around texts, we carefully read the texts we will use, analyze them for what they afford in terms of science learning and language development, and collaboratively plan worthy questions that will promote a lot of thinking and talking among students, keeping our eye on the inquiry questions, big ideas, and culminating writing task(s) we've established for the unit of study. Since we read the same texts with students over multiple days, we plan increasingly complex questions for students to ponder and discuss in peer-to-peer, multi-exchange interactions. We like to use sticky notes to write the questions we will ask students and place them directly in the book, since referring to a lesson plan and holding a book during a read aloud can be awkward. We also use sticky notes to help us remember any vocabulary terms we want to pause to explain or illustrations we want to highlight to support students' conceptual understanding. Young children are eager to discuss the big science ideas in complex science informational texts. They readily take up the complex disciplinary language they encounter when it is called to their attention and explained and when they have an opportunity to use it meaningfully in extended discussions with open-ended questions.

Expecting all students to engage with rich science texts through interactive reading and scaffolded peer-to-peer interaction demonstrates a strong respect for all children's intelligence and their capacity to grapple with complex ideas through equally complex language. Teachers may feel concern that students are not understanding every word of the text that is read interactively. However, both the linguistic and conceptual knowledge development that students engage in is planned, yet unfolds in an organic and multi-faceted (and sometimes unpredictable) way. Through repeated interactions with rich science texts, along with scaffolding for using disciplinary language purposefully and in a socially and emotionally supportive environment, children weave together the concepts and language needed to interpret and communicate their ideas. When teachers employ quality texts and quality questions that are worthy of children's attention, there is a lot for students to be curious about, talk about, and discover.

Using Routines for Equitable and Quality Interactions

The science disciplinary language development that is possible through the use of rich science texts and concepts in the early years assumes interactive and dialogic approaches to learning. With young children, teachers often guide conversations around central texts through interactive reading. They set students up for success by facilitating their ability to discuss their ideas with their peers in extended, multi-exchange interactions. The learning and practice students do around collegial discussions is the co-requisite work that goes hand-in-hand with learning the language and content. Most children love to talk, but talk is not always equitable. Equitable talk requires that students have clear procedures for conversing with multiple partners; that they know how to take turns, track their discussion partner(s), and focus on active listening; and that they have learned to engage physically during paired conversations. Physical engagement includes showing their discussion partner that they are listening attentively by making eye contact, leaning in, nodding, or using other gestures that are socially recognized in U.S. classrooms. We recognize that not all cultures share these norms for behavior, which means that patience is needed while some students learn to add these new ways of interacting to their repertoires. Teachers also need to consider how they can modify their thinking and behaviors to better include students with unfamiliar communication styles or cultural backgrounds.

To help students acquire discussion skills, early-years teachers can explicitly teach discussion moves, such as prompting students to "hold our thoughts" (sometimes accompanied by a "thinking pose") so that everyone has enough think time before sharing ideas; providing sentence frames to support effective expression; and inviting students to rehearse statements or questions (sometimes by whispering responses into an imaginary microphone) as a way to prepare before they talk with a partner. Learning to take turns and listen while others talk, express one's own understandings and ideas, and ask questions to extend discussions supports students' social-emotional, academic, and linguistic development.

Exploring practical and culturally responsive routines for each classroom community offers an opportunity for teachers to honor the assets young learners bring with them to school. We have witnessed students in grades PK–1, full of joy for learning, who insist on standing in front of their classmates to teach alongside the teacher. We have also witnessed students engaging readily and joyfully with a call-and-response approach and asking for more of this approach because it reflects a communication style some students bring from their home communities. Teachers, being the great innovators that they are, can take students' ways of interacting and combine them with other important structures they've put into place to create a successful space for interactive learning.

OVERVIEW OF THE TLC STAGES

The stages of the TLC (Figure 6.2) are presented as steps toward standards-based learning goals around big science ideas, culminating in a writing task that helps students progress in their science disciplinary thinking and writing. However, in reality, the stages do not occur in a lockstep fashion. Typically, there is a lot of back and forth from one stage to another, and stage one (building the field) continues throughout the cycle. Here, we provide a brief overview of the different stages of the TLC, along with some sample activities, in order to distinguish their purposes in the scaffolding process and illustrate how each stage flows from one to the next.

Stage One: Building the field

The first stage of the TLC focuses on meaning making, or "building the field" of knowledge about a science topic, accomplished through language-rich experiences. We like to start a TLC science unit by inviting children to share what they already know about the topic from their home and previous school experiences, and what they are curious about. All ideas are entertained, and, as is the case throughout the unit, we encourage the children to express themselves using their home languages or dialects of English, as they choose. We use a "K-C-L chart" (what we *know*, what we are *curious* about, what we *learned*) to record ideas and keep it posted in the classroom so that children can add their questions and learnings as the unit progresses. We do a lot of charting throughout the TLC unit in order to create a text-rich environment and provide language and ideas that children can use in their own writing.

To support children's curiosity and invite their inquiry into a science topic, we use hands-on activities in which they can freely explore and discuss their thinking with peers. For example, for our honeybees TLC unit, we provide photographs of bees engaging in various behaviors, such as sucking nectar from flowers, gathering pollen on their bodies, and protecting the hive. We also provide models (plastic replicas) of different types of honeybees (e.g., queen, drone, worker) and stages of the life cycle (e.g., egg, larva, pupa, adult). We invite the children to discuss what they observe in small groups and to generate questions they want to explore in the unit. The children record these ideas in their science logs and share them with the whole group so that they can be added to the K-C-L chart. We also have an ongoing science independent learning station where the children can observe photographs, models, or tangible examples of science phenomena (e.g., a classroom butterfly garden, plants growing in different conditions) and record their observations in their science logs.

Creativity in the early learning classroom, including dramatic play, visual arts, or music, can support language development, as children are eager to talk about the concepts they are imagining or creating using newly acquired terms. For example, for the concept of pollination, we have children pretend they are bees flying from flower to flower (replicas we make out of tissue paper) to sip nectar and gather pollen on their "pollen baskets." We put an edible powder, such as powdered sugar, in the center of each flower

Do You Like To Buzz?
(to the tune of "Do Your Ears Hang Low?")

Do you like to buzz?
Are you covered all in fuzz?
Do you call a hive a home?
In the garden do you roam?
Do you gather pollen when it's sunny?
Is your proboscis a little funny?
Do you like to buzz?

Figure 6.3   Singing in science.

to replicate the pollen, which sticks to the children's fingers. While the children are dramatizing the pollination process, we encourage them to verbalize what they are doing using new science terms (e.g., proboscis, pollen baskets), as well as general academic vocabulary (e.g., gather, collect), and we then invite them to orally recount the experience in small groups before writing and drawing about it. Singing is another especially joyful activity that young children readily engage in. One technique we like to use is to take a familiar tune and create new lyrics, ideally with the children, to reinforce the new science concepts and language (see an example in Figure 6.3).

Quality interactions with complex science informational texts are integral to science learning in the early childhood classroom. Interactive teacher read alouds using worthy complex texts should be joyful experiences in which children talk abundantly with their peers to expand their science thinking and develop disciplinary language. We use a multi-day read-aloud routine where we read the text (or key sections of the text) with the children several times over the course of a week, stopping to invite them to discuss with a partner increasingly complex and carefully crafted questions. We use dialogic techniques to support children's cumulative learning, including the following:

- *Ask open-ended questions* so children can engage in extended, multi-exchange peer-to-peer discussions (e.g., "Why do you think the bees are gathering all of this pollen on their bodies?").
- *Ask known-response questions* that they can all respond to chorally to reinforce concepts and language (e.g., "What do we call this body part?").
- *Respond to children's responses* to stretch their thinking and language: Affirm their responses, prompt them to elaborate on their responses, recast their ideas to model the appropriate use of new language, and repeat responses so all children can hear.

In addition, because there is a lot of technical language as we read aloud these complex texts, we explain new technical science vocabulary (e.g., pollen), act it out with the children, or point to illustrations that match the new terms while we are reading, and we have the children say the words with us so they become familiar with the terms. Since children need to build up a repertoire of sophisticated general academic terms (e.g., survive), after first explaining some of these words while reading, we also explicitly teach a select set of general academic vocabulary words using a predictable routine (Figure 6.4), which helps the children use the words in their speaking and writing (see Spycher, 2009 for additional information on this approach).

These are just some of the ideas we incorporate as we plan a TLC science unit, and the activities we select vary by science topic. Many of the activities we suggest are likely to be familiar to early childhood teachers, although all of us could spend a lifetime refining and enhancing our methods.

General Academic Vocabulary Instruction Planning Template
Timing: about 8 min.

Word: Select a general academic vocabulary word from the complex text with which the children have already engaged at least once. The word should be useful to them for better understanding the text and topic and for effectively communicating about this and other texts and topics.

Teaching Routine:

I. Introduce the Word: (2 min.)
- Say the word, invite the children to say it with you, and briefly remind them where they first heard it in the text. Write the word and highlight the first letter. Point out any cognates. (e.g., *investigate* in English is *investigar* in Spanish).
- Explain what the word means in child-friendly terms (1–2 sentences). Use the word in a complete sentence so you don't sound like a dictionary.
- Provide a few examples of how the word can be used in other contexts. Show pictures and use gestures to support comprehension.

II. Children Use the Word Meaningfully: (5 min.)
- Guide students to use the word meaningfully in one or two think–pair–shares (three, if needed), with open-sentence frames that are appropriately grammatically complex (e.g., I want to *investigate* _____ because _____.)
- Use pictures as prompts where useful. (For example, for *investigate*, show a picture of a meadow and ask students what they might investigate there.)

III. Check and Develop Word Knowledge: (1 min. plus repeatedly over time)
- Ask short-answer questions to check for understanding. (Is this something you'd investigate? If yes, say "*investigate*." If no, say "wouldn't *investigate*.")
- Invite the children to teach the word to someone when they get home, and encourage them to use the word as much as they can in speaking and writing.
- Post the word, and model using it over time as appropriate.

Figure 6.4 General academic vocabulary instruction routine.

Stages Two and Three: Exploring Language and Jointly Constructing Texts

What often happens is that teachers spend a lot of time on building content knowledge and then ask children to write independently, with varying results. By adding some activities where the language of the genre is talked about explicitly and where children can co-construct the genre writing with skillful teacher guidance, more students will be able to successfully engage in the culminating writing task and meet genre expectations. We explain stages two and three together because language that is deconstructed in stage two is often reconstructed in stage three. We outline some of the activities we use below.

Stage Two

In this stage, the focus is on helping children to explore the language of the genre, or text type. Here, we help children to notice the language at different levels and talk about it meaningfully. Teachers might analyze a short passage of the text with children by writing it on a large piece of chart paper so all students can see it and then drawing their attention to how all of the information in the passage is about the same category (e.g., describing honeybees' bodies) and how the sentences are organized. The class might "unpack" a complex sentence by identifying some of the "linguistic boundaries" (e.g., prepositional phrases, noun groups), which form "chunks" of meaning. We use metalanguage, or language for talking about language,[4] in these discussions. One meaningful chunk we like to help young children notice is the "that chunk," a type of embedded clause, which, when tucked into a noun group (e.g., long proboscises) expands and enriches its meaning by providing important detail. We talk with children about how the sentence "Bees have <u>long proboscises</u> *that they use for sucking and tasting nectar*" has a "that chunk" that gives readers more information about the noun group (long proboscises). Using such metalanguage (language to talk about language) supports discussions about genres. Children readily take up child-friendly terms (e.g., "that chunks," "noun groups") and may even make up their own metalanguage.

Stage Three

Here, the teacher serves as a "facilitative scribe" to jointly construct a well-crafted text with children, scaffolding the use of language they explored in stage two and have been using throughout the unit. The class, or small group, could craft complex sentences, tight paragraphs, and even longer passages. The teacher's job is to listen closely to what students say and scaffold their use of language appropriate for the genre, always attending to accurate science meaning. This helps the children "rehearse" for independent writing of the genre. For example, we might start off inviting ideas about what to write (e.g., "How should we start our description of bees?") and negotiate with the children about which language to use. As we craft the text with the children, we ask probing questions to encourage precision (e.g., "Is there another more scientific word we could use for bees' tongues?") and expansion (e.g., "Can you say more about what worker bees do? Is there a 'that chunk' we could use?"). We affirm what students say and sometimes recast it to model disciplinary language (e.g., "Yes, they do get pollen on their legs, or on their pollen baskets!"). We also ask students to make revisions as we go (e.g., "What do you think about adding a connector here so that these ideas are linked?").

Stages Four and Five: Independently Constructing Texts and Reflecting on Own Texts

Stages four and five are an opportunity for children to spread their wings with independent science disciplinary writing, support their peers as they write, and reflect on what they learned and wrote.

Stage Four

By this time in the TLC, the children have been writing daily and are now well-prepared to independently write texts that meet the expectations of the genre. By "independently write," we don't mean that children are completely on their own. Young children still need supports, such as graphic organizers to categorize information, charts around the room with exemplary texts, science terms posted on charts or on a science word wall, and consultations with peers and teachers. In stage four, we always post and discuss with children the "success criteria" for the writing task (e.g., "My ideas are clear to me"; "I describe what bees are, have, and do"; "I use precise words"). The children also like to add their own success criteria, based on the learning they've engaged in throughout the unit (e.g., "I use 'that chunks' to add detail").

Stage Five

This final stage is an opportunity for children to reflect on their own writing and what they have learned, which sets them up for success in the next TLC. For example, teachers might ask students to analyze their own science information reports, using the same success criteria they used to write it, and identify strengths and areas for improvement. They might structure peer feedback sessions where the children analyze one another's texts, using norms (e.g., "Listen carefully when others talk") and protocols (e.g., "Use the success criteria when you give feedback to your friend") to help children become peer mentors and cultivate a learning community. Importantly, teachers also provide an opportunity for children to reflect on and share about what they learned during the unit, which helps them to become mindful of their own learning processes.

CLASSROOM EXAMPLE: HUMAN IMPACT
ON EARTH SYSTEMS

The following classroom example highlights how one teacher, Ms. Flores (a pseudonym), used the TLC to guide her kindergarten class through an environmental science unit on human impact on earth systems, specifically focusing on how the choices that humans make impact other living things. The culminating task for this unit was for students to write an argument persuading people to take care of our water systems. The children's arguments were realized through collaborative advocacy posters in which they described what fish need, explained the plight of fish due to water pollution, and argued for steps we should all take to create clean water in a call to action. Through this example, we hope to illustrate the potential of the TLC in multilingual and multidialectal early childhood settings. While the example provided is from a bilingual classroom, the ideas and activities can be easily adapted for other contexts.

During the course of the unit, students engaged in scientific inquiry tasks, including observing fish and recording their observations and labeled drawings in a science journal. They read and discussed (through interactive teacher read alouds) how fishes' different body parts help them survive and what additional things fish need to survive. These discussions and learning tasks segued into a focus on the importance of clean water and the impact humans have on water systems.

Stage 1: Building the Field

In this part of the TLC, students learned about fish, their characteristics, and their survival needs. Pedagogical practices and classroom tasks in Stage 1 focused on building content knowledge about the topic of fish. To begin the unit, students were invited to share their background knowledge about fish and generate initial questions about them. They engaged in multiple interactive read alouds with science informational texts and viewed and discussed short science videos to build content knowledge. The classroom had fish tanks with small goldfish and guppies so that students could observe the fish daily and take notes in their science journal, which they used in discussions with their science team (small groups of students). Students then engaged in collaborative group work, where they discussed observations about fish using different images; engaged in extended, scaffolded conversations as a class about their observations; and then collaboratively created a visual representation to explain what fish need to survive and to record questions they had. Each group then presented their posters to the class, after which Ms. Flores helped the class create a list of observations and questions (Figure 6.5).

Figure 6.5 Collaborative group work in science.

To build students' understanding of human impact on water systems, students engaged in a hands-on inquiry task, where they learned about water pollution by adding waste to clean water and then trying out different ways to clean it. Working in science teams, students followed the protocol for the inquiry task (Figure 6.6): they observed, took notes, discussed their observations, and came to conclusions about the difficulty in cleaning polluted water.

After the inquiry task, the class engaged in a debrief discussion about their new insights about water pollution and began to discuss the implications for

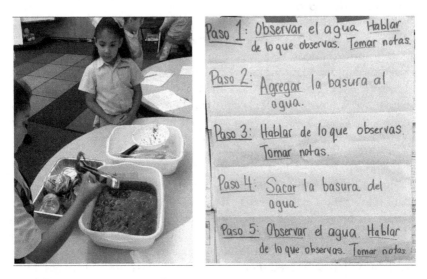

Figure 6.6 Science inquiry task.

fish and people. Students shared their ideas about why clean water is important and what people should do to maintain clean water. This discussion fostered students' use of the language of causal explanation, which was later revisited in Stage 2 of the TLC and used in writing in Stages 3 and 4. For example, within student discussions, students expressed statements such as, *"Cuando la gente tira basura al agua, se contamina, y se enferman los peces"* ["When people throw trash into the water, it gets contaminated, and the fish get sick"] and *"Los peces se mueren porque el agua está sucio por la gente que tira basura al agua"* ["Fish die because the water is dirty from people throwing trash into the water"]. Through these discussions, students were able to articulate the relationship between human actions and their effects on fish and their habitat (Figure 6.7).

Stage 2: Exploring the Language of the Text Type

This unit of study offered opportunities for students to explore the language features of description, explanation, and argument. Once students

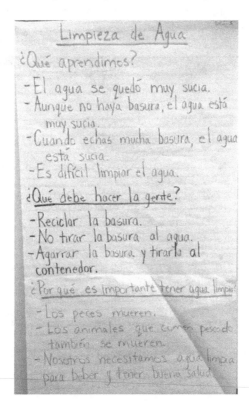

Figure 6.7   Class inquiry task debrief discussion.

had built up content understanding of fish and their survival needs, Ms. Flores wanted to further draw students' attention to how they might expand on and enrich their sentences with additional details to be more precise. To do this, the students engaged in a pedagogical practice called *collaborative sentence reconstruction,* where they listen to a mentor sentence several times and take notes by drawing pictures, and then work together in pairs to reconstruct the sentence (Figure 6.8).

The purpose of this lesson is for students to gain deeper understanding of the meanings in the sentence—an important comprehension skill—and to be able to demonstrate metalinguistic awareness by discussing how the sentence is structured and how different language features are at work in the sentence. In this case, Ms. Flores wanted to raise students' awareness of descriptive language and of how the author of the original sentence, which was excerpted from one of the science informational texts students had read multiple times, provided details about how and where fish move. The original sentence students reconstructed and then unpacked was *"Los peces nadan hacia arriba para comer la comida que flota encima del agua"* ["Fish swim upward to eat the food that floats on top of the water"].

Collaborative Sentence Reconstruction in Kindergarten

1. Select a sentence with complex syntax from a text students have already interacted with.
2. Read the sentence aloud once: Students just listen and do not see the sentence.
3. Read the sentence a second time: Students listen and draw and label what they hear.
4. Partner sharing: In pairs, students share their labeled drawings and orally reconstruct the sentence together.
5. Group sharing: A few sets of partners share their oral sentence with the whole group, and the teacher records a group word and phrase list on chart paper so all can see. Students chorally read what is on the list.
6. Read the sentence a third time: Students add to their labeled drawings.
7. Partners reconstruct the sentence: The same pairs work together to write a sentence, as close as they can to the original sentence, using their drawings and notes from the three readings.
8. Share and compare: The teacher writes the original sentence, and invites the students to compare their sentence with the original one, prompting them to notice particular language features (e.g., specific words used, prepositional phrases, "that" chunks, long noun phrases).
9. Unpack meanings: The teacher facilitates a discussion about the meanings of the different parts of the sentences by "unpacking" them and then focusing on how each part adds detail and precision to the whole sentence.

Figure 6.8 Collaborative sentence reconstruction in kindergarten.

As they discussed the sentence, Ms. Flores asked the students two main questions: "Who is this sentence about?" and "What is happening?" The question about what is happening elicits responses about the movement, or behavior, of the fish. The language feature that Ms. Flores focused on when asking these questions was "doing processes,"[5] or in more familiar terms, "action verbs," which are critical for describing the behaviors of animals with precision. The lesson also drew students' attention to how authors elaborate on ideas by including additional information through prepositional phrases. The teacher elicited awareness of this language feature by asking the questions, "Where/when/how/why/in what ways does the animal move?" Prepositional phrases are one way that authors add detail about the *circumstances* related to processes (e.g., from side to side, under the water, through the opening). Highlighting these prepositional phrases—for instance, through questioning about where something happens—is a way to support students in adding detail to their writing.

The class drew and labeled their interpretations of sentences they heard, and reconstructed the sentences together as a whole class first (Figure 6.9). Then students reconstructed sentences with their partners (Figure 6.10).

After sharing and discussing the reconstructed sentences, the students engaged in "unpacking" or deconstructing the sentences to discuss the meanings in the different parts of the sentences (Figure 6.11).

This final step of unpacking the sentence provides another opportunity to closely analyze both the language and the meanings in each portion of the sentence. The students co-construct a list of simple sentences from each portion that, when combined, express the complete meaning of the complex sentence. This activity is interactive, and questions asked of the students include "What is this part about?" and "What information is it telling us?" Sentence deconstruction simultaneously provides an opportunity to focus on meaning and form by drawing students' attention to important information in the sentences and what the meaningful chunks are (such as specialized vocabulary used or prepositional phrases that add detail).

Figure 6.9　Class text reconstruction.

Figure 6.10 Partner sentence reconstruction.

Figure 6.11 Sentence unpacking.

Additional sentences that the class deconstructed in Stage 2 of the TLC focused on the same language features and metalanguage (i.e., doing verbs and prepositional phrases) in order to provide multiple and repeated opportunities for students to discuss the language, reinforce content understandings, and build metalinguistic awareness (Figure 6.12).

Class Chart Podemos describir lo que hacen los peces y añadir detalles de cómo se mueven			
¿Quién/Qué?	**¿Qué Hacen?**	**¿Cómo? ¿Donde? ¿Pour Qué?**	**Apuntes (dibujo)**
Los peces	nadan	moviendo su cuerpo de <u>un</u> <u>lado a otro lado</u>.	
Algunos peces	descansan	<u>en el fondo</u> de la pecera.	
Los peces	mueven las aletas	para nadar <u>hacia</u> <u>delante y hacia</u> <u>atrás</u> en el agua	
(Los peces)	nadan	<u>hacia arriba</u> para comer la comida que flota <u>encima</u> <u>del</u> agua.	
Los peces	se esconden	<u>dentro de</u> las rocas o en un hueco cuando tenga miedo.	
Los peces	usan las branquias que están <u>en cada</u> <u>lado</u> de su cuerpo,	parra respirar <u>debajo del</u> agua.	

Figure 6.12 Describing what fish do with details.

In addition to enabling students to expand and enrich their descriptions about fish, Stage 2 also introduced language for explaining causal relationships. To do this, Ms. Flores leveraged the student conversations from the water pollution inquiry task to introduce the language of causal explanation. She further engaged students in using specific language (i.e., causal language, such as "when" and "because") to help them explain the causes or effects of water pollution with precision. She introduced open sentence frames to support effective communication, such as *"Cuando* [when] _____, _____.; _____ *porque* [because] _____." The students then drew upon their experience participating in the water pollution inquiry task, as well as their background knowledge from their interactive reading tasks about fish, to orally construct sentences that explain the causes and effects of water pollution, highlighting the subordinating conjunctions *"cuando"* [when] and *"porque"* [because].

Through these various language analysis tasks, the teacher raised students' awareness of how particular language features in science writing work in order to support both their comprehension of the complex science content and scaffold their use of key language features in their writing.

Stage 3: Joint Construction of Texts

In Stage 3 of the TLC in Ms. Flores's unit on human impact on earth systems, students had an opportunity to "rehearse" writing through teacher facilitation. This stage occurred after students had built up considerable knowledge about the characteristics of fish and their needs for survival, as well as how water pollution affects fish. To build on the classroom activities in Stage 2 and further prepare her students for independent writing, Ms. Flores co-constructed sentences with students about the causes and effects of water pollution on fish. She drew on students' knowledge about the topic and the language features of description (e.g., prepositional phrases, doing verbs) and causal explanation (e.g., the subordinating conjunctions "*cuando*" [when] and "*porque*" [because]), introduced in Stage 2. As the students and teacher jointly constructed sentences, she modeled the process of writing, and co-created with them a model they could later use in their independent writing. Ms. Flores elicited ideas from the students and asked them to think about and discuss how they would put their ideas together in order to write about the topic. The class jointly constructed several sentences to explain the causes and effects of water pollution. Ms. Flores facilitated a discussion about how to write the first sentence and wrote the agreed-upon sentence on a chart, modeling for students. Then, she continued to jointly construct sentences with the students, pulling in their ideas and asking them to add details, reword, or combine ideas, as needed. The sentences they co-constructed included the following:

> "*El agua está contaminada porque la gente no recoge la basura.*" ["Water gets polluted because people don't pick up their trash."]

> "<u>*Cuando*</u> *hay mucha suciedad en el agua, los peces se enferman y mueren.*" ["When the water is very dirty, fish get sick and die."]

> "*Los peces mueren* <u>*porque*</u> *la gente tira basura al agua.*" ["Fish die because people throw trash into the water."]

> "<u>*Cuando*</u> *las personas tiran la basura al agua, los peces pueden morir.*" ["When people throw trash into the water, fish can die."]

After constructing these sentences together as a class, the students wrote the sentences in their science journals (Figure 6.13).

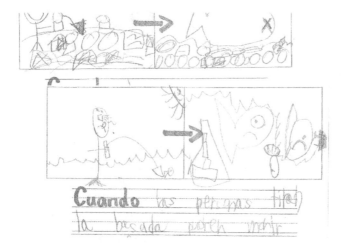

Figure 6.13 Jointly constructed causal explanations.

Stage 4: Independent Writing

The children were now ready to work with their table teams to complete the final writing task, which was to create a poster to advocate for clean water. Students used success criteria that outlined the requisites for the task and worked together to create posters that explained what fish need (clean water), why fish die (polluted water), and an action step, or recommendation, that people should adopt to maintain clean water systems. Student advocacy posters (Figure 6.14) included sentences, drawings, words, and phrases relevant to the topic and task. As students wrote, Ms. Flores was available to assist as needed and continue the rich conversations around the topic to aid this final writing piece. Students utilized many of the collegial discussion skills they had worked on thus far, asking their student team members for ideas and negotiating where the drawings, sentences, words, and phrases would be located on the posters and what messages they would share.

Stage 5: Reflecting on One's Learning and Writing

In the final stage of Ms. Flores's TLC about clean water systems, students carefully reviewed and then presented their posters in order to teach their classmates about water systems. To carry out this activity, the class referred to the poster success criteria and were provided with sentence frames to give targeted feedback to their classmates, such as "*Me gusta* _____" [I liked _____], "*¿Puedes explicar* _____?" [Can you

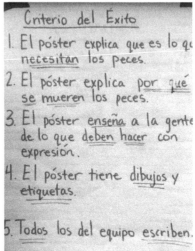

Figure 6.14 Student advocacy posters.

explain _____], and "*Tengo una pregunta acerca de* _____" [I have a question about _____]. The final task of the unit consisted of students writing about their reflections on their own learning (Figure 6.15).

This final writing task helped Ms. Flores to gauge what students had learned and where they were in their academic writing development, which also helped her evaluate how well she had scaffolded the teaching and learning experiences within the unit.

DISCUSSION AND NEXT STEPS

The TLC offers a cohesive and comprehensive approach to supporting young multilingual children's academic writing development within the context of science learning. Through a predictable, yet flexible, five stage process, students learn to think, listen, speak, read, and write like a scientist and become increasingly aware of how language works in science. Building language skills and metalinguistic awareness in science is empowering for young learners because it helps them to be more attuned to language as they are listening to teacher read alouds or reading on their own, and to be more conscious of the language they select to communicate in speaking and writing.

Embracing the TLC comes with a committed belief that all children can learn at high levels and develop rich academic language with the right kind of support. Teachers, in their quest to find ways to amplify and enrich their

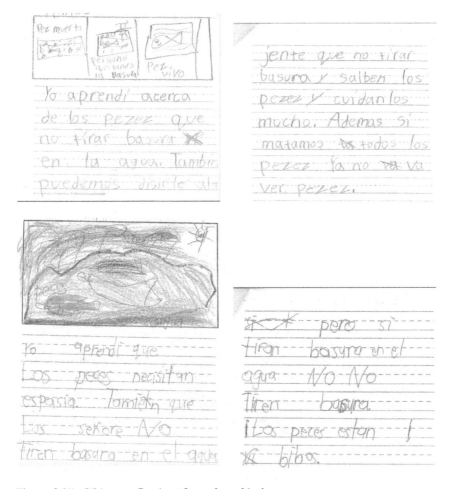

Figure 6.15 Written reflections from three kindergarteners.

students' learning and progress, can look to the TLC as a solid framework for continuous student development as well as their own development as educators.

Inquiry Questions for Researchers and Teacher Educators

- How can early-grades teachers be better supported to scaffold early academic writing in science for emergent bilingual children?
- In what ways could the TLC approach support effective planning?
- How does the TLC approach amplify the goals of new science, ELA, and ELD standards?

- What challenges and opportunities does the TLC offer our youngest learners and their teachers?

Action Research Suggestions for Teachers

- Work with your grade-level team to identify complex science informational texts that address some of the big ideas you'd like students to learn in science. How could you leverage the rich language in these texts to support your students' early academic writing?
- Work with your grade level team to identify a culminating writing task in science and try out some of the activities presented in this chapter in a sequence, following the stages of the TLC. What do you notice students saying and writing? What challenges do you encounter?

NOTES

1. These crosscutting concepts are (a) patterns; (b) cause and effect: mechanism and explanation; (c) scale, proportion, and quantity; (d) systems and system models; (e) energy and matter: flows, cycles, and conservation; (f) structure and function; and (g) stability and change.
2. The term "clause embedding" may be unfamiliar to some teachers. A clause is a complete idea and contains a verb. When a clause is "embedded" it becomes part of another grammatical element, thereby modifying it. In the sentence, "Bees pollinate the plants *that people need to survive*," the dependent clause, "*that people need to survive*," is embedded in the noun group "the plants." This type of complex grammar is common in science texts.
3. Keystone species are plants or animals that are so important to their ecosystems that if their population were significantly reduced or removed, the ecosystem would be negatively impacted or even collapse.
4. The type of metalanguage we use with teachers is often different from that which we use with children. For example, instead of the more sophisticated term "embedded clause," which we use with adults, we use the term "that chunk" with children. Using metalanguage is not about right and wrong, but about finding a way to talk about language itself.
5. We use the metalinguistic term "processes" from systemic functional linguistics to refer to verbs since they help children to talk about language. We talk about "doing processes" (e.g., swim), "saying processes" (e.g., say, shout), "thinking/feeling processes" (e.g., wonder, want), or "being/having processes" (e.g., is, has).

REFERENCES

Christie, F. (2012). *Language education throughout the school years: A functional perspective.* West Sussex, England: Wiley-Blackwell.

Derewianka, B., & Jones, P. (2016). *Teaching language in context.* South Melbourne, Australia: Oxford University Press.

Gibbons, P. (2015). *Scaffolding language, scaffolding learning.* Portsmouth, NH: Heinemann.

National Research Council. (2012). *A framework for K–12 science education: Practices, crosscutting concepts, and core ideas.* Washington, DC: The National Academies Press.

NGSS Lead States. (2013). *Next generation science standards: For states, by states.* Washington, DC: The National Academies Press.

Rose, D. (2010). Genre in the Sydney school. In J. P. Gee and M. Handford (Eds.), *The Routledge handbook of discourse analysis* (pp. 209–225). London, England: Routledge.

Rothery, J., & Stenglin, M., (1995). *Exploring literacy in school English (Write it right resources for literacy and learning).* Sydney, Australia: Metropolitan East Disadvantaged Schools Program.

Schleppegrell, M. J. 2004. *The language of schooling: A functional linguistics perspective.* Mahwah, NJ: Erlbaum.

Spycher, P. (2009). Learning academic language through science in two linguistically diverse classrooms. *Elementary School Journal, (109)*4, 359–379.

Spycher, P. (2017). *Scaffolding writing through the "teaching and learning cycle."* San Francisco, CA: WestEd.

Spycher, P., Austin, K., & Fabian, T. (2018). The writing-centered classroom: Demystifying language and promoting student voice. *Educational Leadership, 75*(7), 54–59.

Spycher, P., & Linn-Nieves, K. L. (2014). Reconstructing, deconstructing, and constructing complex texts. In P. Spycher (Ed.), *The Common Core State Standards in English language arts/literacy for English language learners: Grades K–5* (pp. 51–68). Alexandria, VA: TESOL Press.

CHAPTER 7

SUPPORTING *Enjoy* ☺
3rd–8th GRADE ENGLISH
LEARNERS WITH SCIENCE
INFORMATIONAL TEXTS
THROUGH SUMMER SCHOOL
TEACHER PROFESSIONAL
LEARNING

Karin Linn-Nieves
San Joaquin County Office of Education

In this chapter, I share lessons learned from the first 2 years conducting a month-long demonstration summer school model in which a county office of education joined forces with a local large urban school district to provide teacher professional learning and a summer school experience for Grades 3–8 English learners (ELs) classified either as long-term or at risk for becoming long-term. The term *long-term English learner* refers to students who speak English as an additional language, have been enrolled in U.S. schools

Culturally and Linguistically Diverse Learners and STEAM, pages 145–168
Copyright © 2019 by Information Age Publishing
All rights of reproduction in any form reserved.

for six or more years, are in 6th–12th grades, and who have remained at the same English language proficiency level for two or more consecutive years (or have regressed). Our model has three interconnected purposes. The first purpose is to accelerate science academic language and literacy development for students. The second is to provide professional learning that deepens teacher knowledge and supports critical shifts in teacher practice as they learn how to target the specific language needs of this particular population of ELs. Third and lastly, we want district leaders to be able to observe what this type of teaching and learning could look like in a school setting with ELs so that they can help lead and support our initiative. The outcome of this combination was deep learning for all. We describe the model we used for the summer school, the teaching approaches and instruction we used, and some illustrative examples. We also report some results from students and teachers and discuss the lessons we learned.

DISTRICT CONTEXT

Stockton Unified School District is a diverse urban district serving over 40,000 students in transitional kindergarten through Grade 12. It is located in the Central Valley of California, an hour south of the state capital of Sacramento. While ELs represent 28% of the population, another 30% come from bilingual homes and were either identified as Initially Fluent English Proficient (20%) upon entry to the school district or are former ELs who have been reclassified (10%). Over 2,100 students are classified as long-term ELs and another 1,400 are ELs at risk for becoming long-term ELs. More than 70% of students in Stockton Unified School District qualify for free and reduced-price meals, an indicator of low-income status. Last spring, less than 1.7% of ELs in Grades 6–8 met or exceeded standards in English language arts on the state standardized assessments. Unlike the rest of the districts in San Joaquin County, Stockton Unified School District has not adopted a published English language arts/English language development curriculum. They have opted to hire a cadre of classroom teachers and coaches to work with their English Language Arts Department and language development office to write their own grade level English language arts/English language development units of study. Leadership at Stockton Unified School District feels that they know their students' needs better than a publisher could.

SHARED LEADERSHIP

When Adrienne Machado became the new director of the language development office for Stockton Unified School District, she called me at the San

Joaquin County Office of Education where I am the director of language and literacy, to discuss possibilities for teacher professional learning focused on the needs of EL students. My initial two-prong professional learning proposal included offering opportunities for cohorts of administrators and coaches to attend our 3-day English Language Development Standards Institute to learn about the state's English language development standards (California Department of Education (CDE), 2012) and English Language Arts/English Language Development K–12 Curriculum Framework (CDE, 2014). The overarching goal was to provide EL students the opportunity to have their specific academic science language and literacy needs analyzed and then strategically addressed through high quality teaching. We would accomplish this goal by providing foundational professional learning for all principals, vice-principals, coaches, and program specialists on current practices and policies effective for EL students and the leadership skills needed to implement them. The second aspect of the proposal was to offer an opportunity for district leaders who had attended the English Language Development Standards Institute to observe a concrete classroom example of effective teaching and learning for ELs in an actual school setting. It was important for administrators and coaches to see what our vision looked like so that they could support the site leadership necessary to transform practices across the district. In creating this model, we had specific goals for the participating students and their teachers.

1. For the Grades 3–8 EL students who attended, we wanted to improve their academic language and literacy achievement in science, increase their confidence in active classroom participation, and prepare them to transfer the strategies they learned to their school-year classroom contexts.
2. For the participating teachers, we wanted to improve their understanding of how to implement the California English Language Development Standards and the powerful teaching described in the California English Language Arts/English Language Development Framework. We also wanted them to align evidence-based practices designed to accelerate language and literacy development in science, and prepare them to take the learning back to their classrooms for school-year implementation.

Our intent was to provide teachers with a structured, supportive environment and opportunities to apply their learning in real time in the summer school classrooms. We also wanted teachers to become teacher ambassadors of this work at their home sites.

While only 23 site and district leaders signed up for the first English Language Development Standards Institute, once the word got out, 58 attended in the second year. The institute familiarized leaders with the state's newer English language development standards and how the standards could be used in tandem with the Common Core State Standards for English language arts/literacy and other content standards. A critical resource used during the institute was the California English Language Arts/English Language Development Framework, which provides guidance on standards-based teaching, including detailed vignettes of classroom activities. During the institute sessions, classroom activities are modeled using a unit of study taught in a local school district. Participants leave with a better understanding of what effective teaching and learning for EL students looks like, ready to support their teachers with their units of study using the English Language Development Standards in tandem with other content standards, and prepared to provide leadership around current EL practices and policies.

The next task was to create a month-long summer school program where students and teachers could experience, and leadership could observe, the instructional approaches promoted in the English Language Development Standards Institutes, which were brought to life from the English Language Development Standards and the California English Language Arts/English Language Development Framework. We wrote course content, created and prepared corresponding materials, and planned robust professional learning. We took the idea of shared leadership to heart and divided our responsibilities into two categories. Adrienne would lead the logistical work, creating conditions for effective content learning, and I would lead the creation of the units and professional learning. Adrienne recruited Stagg High School to be our summer school site, because their principal, Mr. Phillips, is a known advocate for marginalized students; Adrienne knew our program would be welcomed on his campus. Although the summer school was open to qualifying students throughout the district, during the first pilot year the bus schedule Adrienne created targeted the five K–8 schools with the largest numbers of long-term ELs and Els at-risk for becoming long-term Els. We increased transportation capacity to 10 buses during our second year to accommodate for program expansion. As part of the teacher selection process, teachers had to agree to a two teachers per class co-teaching model; attend all of the professional learning sessions; be willing to follow lesson plans and try out new strategies; be coached; and be videotaped and observed by summer school professional learning staff as well as visitors (administrators, coaches and teachers) from the district and neighboring districts. Teachers also had to commit to apply their new learning to their regular school year context and become teacher ambassadors for this work. Since we wanted students to be able to eat free breakfast and lunch on campus, coordination of these meals was another important component. Materials preparation included ordering all of the supplies teachers and students would need (one set of seven books per teacher, abundant chart paper, blue tape and markers, one journal per student, and pencils) and preparing all of the classroom materials that the teachers would be using for the first week and most of the second week (primarily charts, pictures, and photocopies). We share these logistical details because they made a significant impact on creating the conditions necessary for the summer school experience to be successful. This careful planning supported teachers to focus on learning and applying the new strategies, not on lesson planning or preparing materials.

PROFESSIONAL LEARNING CONTENT

While Adrienne and her staff worked on the logistics, my San Joaquin County Office of Education colleagues and I planned how to create the units of study and prepared the professional learning content. We began this by selecting engaging science topics and finding complex science informational texts. Then we set out to craft the units of study using these texts in ways that afforded the use of new strategies that would bring the California English Language Development Standards to life while concentrating on the productive science literacy skills—speaking and writing. We intentionally used a gradual release model so that over the course of the month-long professional learning/summer school experience, the responsibility would shift from San Joaquin County Office of Education and Stockton Unified School District planning and preparing all materials to teachers co-prepping and co-planning, and then finally teachers planning and prepping collaboratively with their grade level teams. Figure 7.1 shows how the gradual release model was implemented over 4 weeks.

The first year, we selected two keystone species as our focus for the units of study that teachers learned in professional learning sessions and applied in summer school. Keystone species are animals or plants that play very important roles in the way an ecosystem works. Students in Grades 3–5 learned about sea otters, and in Grades 6–8, students learned about honeybees. During Year 2, we selected just one keystone species, salmon, which

Week 1	Week 2	Week 3	Week 4
San Joaquin County Office of Education staff lesson plan and Stockton Unified School District staff prepare all materials for teachers.	San Joaquin County Office of Education staff lesson plan and Stockton Unified School District staff co-prepare all materials with teachers.	San Joaquin County Office of Education staff co-lesson plan with teachers, and teachers prepare all materials.	Teachers plan and prepare all materials.

Figure 7.1 Planning and preparing gradual release model.

allowed us to be more focused and strategic during both lesson planning and professional learning. Both years, all students focused on their animal's role as a keystone species, the unique anatomical features that help them survive, their life cycle, the impact humans have on their ecosystems, and why we should advocate for their survival.

To create each unit of study, we first determined the writing goal, which was to prepare a portfolio of writing that gave both groups of students the opportunity to practice different text types (descriptive, explanatory and argument). Having students write these different text types also gave teachers a chance to think about each of the text types more analytically. We used a text organization matrix (Figure 7.2) to help organize our planning and as a prototype during professional learning. Teachers then co-created weekly text type charts with students to develop their metalanguage and to talk more explicitly about the particular features of each (Schleppegrell, 2013).

Once we determined each writing task, we selected a variety of science informational texts that would support students' content knowledge development and serve as mentor texts for their own writing. Each text had to address at least one aspect of the information students were going to write about (e.g., how the animal was a keystone species) and we searched for a variety of complex texts with rich vocabulary and grammatical structures. These included the books we'd purchased as well as online texts. We then used a simple "sentence patterning chart" to identify the domain-specific and general academic vocabulary we could highlight for students and to analyze the syntax in each text. In our analyses of texts, we started to notice nuances in the vocabulary used, which types of verbs and verb tenses were used, and in what ways noteworthy adjectives, adverbs, or prepositional phrases were used. Our awareness of the language in the text deepened with subsequent analyses, which helped us determine how we could leverage different parts of the texts and use grammar-based activities in context to highlight for students (and their teachers) how science language works. In subsequent analyses, we looked for complex sentences we could unpack with students, grammatical features to highlight, examples of language features that are typical of the text type (e.g., sequential and temporal text connectives such as "later," "after spawning," "in the spring," used in explanatory texts on the salmon life cycle), and where we might be able to be playful with language (e.g., writing a simple song using precise verbs that students would create gestures for). Additionally, we used a color-coding system when highlighting parts of speech and how the parts of speech work together to make meaning (Figure 7.3).

We also selected domain-specific vocabulary from the texts that we would use as a daily key vocabulary word to teach, highlight throughout the day, and use during transitions (Figure 7.4).

Text Type	Informative: Descriptive	Explanatory: Sequential	Explanatory: Causal	Argument
Writing Task	Write a descriptive paragraph about salmon.	Write a sequential explanation of the salmon life cycle.	Write a causal explanation of the impact humans have on salmon.	Write a letter to the editor about how to save/protect salmon.
Purpose	Describe, define, classify or categorize information.	Understand how something happens.	Understand why something happens.	Persuade the reader to agree to a certain viewpoint or take action. Develop a stance in relation to an issue.
Organization	General statement/ classification statement (topic) Facts/details about the topic (whole to part) Order not important	Description Sequential explanatory sequence	Description Causal explanatory sequence	Statement/claim Supporting arguments Details Reaffirmation
Language Features	Densely packed sentences: long noun phrases Verbs: timeless present tense being/having verbs (is/are, has/have) doing verbs (migrate, hatch) Vocabulary: domain specific and general academic	Densely packed sentences: long noun phrases Verbs: timeless present passive voice (have been spawned) Sequential + temporal text connectives (during, after, in the spring) Vocabulary: domain specific and general academic	Densely packed sentences: long noun phrases Verbs: timeless present passive voice (become polluted) Causal text connectives and Conjunctions (when, due to, as a result) Nominalization (siltation, destruction) Vocabulary: domain specific and general academic	Text connectives and conjunctions (in addition, as a result, furthermore) Verbs: Modal verbs (can, should, must) Evaluative language (necessary, deserve, safer) Citation phrases (according to, states, found) Vocabulary: domain specific and general academic

Figure 7.2 Text organization matrix.

Next, we began writing instructional sequences to match each writing text type to be addressed throughout the unit of study. We developed these using a highly scaffolded apprenticeship model for writing, which has been developed over the past couple of decades in Australia and more recently used in the United States, called the teaching and learning cycle (TLC;

adjectives (red)	nouns (black)	verbs (green)	adverbs (orange)	prepositional phrase (purple)
extinct	survival	forage	carefully	in the kelp forest
diurnal	kelp	protect	quickly	under the ocean
retractable	sea urchins	survive	slowly	along the coastline
warm-blooded	prey	protect	forcefully	between the rocks
closable	protection	groom	gently	near the shore

Figure 7.3   Example of a sentence patterning chart.

Word + Part of Speech + L1	Definition + Picture	How to use it + Example from text	Definition + Picture
pollen **noun** *pollen*	a powder made by flowers	Bees visit many flowers to collect <u>pollen</u>. *Bees transfer the <u>pollen</u> that sticks to their body from flower to flower.*	pollinate **pollinator, pollination**

Figure 7.4   Example of a key vocabulary chart.

Derewianka and Jones, 2012; Rose and Martin, 2012; Spycher and Linn-Nieves, 2014). The TLC (Figure 7.5) is also the scaffolding model used in the California English Language Arts/English Language Development Framework for all of the units of study in the "English Language Arts With Integrated English Language Development" and corresponding "designated English language development vignettes."

The Language and Literacy Department at San Joaquin County Office of Education uses this systematic and explicit approach to scaffolding students' writing development in all of our units of study, and we have had great success using it with both students and teachers. The cycle addresses what we have observed is missing from most writing instruction. In many classrooms, we find that teachers do a good job building content knowledge. They often activate prior knowledge, read some texts, and co-create graphic organizers with students. When students are then asked to write about the topic, typical responses include: "I don't know how to start"; "I don't know what to write"; or "How long does this have to be?" Teachers believe there is plenty to write about from the information read, instructional conversations they have led, and the graphic organizers created. The TLC acknowledges that although students must know enough about the topic to have something to write about, much more goes into writing

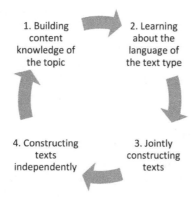

Figure 7.5 The teaching and learning cycle (TLC). *Source:* Derewianka and Jones, 2012; Rose and Martin, 2012; Spycher and Linn-Nieves, 2014.

than just content knowledge. Students also need abundant practice to understand how English works in different ways with different text types and in different content areas. Writing is structured differently across text types, and knowing this helps students match their writing to the task, purpose, and audience. The following is a brief overview of the four stages of the TLC and how we approach each stage in our summer school professional learning model.

Stage 1: Building Content Knowledge

This stage is focused on content knowledge building and sets the stage for all subsequent learning. The texts students will read and information taught are carefully selected with a critical eye on the writing goals. During this stage, teachers find out what students know and begin building meaning about science phenomena. Strategic planning for the content learning includes a variety of opportunities to learn and discuss information in meaningful ways that also generate enthusiasm and a sense of purpose for the unit of study.

A few of the tasks from this stage that we included in summer school were abundant reading and writing about the keystone species students were learning about, video viewing and discussion, note making while listening, structured academic discussions about the texts and videos, attention to domain-specific and general academic vocabulary, and simulation science experiments. It is very important to note that this stage, although presented here first sequentially, is not prescriptive; new texts providing additional content knowledge are continually introduced throughout the unit.

Stage 2: Learning the Language of the Text Types

This stage focuses on developing language awareness and learning about how English works. Once students are familiar with a piece of text, teachers can begin to dig deeper into learning about the language of that text. In our experience, this stage is missing from most writing instruction and curriculum materials and is of utmost importance in order for our students to understand text types, their different purposes, how they are structured, and the language features that are typical of each. Knowing about the language in different text types helps students attend to how the text is structured and to the specific language used in the text, which supports their reading comprehension and gives them a model for their own writing.

A few of the many tasks we included in the summer school model were examining mentor texts, reconstructing and deconstructing texts, and focusing on particular language features in science informational texts, such as the verb types, domain-specific vocabulary, and text connectives.

Stage 3: Jointly Constructing Texts

This very important stage is rarely part of older students' writing instruction yet is critical for helping them to become independent writers. The focus is on guided practice, where teachers and students construct a text together. The teacher acts as a scribe, drawing attention to the text type and structure, and scaffolds the writing by asking students questions, making suggestions, and providing prompts or rewording where necessary. Students collaborate to share ideas and contribute to the process. Throughout the process, the text is read, re-read, and edited.

During summer school, we engaged in joint construction daily. Some of the ways we jointly constructed texts were through jointly constructed complex sentences, summaries of texts, and concise paragraphs or multiparagraph sections on various topics about the keystone species.

Stage 4: Constructing Texts Independently

Once students have had multiple opportunities to closely read and analyze mentor texts, to understand their purpose, structure, and language features, to deconstruct and reconstruct those texts, and to write and edit collaboratively through joint construction, they are much better prepared to write independently. At this point in the TLC, students have the opportunity to apply their new understanding of the topic and text type by writing about a new related topic or another aspect of the original topic. In addition to guided peer editing, teachers provide explicit feedback on students' plans and drafts. Students also participate in targeted small group instruction based on teacher formative assessment, and receive teacher feedback.

PRE-SERVICE PROFESSIONAL LEARNING

We planned two and a half days of foundational professional learning to prepare teachers for the month-long summer school. Topics for these days included team building, the importance of a growth mindset, characteristics of long-term ELs, the CA English Language Development Standards and English Language Arts/English Language Development Framework, the TLC, co-teaching models to be used, and instructional sequence and materials.

Day 1

The first day took place on a Saturday, a couple of weeks prior to the start of summer school. We spent the majority of the day learning about the English Language Development Standards through a demonstration lesson, showing examples of the standards in action in classrooms. Teachers learned about the TLC for the first time, the organizational model for their keystone species unit. They read the Grade 5 English Language Arts/Science With Integrated English Language Development vignette and its corresponding designated English Language Development vignette from the California English Language Arts/English Language Development Framework, which focuses on a unit of study on the ecosystem and models several strategies they would be using. To apply their beginning understanding of the TLC, teachers collaborated to determine in which stage of the TLC they thought the strategies used in each vignette belonged and why. A few of the strategies included:

- The use of mentor texts
  - used to teach students how to read complex informational texts more closely
  - models for students to see the kind of writing they should produce
- Deconstructing texts
  - unpacking the meanings in a text by discussing the language used
  - analyzing the language features in texts and how they work to make meaning
- Analyzing text organization
  - creating an outline for an informational report to help them structure writing
  - learning about cohesion

The participating teachers' homework assignment was to closely read the first book they would be using during the first instructional sequence in summer school in order to familiarize themselves with their keystone species (science content) and the vocabulary and language utilized in that text (science language).

Day 2

We held our second professional learning day on the Saturday before summer school. We revisited the TLC and then experienced and debriefed each strategy teachers would be using during the first day of instruction. The first year, I demonstrated each of the strategies using a different keystone species, the Mexican free-tailed bat, which served as a model teachers could use to practice the same strategies they would apply to their particular keystone species. This demonstration proved to be somewhat overwhelming as teachers were unfamiliar with the terminology I was using and the strategies I was modeling. During the second year, we opted to use only one keystone species, which helped focus our professional learning and significantly lessen teachers' overwhelmed feelings, as they could experience the strategies using the exact content they would be using with their students.

Day 3

On the following Monday, the day before summer school started, we reviewed several models of co-teaching and took partners through structured conversations so they could plan how they would work together. We then reviewed the instruction for Day 1 of the summer school and gave partners time to decide which co-teaching models they would try during the different activities throughout their first day. Next, everyone gathered their prepared instructional materials and spent the afternoon planning and organizing their classrooms together.

SUMMER SCHOOL

During the month-long summer school, students cycled through four instructional sequences (Figure 7.6) that each lasted about a week. Each instructional sequence was a "mini-TLC" that scaffolded students' writing around a specific text type (description, explanation, argument). We describe the first instructional sequence to provide an idea of what the summer school classes looked like.

Week 1	Week 2	Week 3	Week 4
Text Type in Focus: Informative-Description	Text Type in Focus: Explanatory-Sequential	Text Type in Focus: Explanatory-Causal	Text Type in Focus: Argument

Figure 7.6 Summer school instructional sequences.

We carefully designed the first instructional sequence to include most of the ideas/strategies that were new to the teachers, the ones we wanted them to learn first and learn well and use during the upcoming three instructional sequences. During professional learning, I modeled each strategy so they could experience the strategy first hand and provided time for teachers to process. I had personally used each strategy that I modeled multiple times at different grade levels, which gave me the first-hand knowledge needed to provide helpful teaching tips from my experiences working with students. I was also able to share pictures, videos and samples of student work. Because teachers experienced the strategies themselves, they were much more familiar with and could better lead their students' learning than if they had just read lesson plans created by someone else.

Instructional Sequence 1

To prepare students to write a descriptive informational text about their keystone species (a description), we began each day with a quick routine using the key vocabulary chart and signal word of the day. Students shared what they already knew about their keystone species, and then participated in a *give one, get one* activity which helped them leverage their existing knowledge and build some new content knowledge. Students closely read complex science texts multiple times for different purposes and nominated domain-specific vocabulary for a class *notice and note* vocabulary chart. *Text puzzles,* an activity in which students collaboratively reconstruct texts they had previously read closely, gave students additional experience discussing the science content and also the syntax used in the science informational texts they were reading. In text puzzles, sentences are cut into words or chunks of meaning, then mixed up. Two students work collaboratively to put the sentence back together and discuss what it means. We created stations students could rotate through and cut the sentences up at the word level and phrase level (e.g., noun phrase, prepositional phrase) of meaning (Figure 7.7).

Another task introduced in the first instructional sequence was the *noodles* (notes plus doodles) strategy, which gives pairs of students an

Sea otters   live   in the cold waters   of the Pacific Ocean   off the coasts

of the United States,   Canada,   and Russia.

Figure 7.7 Text puzzles example.

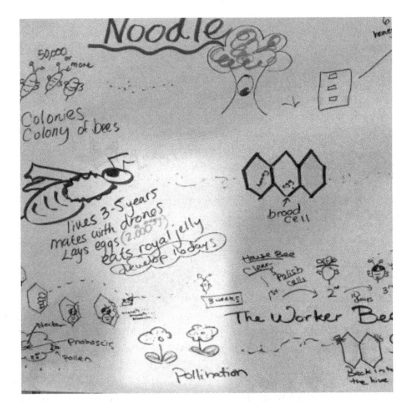

Figure 7.8 Noodles example.

opportunity to summarize the key ideas from a text the teacher reads aloud (Figure 7.8).

Students then offer up ideas for doodles to help them remember the key ideas and suggest words/phrases to be added into "note-making" charts, which are used for discussion and writing tasks (Figure 7.9).

Once students have developed some content knowledge around a science topic, they can move into Stage 2 and analyze new complex sentences, larger sections of text, or whole texts that the teacher has deemed worthy of deeper understanding and exploration. For example, the Grades 3–5 classes, who were learning about sea otters, listened to the following sentence

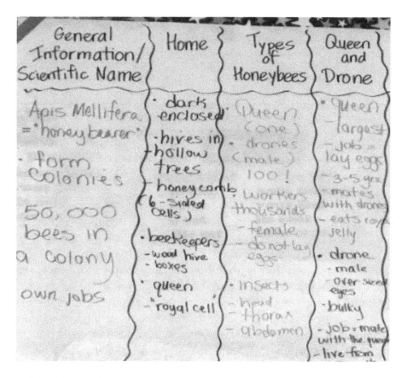

Figure 7.9   Note-making example.

twice, took notes on key words, created a class list of the words, and then collaboratively reconstructed it orally:

> Just offshore, the shallow coastal waters are also a refuge for marine mammals, such as the sea otters.

Once they had heard the sentence, reconstructed it and read it a couple of times, the teacher first led them in unpacking the sentence for meaning and then highlighted specific grammatical features that lend nuance to the sentence but that students may miss (e.g., "also," "such as"). Through guided questioning, the students unpacked many meanings from this one complex sentence, such as:

Sea otters live near the land.
Sea otters live in the ocean.
Sea otters live in water that is not deep.
The water that is along the coast is not deep.
Sea otters are mammals.
Some mammals live in the ocean.

Day 1	Day 2	Day 3	Day 4	Day 5
Close reading Text 1, peer discussions, text type chart (text type and purpose), can–have–are chart	Close reading Text 1, peer discussions, text puzzles, text type chart (text organization and language features), noodles, note-making	Close reading Text 2, peer discussions, note-making, collaborative sentence reconstruction, sentence unpacking and sentence combining	Close reading Text 2, text puzzles, text type chart, running dictation, sentence unpacking, joint construction—descriptive paragraph	Students write descriptions, give and get feedback from peers, then teachers, revise

Figure 7.10   First instructional sequence outline.

Next, students engaged in sentence combining to create novel sentences using the information they'd pulled out of the complex sentence such as, "Sea otters are mammals that live in the ocean." Later in the week, teachers jointly constructed complex sentences with students, using the information derived from noodles, note-making, text puzzles, sentence unpacking, and sentence combining. Each day, students wrote increasingly sophisticated sentences, and through this sequence of scaffolding, by the end of the week, they were able to write science descriptions with nuance and complexity (Figure 7.10).

AFTERNOON PROFESSIONAL LEARNING

Adrienne and I walked through the classrooms daily, sometimes jumping in and teaching upon request, sometimes answering questions, observing students and frequently finding topics to revisit during the afternoon professional learning sessions. Our daily professional learning occurred from 12:30–2:30 p.m. after students had left at noon and teachers had eaten their lunch. We began each afternoon by sharing things that went well (e.g., a lesson, something one teacher observed their partner do, an example of what students did). Each day, we found things to highlight from our walkthroughs that we asked teachers to share. For example, one group of teachers incorporated some materials from two activities in a novel way that was highly effective with their class. They shared the chart they had created and the following day many of their colleagues were using their idea. In addition to sharing ideas and reflecting on our practices, we also reviewed the next day's instructional sequence, clarified strategies, unpacked English language development standards, and over time began to collaboratively plan lessons. During the fourth week, when teachers were collaboratively planning lessons on stewardship, each group led different topics (e.g., key vocabulary, texts, interactive activities, and videoclips). After about 20 minutes, they each presented on what they had found/created and were amazed to discover that the majority of the planning could be accomplished so quickly. Teachers commented multiple times that now they had so many ideas of ways to work more deeply with texts, which were previously unknown to them.

Each week's writing task included lots of discussion about the scaffolding necessary to get the results we wanted. I created success criteria and editing tools based on the Language Analysis Framework for Writing (Figure 7.11; CDE, 2014, p. 852) that were adapted to each week's writing text type and specific writing task. For example, explanatory sequential writing describing the salmon life cycle requires different text connectives from explanatory causal writing describing human impact.

Each day we reviewed the upcoming day's lesson plans and by Week 3, collaboratively wrote lesson plans. During Week 1 of summer school, we conducted our first walkthroughs with teams of teachers so they could all observe

Content Knowledge and Register	Text Organization and Structure	Grammatical Structures	Vocabulary	Spelling and Punctuation
Is the overall meaning clear? Are the big ideas there, and are they accurate? Is the text type (e.g., opinion, narrative, explanation) appropriate for conveying the content knowledge? Does the register of the writing match the audience?	Is the purpose (e.g., entertaining, persuading, explaining) getting across? Is the overall text organization appropriate for the text type? Are text connectives used effectively to create cohesion? Are pronouns and other language resources used for referring the reader backward or forward?	Are the verb types and tenses appropriate for the text type? Are noun phrases expanded appropriately in order to enrich the meaning of ideas? Are sentences expanded with adverbials (e.g., adverbs, prepositional phrases) in order to provide details (e.g., time, manner, place, cause)? Are clauses combined and condensed appropriately to join ideas, show relationships between ideas, and create conciseness and precision?	Are general academic and domain-specific words used, and are they used accurately? Are a variety of words used (e.g., a range of words for "small": little, tiny, miniscule, microscopic)?	Are words spelled correctly? Is punctuation used appropriately?

Figure 7.11 Language analysis framework for writing.

one another's classrooms. While debriefing, one of the teachers said that she "did the strategy all wrong," and that she would go back to her classroom and, "do it again the right way." We immediately had a crucial conversation with her regarding her expectation of "perfection" while in the process of learning, and how that expectation was not only unrealistic, but could be stifling. If we are expecting teachers to be brave and try out new strategies, it must come with support and guidance rather than a focus on "wrong and right." With her permission, we shared the incident during that afternoon's professional learning and we came up with the motto, "Perfectly Imperfect."

Summer school was as much about the teacher learning as it was about the student learning, and it was important for teachers to demonstrate to their students that they were learners too. Without taking risks to learn, it is impossible for teachers to understand their practice more deeply and move ahead or grow (Darling-Hammond & Richardson, 2009). From this day on, we opened up our professional learning each afternoon with different quotes (e.g., "Mistakes are proof that you are trying"; "I embrace the imperfections and celebrate them"; and "Imperfection is the new perfection"). We made a very conscious effort to use an asset-orientation and asset-based language with both our students and with our adult colleagues. Instead of using words like "errors" or "mistakes," we used "approximations" when referring to both student and teacher learning. When referring to students, we used the acronym EAL, English as an additional language, and we talked about the use of the word "yet"—as in, "I do not know how to do that *yet*" (Dweck, 2006).

For additional collaboration, classrooms were partnered, so that students could teach one another about their keystone species. Once a week, the two classrooms would meet and share what they were learning and engage in some activities together. The students enjoyed working with their cross-age peers tremendously. Due to the two teacher per classroom model, some innovative peer coaching practices emerged. We were able to gather several teachers at once to demonstrate lessons and then the observers could go back and model the strategy for their partner. Our culminating activity was to hold an open house where families, friends, and community members could tour the classrooms and learn from the students, who served as docents, sharing all the learning that had occurred in their classrooms and demonstrating several of the strategies for their guests.

FOLLOW-UP PROFESSIONAL LEARNING

We reunited for three follow-up days over the course of the following school year so that our teacher ambassadors could continue to refine their skills, deepen their knowledge and apply this learning to their contexts. Each reunion began with everyone sharing concrete examples of something they had tried with their current students based on their summer school learning. The two-fold purpose was to continue supporting teachers' implementation of the practices they'd learned in the summer professional learning and to use it as a formative assessment opportunity for us so that we could continue to make refinements to the model. Occasionally, we could see that teachers might have missed where a strategy belonged in an instructional sequence, or missed some of the critical aspects of the steps or prompts to students. To reinforce the notion of purposeful implementation of the strategies teachers learned and applied in the summer school model, we revisited the TLC at each reunion meeting. This practice continued to ground our discussions and our understanding of how this theoretical framework supports teachers' efforts to scaffold students' writing. During our first reunion, I narrated each stage of the cycle and then had participants paraphrase the gist with partners. At our second reunion, we read more vignettes from the California English Language Arts/English Language Development Framework and identified stages in the TLC the strategies addressed. At our third reunion, we read Gibbons' (2015) description of the TLC and practiced using some of the strategies she recommends for each stage. We always ended each session with time for teachers to collaborate on refining their own units of study, where they embedded these strategies and the TLC framework into their existing practice.

PRE–POST WRITING ASSESSMENTS

Students completed the same on-demand writing sample on their first and last days of summer school so that we could determine what they had internalized over the 19 days of instruction. In their initial samples, we did not expect students to know much about the content, and we were more focused on examining their writing. We tallied "approximations" students made to help us determine particular areas of focus for instruction. The top areas of instructional need were subject–verb agreement ("Bees are little insects that fly"), an almost exclusive use of simple sentences ("Salmon are fish"), pronoun reference ("Bees have wings and bees fly"), prepositions ("Sea otters live on the water"), and academic vocabulary ("Bees make honey from their tail"). At a glance, the growth students made in their post-assessments was substantial, simply due to the difference in quantity as compared to the pre-assessments. Upon further analysis, the frequent use of complex sentences and precise vocabulary were now notably present (see Figure 7.12).

On our first day of professional learning, teachers listed practices they currently used in the classroom to support their EL students' writing. Responses included generic ideas such as total physical response, visuals,

Student	Pre-Assessment	Post-Assessment	Analysis
Angel (3rd grade)	*Sea otter are cute.*	*Sea otters are important animals because they are a keystone species.*	– subject verb agreement – domain-specific vocabulary – complex sentence
Maya (6th grade)	*Bees are little insects that buzz when they fly.*	*Bees fly from flower to flower collecting pollen and nectar and then store it in hive cells.*	– domain-specific vocabulary – precise verbs – complex sentence

Figure 7.12   Pre- and post-writing assessments. *Note:* Student names are pseudonyms.

graphic organizers, sentence frames, think-pair-share, brainstorming, modeling, frontloading vocabulary, and wait time. In terms of what they wanted to learn, a common thread included ideas to help students become more confident and independent. They also expressed interest in language development and use of the standards. On the last day of summer school, teachers filled out a survey, rating themselves on the following questions using a scale of 1–3 (1 = *not at all,* 2 = *some,* 3 = *greatly*):

Do you feel you have grown professionally as a teacher as a result of summer school?

Has your knowledge of the California English Language Arts/English Language Development Framework expanded?

Do you feel your students' language has grown as a result of summer school?

Do you feel better prepared to teach ELs in the fall?

Nineteen of 20 teachers rated all of their answers *greatly* while one used the *some* rating.

In response to the questions "How often did you apply the English language development standards in your lessons this summer?" and "Check all that contributed to your growth as a teacher," all 20 teachers marked *daily* on the first question and everyone agreed that the combination of initial professional learning, daily professional learning and collaboration, and in-class support accounted for their shifted practice. Additional sample questions and responses included:

- "If students' language has grown as a result of summer school, how do you know?"
    - Instead of writing simple four word sentences, students are now able to write complex sentences. They know how to use transi-

tions to show sequence while introducing the content they learned about bees.

  – I could hear their growth in their language, see their growth in their writing, and feel their growth in their confidence to speak in front of peers and adults.
- "How has your language awareness increased during summer school and how will it impact your teaching?"
  – My language awareness has improved dramatically. I added more than a dozen easy teaching strategies that are both academically challenging/rigorous and fun that can be applied to my units of study. I now know what to do during integrated and designated English language development.
  – I am much more thoughtful of the language I choose to utilize when speaking and writing with my students. I now realize how important it is to teach students academic language, read for *meaning* first and learn the structure of text types.
- We recorded video clips of teachers, students, and parents to share. One teacher stated, "The strategies that I learned at this summer school were the strategies I'd been looking for, for 30 years. Using them this summer and using them in my school now, I see the students understanding and being able to construct sentences and paragraphs in a way I've never seen before. It has filled my toolbox up with things I'd always needed."

A parent told us that her 6th grade son loves learning again and came home daily to teach his little sister about all that he had learned that day. Her son said that he thought summer school was going to be boring, but that when he came, he really loved it. He added that bees were a very interesting subject, that he learned a lot about them and said he will never look at bees in the same way.

LESSONS LEARNED

The type of quality summer school and professional learning model we've described takes a lot of planning and dedication, but with collaboration between district leaders and support providers (e.g., county offices of education), it can be done well with positive results. For the first few days of the summer school, there was definitely a "strategy overload" for teachers since they were using so much new science content and so many new strategies with new names, not to mention new standards. To minimize stress, one teacher started labeling all of her charts, which was a simple, brilliant move we began to incorporate during the second week. And all charts were labeled from the outset during our second year.

We contacted both the local newspaper, *The Stockton Record*, and the San Joaquin County Office of Education's *Outlook* magazine. Both came to visit and conducted interviews with students, teachers, and parents; and both really captured the essence of what we were trying to accomplish in their publications (Carpazio, 2017; Johnson, 2017). We organized site tours to begin during the third week of instruction. This gave teachers the chance to learn the strategies and become comfortable with them before being observed. It also gave teachers and students the opportunity to decorate their bare classrooms, so that by the end of the second week, classrooms were bursting with rich science content and language. We met with each group of visitors to present the summer school model and then divided into smaller groups to take them on classroom tours. After, when we regrouped to debrief and answer questions, we brought in a teacher to share about their personal experience.

Another reflection was how difficult many teachers found joint construction during the first year. This high-leverage strategy is of critical importance to support students to practice using a more academic register when writing. However, we observed that teachers did not really quite understand how to do it or felt intimidated by it as novices since they had little experience with how to guide it. As a result, we paid particular attention to the scaffolding of this powerful strategy during our second year, through more careful sequencing. On the first day, teachers did a close reading of the initial mentor text, and then partners collaboratively categorized key words and phrases into a *can–have–are* chart. From there, the teacher facilitated sentence combining using the words and phrases from the chart, leading to joint construction. Students wrote compound and complex sentences about salmon, and teachers arrived at our afternoon professional learning having experienced immediate success. We learned to provide an initial focus on teachers getting good at jointly constructed complex sentences before moving on to a scaffolded paragraph (i.e., partially filled in) and then, a jointly constructed paragraph.

While observing at one site last spring, we spotted a bulletin board near the copy machine where a strategy from summer school was on display. As part of staff professional learning, one of our summer school teachers, Irene, had modeled the *noodles* strategy and then offered to come in and demonstrate it if anyone was interested. She made copies of the instructions available to her colleagues and posted a sheet of paper for teachers who tried the strategy out to sign. There was a copy of the TLC highlighting the stage where the strategy belongs, alongside a list of possible extensions. Needless to say, we were thrilled about this "ambassador's" work!

NEXT STEPS

Our demonstration summer school is now part of a multi-year plan for the Stockton Unified School District. As previously stated, one of the purposes for developing the model was so that administrators and instructional coaches could see the teaching and learning described during the English Language Development Standards Institutes they had attended in action with ELs. In order to deepen literacy practices that scaffold the understanding of the English language and how it works, we believe it is critical for administrators and coaches to understand the work so they can help lead it. During Year 2 of our collaboration, San Joaquin County Office of Education brought several English Language Development Standards Institutes to Stockton Unified School District teachers and continued to add to the cadre of administrators and coaches. In our second year of summer school, we expanded to incorporate three new units of study that included a K–2 grade span focused on migrant students and a 9–12 grade span focused on argument writing with long-term ELs in high school, significantly augmenting the number of students and teachers involved in the model. We partnered a cadre of teacher leaders with new teacher hires, and observed them blossom as mentors. Several shared how they developed a much deeper understanding of the work during their second opportunity to participate in summer school. With these efforts and our model of strong county office and district office collaboration, our goal is to support all teachers in our county to scaffold science language and literacy so that we eliminate the creation of long-term ELs.

Moving forward, these are the inquiry and action research questions we aim to pursue, or that we would like to see the field pursue:

Inquiry Questions

- How can we meet the different linguistic needs of diverse ELs?
- How can the professional learning model and instructional approach in this chapter be used to better support students, teachers, and administrators?
- What are the benefits of organizing instruction using the teaching and learning cycle?

Action Research Questions

- How does the model described in this chapter compare to the curriculum, instruction, and professional learning used in your school or district?

- How similar or different are these ideas from how you currently organize writing instruction?
- What are some takeaways that you can apply to your context to support student writing?

REFERENCES

California Department of Education. (2012). *California English language development standards: Kindergarten through grade 12.* Sacramento, CA: Author. Retrieved from https://www.cde.ca.gov/sp/el/er/documents/eldstndspublication14.pdf

California Department of Education. (2014). *English language arts/English language development framework for California public schools: Kindergarten through grade twelve.* Sacramento, CA: Author. Retrieved from https://www.mydigitalchalkboard .org/cognoti/content/file/resources/documents/8c/8cf4adf5/8cf4adf587 da2b191c07b09831798d521bc05adc/FrameworkFINALJuly2015.pdf

Carpazio, A. (2017, June 27). Inaugural summer school program gives English learners a boost. *The Stockton Record.* Retrieved from http://www.recordnet .com/news/20170629/inaugural-summer-school-program-gives-english -learners-boost

Darling-Hammond, L., Hyler, M. E., & Gardner, M. (2017). *Effective teacher professional development.* Palo Alto, CA: Learning Policy Institute. Retrieved from https://learningpolicyinstitute.org/product/teacher-prof-dev

Darling-Hammond, L, & Richardson, N. (2009, February). Teacher learning: What matters. *Educational Leadership, 66*(5), 46–53.

Derewianka, B., & Jones, P. (2012). *Teaching language in context.* Melbourne, Australia: Oxford University Press.

Dweck, C. (2006). *Mindset: The new psychology of success.* New York, NY: Ballentine Books.

Gibbons, P. (2015). *Scaffolding language, scaffolding learning: Teaching English language learners in the mainstream classroom.* Portsmouth, NH: Heinemann.

Johnson, Z. (2017). Words were everywhere. *The San Joaquin County Office of Education Outlook, 71*(1), 18–21. Retrieved from https://indd.adobe.com/ view/53f44ebb-d605-4a9a-9b72-c82652d17368

Rose, D., & Martin, J. (2012). *Learning to write, reading to learn: Genre, knowledge, and pedagogy of the Sydney school.* Sheffield, CT: Equinox.

Schleppegrell, M. (2013). The role of metalanguage in supporting academic language development. *Language Learning, 63*(s1), 153–170.

Spycher, P., & Linn-Nieves, K. (2014). Reconstructing, deconstructing, and constructing complex texts. In P. Spycher (Ed.), *The common core state standards in English language arts for English language learners: Grade K–5* (pp. 51–68). Alexandria, VA: TESOL Press.

CHAPTER 8

BALANCING CULTURAL AND SCIENCE IDENTITY FRAMEWORKS FOR AMERICAN INDIAN/ALASKA NATIVE HIGH SCHOOL STUDENTS

A Summer Research Journey

Carolee Dodge Francis
American Indian Research and Education Center

Noehealani Bareng-Antolin
American Indian Research and Education Center

Kira Tran
American Indian Research and Education Center

The need for Native Americans (NA) in the biomedical, behavioral, clinical, and social sciences research workforce has never been so pronounced. The American Indian/Alaska Native (AI/AN) population reflects high

Culturally and Linguistically Diverse Learners and STEAM, pages 169–187

rates of chronic disease that continue to rise rapidly. The multifaceted disparities in access to education and educational achievement contribute to and complicate the resolution of health disparities (Nesbitt & Palomarez, 2016). Research suggests that the health and health care of underrepresented minorities are improved when providers of similar ethnic and racial backgrounds provide the care (Brown, DeCorse-Johnson, Irving-Ray, & Wu, 2005; Smedley & Mittman, 2011). This chapter provides perspectives related to drawing AI/AN students into these fields through cultural grounding, gathering and experiencing scientific knowledge, and making meaning for the students and their tribal communities.

THE NEED FOR AI/AN STUDENTS IN STEM

The disease burden that occurs across the marginalized populations in the United States, related to gender, race/ethnicity, education, income, and disability, has a profound impact on the health of our nation. Chronic diseases disproportionately afflict minority populations, including diabetes, obesity, kidney, liver, urologic diseases, and cancers. This disproportionately burdensome health trend translates into health disparities, and strongly correlates with lower socioeconomic status, less education, lower paying jobs, higher levels of unemployment, and often less health care coverage found among rural residents.

In the United States, 2.9 million people identify as AI/ANs alone. The AI/AN population experienced rapid growth in the first part of the century, increasing by 26.7% since 2000, compared the 9.7% for the U.S. population as a whole (Norris, Vines, & Hoeffel, 2012). The AI/AN population is also younger than the overall United States population, with a median age of 30.2 years, compared to 37.8 years overall (United States Census Bureau, 2016).

The disparate type 2 diabetes burden that AI/ANs bear (Centers for Disease Control and Prevention, 2017) has created an unparalleled epidemic among native populations (Valway et al., 1993) across the nation. AI/ANs are 2.3 times more likely to have diabetes as non-Hispanic Whites of similar age (Centers for Disease Control and Prevention, 2011). From 1994 to 2004, the age-adjusted prevalence of diagnosed diabetes doubled among young (under 35 years) AI/ANs served by the Indian Health Service (Acton, Burrows, Wang, & Geiss, 2006). According to the Indian Health Services Division of Diabetes Statistics, between 1990 to 2009 there was a 110% increase in diagnosed diabetes in American Indian and Alaska Native youth age 15-19 years old (2012). Building tribal capacity to eliminate diabetes disparities is closely tied to the education and professional development of the next generation of researchers and teachers (Moore, Dodge Francis, & DeBruyn, 2009).

Overall, health disparities are best addressed by a diverse science workforce with vested interests in these issues. According to a 2005 assessment by the National Research Council,

> The participation of minorities broadens and deepens science as individuals with diverse backgrounds address familiar and new problems, formulate novel questions, and employ alternative strategies for solutions. This is seen especially in clinical and public health research areas, such as health disparities and medical care, and in targeted efforts at specific diseases. (p. 21)

In the United States and within our U.S. territories, minority scientists in biomedical research are significantly underrepresented (Villarejo, Barlow, Kogan, Veazey, & Sweeney, 2008). Individuals from disadvantaged backgrounds are underrepresented in higher education, and in particular science education (Halpern-Felsher & McLaughlin, 2016; Sánchez, Poll-Hunter, & Acosta, 2015).

Because minority groups are less likely to engage in science, technology, engineering, and math (STEM) education, they are subsequently less likely to pursue careers in the biomedical research workforce (McGee, Saran, & Krulwich, 2012). The same can be said of AI/AN students: They do not see themselves as researchers, scientists, health professionals, or even going into careers that require a science background. The number of AI/AN professionals in biomedical fields is dismally small—they represent only 0.6% of the biomedical workforce, and only 0.3% of physicians. Achieving buy-in to the scientific enterprise requires not only that students become excited about science, but also that they see that tribal communities share and understand the nuances involved with a summer research experience.

Summer research experiences that increase research-specific self-efficacy by providing situational mastery experiences through a hands-on research internship that includes doing, interpreting, and presenting research under the direct supervision of research mentors reinforces Bandura's (1997) general theory of self-efficacy beliefs. Thus, investing in AI/AN students would support the development of a workforce capable of designing culturally grounded health promotion and chronic disease prevention strategies that currently do not exist in some tribal communities. In order to reduce health disparities within AI/AN communities, it is imperative to include them in research education, research plans, and discussions of the potential impact of the research (Davis, 2000).

Studies have shown that exposure to research opportunities not only broadens but transforms underrepresented students' interest in pursuing science degrees and that by applying that same strategy to the broader fields of biomedical/public health, the number of underrepresented students pursuing degrees and careers in biomedical/public health research should increase (Villarejo et al., 2008). Additionally, exposure to research experiences helps students "think like a scientist," clarify and confirm their career plans including their desire to apply for graduate school, and ultimately enhance the strength of their graduate school applications (Seymour, Hunter, Laursen, & DeAntoni, 2004).

Academic preparation is key to achieving parity in health and science professions (Patterson Silver Wolf & Carline, 2004; Winkleby, Ned, Ahn, Koehler, & Kennedy, 2009). The ability to provide high school adolescents with opportunities and exposure to scientific environments fuels the passion and pursuit of education in the sciences (Halpern-Felsher & McLaughlin, 2016). For AI/AN students the caveat to this path must be the recognition of *bicognition,* the ability to think in dual cultures (Ibarra, 2001). Such *bicognitive* opportunities are especially critical in promoting research and science interest among AI/AN students.

SHORT-TERM EDUCATION PROGRAM FOR UNDERREPRESENTED PERSONS (STEP-UP)

The National Institute of Diabetes and Digestive and Kidney Diseases originally started its summer high school research program at Howard University Minority High School and was comprised of 13 different states and 26 high school students per year. The program was relocated to create the Coordinating Center at Charles R. Drew University of Medicine and Science, and under the leadership of Dr. Keith Norris and program coordinator, Emma Taylor, the National High School Student Summer Research Apprentices Program (NHSSSRAP) was established under the joint collaboration of the National Institutes of Health, Charles R. Drew University of Medicine and Science, and the National Institute of Diabetes and Digestive and Kidney Diseases. The program aimed to expose underrepresented minority high school students to scientific research experience. As one of the first biomedical pipeline programs to focus on this population, NHSSSRAP's mission was to increase the number of disadvantaged, underrepresented students in the biomedical science workforce.

The program expanded to reach 75 high school students each year from across the country including Alaska, Puerto Rico, and Hawai'i. It provided underrepresented mentorship and researchers for academics in the sciences. Despite the trend of increasing diversity across the nation, in 2003, the Sullivan Commission on Diversity in the Healthcare Workforce gathered to discuss the inadequate number of minorities in healthcare professions (Norris & Agodoa, 2009). To increase support and awareness of health profession career options and opportunities for underrepresented minority students, the 2004 Sullivan Commission Report urged partnership with public school systems to provide counseling, mentoring, and test taking skills (Williams, 2008).

Since 2001, NHSSSRAP had been creating opportunities for high school students across the nation by matching selected students with mentors in local research centers in their home states. The National Institutes of Health/National Institute of Diabetes and Digestive and Kidney Diseases provided each student with an initial online research training opportunity, and students were mandated to participate in follow-up laboratory and research trainings specific to the research institution they were trained at over the summer experience. NHSSSRAP expanded to further diversify the program and transitioned to the Short-Term Education Program for Underrepresented Persons (STEP-UP; Caffey-Fleming & Reid, 2016) in 2007.

As the STEP-UP program grew, a National Institutes of Health/National Institute of Diabetes and Digestive and Kidney Diseases research education grant recruited two additional coordinating centers to join as program partners. The new participating sites funded were the University of Hawai'i, Manoa and the University of California, San Francisco. The program continued to focus on training in the National Institute of Diabetes and Digestive and Kidney Diseases mission areas. The fourth coordinating center to join was the University of Nevada, Las Vegas in 2012, which was brought in to focus on more AI/AN student engagement and coordination of AN and Puerto Rican students (Caffey-Fleming & Reid, 2016).

The goal of the STEP-UP program is to increase the number of youth who are committed to and well-positioned for careers in the sciences. The STEP-UP program provides an 8-week summer research experience for 11th and 12th grade high school students to develop critical thinking, research methodology skills, and a science identity within a supportive environment in which they have sustained relationships with mentors (often university faculty, medical and graduate students, and postdoctoral fellows), as well as student peers in the program.

The American Indian Research and Education Center located at the University of Nevada, Las Vegas is entering their second 5-year STEP-UP program funding cycle, with a program called *Journey*. Journey specifically targets and recruits AI/ANs across the nation in an effort to increase exposure of a summer experience within the areas of science and research. The long-term objective of Journey is to provide mentored research opportunities to high school students through the provision of hands-on experiences—which may include the range of biomedical, social science, behavioral, and clinical research—thus encouraging AI/AN students to explore further research experiences and professions, and to pursue biomedical degrees during their undergraduate journey.

The selection process for the STEP-UP program is done through a national application process. Typically, close to 400 students apply from underrepresented populations (i.e., Hispanic, Latino, African American, American Indian, Alaska Native, Native Hawaiian, and Pacific Islander students,

TABLE 8.1 AI/AN Participation by State and Gender (2013–2107)		
State	**Male**	**Female**
Alaska		6
Arizona	3	4
California	1	3
Florida	1	
Georgia		1
Illinois		1
Kansas		3
Maryland	1	1
Michigan	1	4
Nevada	1	4
New Mexico	1	4
Ohio	1	2
Oklahoma	3	6
Oregon		2
South Carolina	1	
South Dakota		1
Texas	1	
Virginia		1
Wisconsin	2	3
Total	**17**	**46**

Note regarding repeat students: From 2013–2017 we had a total of 63 AI/AN students (this number includes the ten repeat students); 16 percent of the students participated for two summers.

and students with disabilities). Unfortunately, Journey can only take about 21–23 students and nationally the STEP-UP program can take 90–95 high school students in total from all four coordinating centers.

The AI/AN participation data in Table 8.1 represents years 2013–2017. It should be noted that the American Indian Research and Education Center is also responsible for recruitment, coordination, and mentorship of students from Puerto Rico. For this chapter, the Puerto Rican student numbers are not included in Table 8.1.

INCORPORATING CULTURAL FRAMEWORKS

When I was in high school I never thought I would go to college. I thought, "I am not going to college." And none of my Native friends ever talked about it either.

—Dodge Francis, 2009, p. 61

Ibarra (2001) discovered that bicognition, the ability to think in dual cultures, was related to Latino graduate student success. A "chronic cultural dissonance" as Ibarra states, stemmed from the students' perceived education values and those of cultural values. The historical passing of culture from generation to generation involves the reconstruction of past frames of reference and of perceiving and understanding new ones, thus creating a hybrid of bicognition, as coined by Ibarra (2001). Cajete (1999) explains that an AI/AN cultural group's way of knowing has a substantial relationship to nature, and thus culture mirrors competencies that are deemed valuable. These may include linguistic and interpersonal intelligence, leadership, and the ability to carry out Native customs and traditions.

Bicognition is a constant angst of give and take with dominant values and ideologies; ever present are traditional values and ideologies that continue to shape and preserve tribal lifeways. While dominant culture might be illustrated and conscious for most to see, understandably the learner's culture may continue to be invisible. As the first author of this chapter noted more than a decade ago, "For students to empower the vision they must see themselves in that vision" of bicognition (Dodge-Francis, 2009, p. 74).

In a study published in the *Washington University Journal of American Indian and Alaska Native Health,* Patterson Silver Wolf, Butler-Barnes, and van Zile-Tamsen (2015) found that self-regulated learning activities foster the culturally responsive pedagogy that AI/AN students may need in order to motivate them to continue in higher education. There has been a long ensuing debate regarding whether AI/AN students have their own cultural learning styles and substantially benefit from thinking and learning when subject matter is grounded within their culture. Patterson Silver Wolf et al. (2015) argue that one of the main reasons underrepresented students, specifically AI/AN students, drop out is due to the unsuitable matching of learning styles.

Who Am I?

Students have a strong cultural belief and value systems with their families. It is the pinnacle to their life structure, and this includes the extended family. This belief and value system is often contra-culture to dominant society.

—Dodge Francis, 2009, p. 65

While the Journey program is responsible for recruitment across the nation, it should be noted that 567 federally recognized tribes exist in the United States. Therefore, it is difficult to know all the traditions, customs, and cultural components associated with tribal communities. It is essential to understand the cultural matrix that shapes an AI/AN student in the context of family, community, and school in order to assist the student with maneuvering within a bicognition perspective. The ability to know and understand the interweaving of student individualism and community is relevant in that it defines the student's world view as it relates to their community lens.

The recruitment of AI/AN students into a summer research experience or bridge program is not only about the student's interest and willingness to participate, but has a strong relationship to family and community needs, beliefs, attitudes, norms, and values. As noted by Chávez and Longerbeam (2016), "Culture underlies everything we do in a learning environment and everything we and our students bring with us to the learning experience" (p. 69).

The ability to reflect and create a dual and an integrative process for teaching and learning across cultures is constantly fluid. The ability to recognize and reflect upon one's own culture is paramount. Individual culture changes as life experiences continue to provide a lens in which we view the world; what we see might not be the reality. When teachers know and understand students' perspectives, it is a starting point for melding cultural frameworks within a learning framework.

Rural Alaska Native Students: Subsistence Synonymous With Culture

The relationship of a cultural context lens as it relates to AI/AN students is imperative for summer research and science bridge programs to be successful. While distance, climate, issues of remoteness, and lack of access to educational opportunities pose challenges to the STEP-UP Journey program, the learning curve for these challenges has allowed the Journey program to ensure that culture is recognizable and respected. As an American Indian enrolled Oneida tribal member, researcher, and educator, and having grown up on a reservation, I (the first author) still see a multitude of barriers and otherness that places AI/AN students outside of the educational taxonomy. It is imperative that Journey understands where each AI/AN student calls home, as this understanding shapes and assists in creating a successful summer research experience.

Subsistence living in Alaska goes beyond the mere need to survive, but constitutes a way of connecting to the land on a spiritual and cultural level. Jobs in rural Alaska are limited, and the cost of groceries can be excessive. Consequently, subsistence hunting, fishing, and gathering are essential for Alaska Natives to survive during the harsh winter months.

Non-native researchers may be unaware of the many challenges Alaska Native students face when conducting research. There are many limitations and barriers to conducting research in rural Alaska. Additionally, many rural Native Alaskan students may be reluctant to participate in summer bridge programs (e.g., STEP-UP Journey program) because it can coincide with their community's subsistence-fishing season. Members from the family and community work collectively during the summer to subsistence fish for the coming fall and winter months. There is a family member hierarchy that ensures a smooth flow of tasks and skills associated with subsistence living.

Scientific research has a distinct prescribed format of hypothesis, research design, analysis, results, and conclusions. AI/AN Journey students may feel a certain angst with this linear research process as it relates to their own culture, values, beliefs, traditional practices, and tribal sovereignty. Students may have cultural considerations when getting tribal approval, collecting data, and presenting their research findings to non-Native scientific communities. The "art of looping linear" (Dodge Francis, 2009) is a metaphoric concept of shaping linear processes to create a circle that encompasses the essence of AI/AN people, thus diminishing the angst from traversing both worlds, Native and non-Native.

The STEP-UP Journey Program came across an example of methodology translation related to cultural subsistence understanding in a student's research. A student from the village of Napaskiak designed her research project to evaluate the levels of mercury in fish found in their local rivers, a health issue that could have serious consequences for her community. This particular student gathered samples during her community's subsistence fishing period, and each sample of fish sacrificed for testing posed consequences to the family and community due to reduced fish runs.

As part of the STEP-UP Journey Program, the student presented to the National Institutes of Health/National Institute of Diabetes and Digestive and Kidney Diseases research panelists, a non-Native scientific community and her peers. It was crucial to explain the relationship of subsistence living and her small sample size as an impact factor of well-being for her family during the winter months.

The ability to understand and plan for cultural nuances within a research context is beneficial for student success; during application process, research design, data collection, and disseminating results back to fellow researchers and tribal communities.

Cultural Recommendations

- The student's success is influenced by the student, family, and cultural context as it relates to the community. Know and understand the historical issues that research has created.
- The research design and accomplishment of the project may have multiple layers of cultural understanding that the AI/AN student faces. Inquiry into their culture as it relates to the student and research needs to be continuous.

- Understand that within a summer timeframe, AI/AN students may have a stronger cultural component to their lives. This is a time for tribal communities to be involved with subsistence fishing, gathering, and ceremony.
- Alaska Native students are typically out of school mid-May, which is much earlier than the lower 48 contiguous states. Educators should be aware that this does add another layer of consideration related to summer milestone timing and accomplishments for summer research/internship programming.
- The cultural and traditional roles that a student is responsible for within the family and community hierarchy is critical to know and understand. It is necessary to also consider this with the tribes in the lower 48 contiguous states. Summer ceremonies and tribal gatherings play an integral role for tribal communities.
- Often students and family members will invite program staff to partake of a meal. It would be deemed culturally inappropriate if one declined food or an invitation to the students dwelling while visiting the area. This an opportunity to discuss the nuances of the program as it relates to the student, family, and community.
- The translation of research projects to a non-Native population may pose presentation issue for the students when illustrating design strategies and results. Be prepared to assist students with addressing these potential translation questions and understanding of cultural context as it relates to a cultural framework.

The introduction of any summer research/internship needs to be relevant to the student, family, and community. Therefore, eliciting and reflecting a cultural relevancy and effectively accomplishing the STEP-UP Journey program parameters ensues a delicate dance of AI/AN culture and a Westernized research system that incorporates cultural and research knowledge and learning for all participants.

Digitally Off-Line at Home

The internet encompasses a huge portion of one's day. A report from the Pew Research Center stated that "low income households with school-age children are four times more likely to be without high-speed Internet access than their middle- or upper- income counterparts" (Horrigan, 2015). Mouza (2008) identifies low-income households as the least likely group to be online and this potentially affects learning opportunities on school-age children. The reality of the digital divide does exist for the AI/AN population and negatively affects the ability of the group to use and access information technology (Brescia & Daily, 2007). President Obama in 2013 launched the ConnectED initiative with the goal of connecting 99%

of K–12 students in America with access to broadband Internet in the classroom by the year 2018. This is an outstanding initiative for school environments. However, if an AI/AN student is unable to access and make effective use of technology at home, then they may continue to be disadvantaged from accessing educational opportunities. The STEP-UP Journey program is constantly reminded of this phenomenon.

The digital divide can be an obstacle for AI/AN students applying for the STEP-UP program. Students interested in the National Institute of Diabetes and Digestive and Kidney Diseases STEP-UP program apply via a National Institutes of Health web-based portal. They must provide a personal statement within the portal, two letters of reference, and current transcripts. The issues that arise are not usually associated with the online personal statement; typically, this can be accomplished at school, with school computers. However, the ability to access a home computer and internet access, as it relates to uploading transcripts and letters of recommendation, presents barriers to completing the application process.

Unknowing program staff, educators, and funders often assume that the student from an underrepresented population is disinterested in the opportunity, or lacks the motivation to finish the application process. In reality, the ability to finish the process is due to the lack of computer access and unattainable internet connectivity outside of school. It often becomes necessary to explore alternative methods for finishing an application process. Students must resort to the old-fashioned method of paper and snail mail, or cell phone shots and texts, or in some cases fax, with original copies mailed.

It seems plausible that with the direction in which information and technology is advancing, on-line would be the natural tendency. Helpser (2008) noted that lower socioeconomic groups do participate in digital activity, but the basic level involves information seeking and individual family communication. The Journey staff understand and agree that web portals make sense and reduce the amount of paper utilized. However, all student internet connectivity is not created equally. Thus, exceptions and modifications need to be considered to the application process.

Once students are in the STEP-UP program, Journey staff members have constant communication interactions between students and mentors during the eight- to ten-week research experience. Since the majority of the students have cell phones, often times communication is achieved through emails, texts, and phone calls. The use of cell phone Skype and FaceTime have become more common tools with students in recent years due to the lack of internet in rural locations. Journey does correspond with the students on a weekly basis and encourages mentors to actively engage in communication with the Journey staff in regard to any questions or concerns.

Past experiences show a lack of technological connectivity and added communication barriers via internet for AI/AN students once outside of school. The ability to plan for technology alternatives to ensure application completion and communication during the research program takes thinking outside of the digital box.

Technology Recommendations

- Create constant communication channels via text, phone, and email in order to understand where the barriers exist in applying. It should be noted that communication often includes parents and guardians. This may be the first time that a student and family have ever applied for a summer educational opportunity online or written a personal statement.
- Develop strong school relationships and maintain constant communication with the school counselors/advisors, administration, and teachers to remind them of deadlines and items needed for application.
- Recognize the lack of Internet connectivity for many of students at home. The use of cell phone photos with regard to letters of recommendation and transcripts is used as a back-up process. Original copies can be mailed, and program staff upload the items into the system.
- Strong communication between the funder and program staff during the application process time frame is crucial for applicants to maneuver any web portals.

Mentoring and Mirroring Science/Research Identity for AI/AN Students

A high school teacher was always telling me that I was never going to be anything— kind of like, "Why do you try?" He also told my sister that she was nothing more than a dead fish floating down the river. At first I wanted to prove them wrong after initially getting mad or whatever. You know, then it's like—you just kind of lose faith in yourself after a while.

—Dodge Francis, 2009, p. 61

The nation's future scientific research workforce is dependent on a diverse pool of highly trained scientists, and the direction that colleges take will have a direct effect on that outcome. As Finson (2002) notes,

> The less stereotypical the image one holds, the more probable it is that one will opt to take more science classes and subsequently consider entering a profession in the sciences. Failure to recognize the presence of such images, to identify them and their specific elements, and to design and implement appropriate interventions may eventually lead to increased erosion in the number of scientists in the workforce. (p. 343)

The literature suggest that learning and teaching does increase when students and mentors connect theory and content to real life experiences. Mentorship is a model for the influence of youth development. Youth can be impacted through the establishment of social, emotional, cognitive, and identity growth (Rhodes & DuBois, 2008). Simpkins, Little, Weiss, and Simpkins-Chaput (2004) provide evidence that out-of-school programs enhance the lives of young people. The incorporation of mentoring among young professionals has been a long-standing tradition (Sipe, 2002). Typically, the conceptualization of youth mentoring is defined as that of an adult mentor that is a non-parental individual, in which the mentor offers guidance and support to the young person.

Journey's goal is to assign students with AI/AN mentors that have a background with the topic area of diabetes, obesity, kidney diseases, and endocrinology (although it often depends on the availability of mentors in the student's geographic area). Mentors may have a differing research background but still provide a strong research experience for the student, which is the ultimate goal. The variety of research projects that the Journey STEP-UP experience are vast in nature and scope. Figure 8.1 provides only a glimpse of the outstanding research that the students accomplish as they learn from and with their mentors. Both abstracts were written by the Journey students and mentors, and these and others can be found online at http://digitalscholarship.unlv.edu/jhdrp/ (*Journal of Health Disparities Research and Practice*, Volume 9, Special Edition 1, 2016, The Pursuit of Young Researchers: National Institute of Diabetes and Digestive and Kidney Diseases STEP-UP).

Research projects may include lab, secondary data analysis, systematic literature review of a research topic, community health assessment, environmental assessments, and occasionally a student may be added to a tribal research institutional review board for a human subjects research project. Typically, Journey stays away from human subject research projects, unless all institutional review board requirements are met by the principal investigator of the project.

Mentoring relationships may help shift youths' conceptions of both their current and future identities (DuBois & Karcher, 2005). It is believed that relationships with mentors may open doors to activities, resources, and educational or occupational opportunities on which youth can draw to construct their sense of science identity (Darling, Hamilton, Toyokawa, & Matsuda, 2002). The model of mentoring plays a strong and important role in the development and interpersonal processes that are part of the STEP-UP Journey program summer experience.

Journey students find that they too become mentors within their communities as they disseminate research methodologies and results back to their community. The passing of old and new knowledge from generation

Polychlorinated Biphenyls and Metabolic Diseases on St. Lawrence Island, Alaska
Jasmine Jemewouk (Journey student), Pamela Miller, MS, PhD (mentor)
Center: Alaska Community Action on Toxics Coordinating Center, University of Nevada, Las Vegas

ABSTRACT: Polychlorinated Biphenyls (PCBs) are industrial chemicals that were used from 1929 until 1979 as a plasticizer in paints, plastics, and rubber products. However, PCBs continue to persist in the Arctic. They enter the Arctic environment through air and ocean currents. Sunlight and weathering help break down chemicals, so the Arctic's lack of sunlight and precipitation during the winter allows PCBs to more readily accumulate. These chemicals settle either on organic films or water and are consequently absorbed by the Arctic food web. PCBs then bioaccumulatep in fatty tissues like omega-3 fatty acids. The higher the animal is in the food web, the greater the accumulation of PCBs in its fatty tissue. The Yupik people of St. Lawrence Island, Alaska rely on a diet that largely consists of bowhead whales, walruses, and seals, all of which are high in omega-3 fatty acids and are near the top of the Arctic food web. Humans occupy the top of the food web and so therefore accumulate the highest concentration of PCBs in their omega-3 fatty acids. Research has shown that high intake of omega-3 fatty acids should promote a healthy endocrine system, therefore protecting against metabolic diseases. However, in recent years, St. Lawrence Island residents have seen a predominate increase in metabolic diseases. A great number of recent scientific evidence suggests a link between exposure to PCBs and endocrine disruption. We hypothesize that consumption of subsistence foods contaminated with PCBs puts these residents at an uncommonly high risk for metabolic diseases. Key Words: PCBs, omega-3 fatty acids, metabolic diseases.

Assessment of Childhood Obesity Prevalence and Prevention Efforts in a Wisconsin Tribal Community
Simone Tucker (Journey student), Lauren Lamers, MPH, PhD (mentor)
Center: Center: University of Nevada, Las Vegas

ABSTRACT: American Indian children experience disproportionately high rates of obesity, yet tribal communities often lack capacity to utilize local obesity data to guide prevention efforts. It is estimated the prevalence of childhood obesity in a Wisconsin tribal community and identified local school-based obesity prevention initiatives. Height and weight data were collected for children ages 2–19 years through routine screenings at local Head Start centers and schools. Weight status was determined based on BMI percentile according to year 2000 CDC growth charts. Summary statistics and chi-square tests were generated to examine differences in obesity prevalence by age and gender. An environmental scan that included key informant interviews, document reviews, and photo-mapping was conducted to identify local obesity prevention initiatives. A total of 820 children were screened during the 2013–2014 school year. In total, 31% of children were obese and 24% were overweight. Obesity prevalence was lower among children ages 2–5 years (20%) than among children ages 6–11 (34%) and 12–19 years (34%) ($p < .01$) but did not differ by gender. Local prevention initiatives included adoption of recommended nutrition guidelines for school meals, school-based programs to improve nutrition and increase physical activity, and changes to the physical environment to increase access to healthy foods and promote physical activity. Childhood obesity prevalence was higher in our sample compared to national prevalence estimates. Local schools have made strides in implementing obesity prevention initiatives. Ongoing monitoring of local childhood obesity prevalence may facilitate planning and evaluation of future prevention efforts.

Figure 8.1   Sample research abstracts written by Journey students and mentors. *Note:* These and other abstracts printed in *Journal of Health Disparities Research and Practice*, Volume 9, Special Edition 1, 2016, The Pursuit of Young Researchers: National Institute of Diabetes and Digestive and Kidney Diseases STEP-UP. http://digitalscholarship.unlv.edu/jhdrp/.

to generation is imperative to the growth, and continuous existence for tribal lifeways. Mentors and Journey staff share a responsibility in shaping and providing opportunities for AI/AN students to share not only their research but also their journey within the research experience.

Mentoring recommendations

- Active learning pedagogy for students is continuous throughout the summer and through the August symposium at the National Institutes of Health/National Institute of Diabetes and Digestive and Kidney Diseases in Bethesda, Maryland. Active learning is the process that might involve reading research publications related to the student's research topic, writing, discussion, problem-solving that promotes critical thinking, synthesis, and evaluation of content in order to achieve the goals of the research.
- Take note that the act of teaching *to* the student is not the same as teaching *with* the student... this is a circular collaboration.
- Consider using cell phone communication as an additional distance mentoring tool. Cell phones are used at a higher rate for mentoring communication with the AI/AN Journey students and staff (as described in the prior section).
- Peer learning and support can include webinars and presentation of research to other students prior to formal symposium or conference. Allow for peer critique and feedback from fellow students.
  - Distance communication platforms, such as *Blue Jeans* or *Zoom* webinars, allow up to 100 participants to videoconference on a variety of applications and to see both participants and presentation content. It should be noted that the majority of Journey students participate through their research site. The meeting or presentation can be recorded and then shared via a link with all attendees and participants unable to attend.
  - The utilization of computer networking also allows STEP-UP Journey program students to practice their *PowerPoint* presentations prior to attending the National Institutes of Health symposium and receive feedback from principal investigators and peers.

CONCLUSION

This article only gives a snapshot of the varied nuances associated with the STEP-UP Journey program. However, Shor (1992) might best describe the process that the Journey program attempts to maneuver when he states that "problem posing does not reinvent curriculum knowledge content (science, literature, math, etc.) but it does incorporate a multicultural perspective that relates to the students' community cultures, and to conditions in society" (p. 35). AI/AN students do not leave their "Indianness" behind when they pursue math, science, research, and higher education opportunities. Therefore, to create an effective AI/AN student summer research experience, the development of such programs must reflect cultural beliefs, values, and ways of knowing, along with scientific pedagogical skills.

The current literature, while limited in depth, illustrates a need for and vigilance to the continuation of summer research experiences within underrepresented high school populations. Journey provides an opportunity for AI/AN students to explore their scientific identity, but perhaps also provides them with the ability to shape their *own* science/research identity and determine how they might want to further explore research and culture for their future.

The importance of addressing cultural connections within STEM for AI/AN students may enhance their motivation to pursue and view science education with a new lens as it intersects with their culture, tribal community, and environment. Thus, the ability to maneuver a bicognition science/research perspective for students as it relates to AI/AN health disparities is imperative for improved health outcomes related to chronic and infectious diseases for tribal people.

We end with inquiry questions and action research suggestions to continue to encourage AI/AN youth to participate in STEM education opportunities.

Inquiry Questions

1. In what ways could programs such as National Institutes of Health/National Institute of Diabetes and Digestive and Kidney Diseases STEP-UP summer research experience, shape, or change students' science/research identity?
2. What mentoring perceptions and knowledge can mentors in STEP-UP programs share for increased effective mentoring?
3. How does bicognition translate for other underrepresented populations in a science/research world?

Action Research

1. Examine what roles a mentor should have as part of a class discussion. What do students expect from mentors? How can they ask that these expectations be met?

2. Interpret the movie *The Immortal Life of Henrietta Lacks.* Since science/
   research does not work in a vacuum, pair students to discuss what science identity and culture mean to them after watching the movie.

ACKNOWLEDGMENTS

The STEP-UP High School program is supported by the National Institute
of Diabetes and Digestive and Kidney Diseases of the National Institutes of
Health, Grant number: R25DK098067.

All authors declare they have no actual or potential competing financial
interest.

REFERENCES

Acton, K., Burrows, N., Wang, J., & Geiss, L. (2006). Diagnosed diabetes among
American Indians and Alaska Natives aged <35 years—United States, 1994–
2004. *Morbidity and Mortality Weekly Report, 55*(44), 1201–1203.

Bandura, A. (1997). *Self-efficacy: The exercise of control.* New York, NY: W. H. Freeman.

Brescia, W., & Daily, T. (2007). Economic development and technology-skill needs
on American Indian reservations. *The American Indian Quarterly, 31*(1), 23–43.

Brown, D. J., DeCorse-Johnson, A. L., Irving-Ray, M., & Wu, W. W. (2005). Performance evaluation for diversity programs. *Policy, Politics, & Nursing Practice,
6*(4), 331–334.

Caffey-Fleming, D. E., & Reid, C. (2016). Preparing underrepresented high school
students to increase diversity in the research and health professions. *Journal of
Health Disparities Research and Practice, 9*(5), 3–5.

Cajete, G. A. (1999). The Native American learner and bicultural science education. In K. Swisher & J. Tippeconnic, III (Eds.), *Next steps: Research and practice
to advance Indian education* (pp. 135–162). Charleston, WV: Eric.

Centers for Disease Control and Prevention. (2011). *National diabetes fact sheet: National estimates and general information on diabetes and prediabetes in the united
states, 2011.* Atlanta, GA: U.S. Department of Health and Human Services,
Centers for Disease Control and Prevention.

Centers for Disease Control and Prevention. (2017). *Native Americans with diabetes:
Better diabetes care can decrease kidney failure.* Atlanta, GA: U.S. Department of
Health and Human Services, Centers for Disease Control and Prevention.
Retrieved from https://www.cdc.gov/vitalsigns/pdf/2017-01-vitalsigns.pdf

Chávez, A. F., & Longerbeam, S. D. (2016). *Teaching across cultural strengths: A guide
to balancing integrated and individuated cultural frameworks in college teaching.*
Herndon, VA: Stylus.

Darling, N., Hamilton, S., Toyokawa, T., & Matsuda, S. (2002). Naturally occurring
mentoring in Japan and the United States: Social roles and correlates. *American Journal of Community Psychology, 30*(2), 245–270.

Davis, S. D. (2000). Groups, communities, and contested identities in genetic research. *The Hastings Center Report, 30*(6), 38–45.

Dodge Francis, C. (2009). *The art of looping linear: Perspectives from tribal college students and faculty.* Saarbrucken, Germany: VDM Verlag.

DuBois, D. L., & Karcher, M. J. (2005). *Handbook of youth mentoring.* Thousand Oaks, CA: SAGE.

Finson, K. D. (2002). Drawing a scientist: What we do and do not know after fifty years of drawings. *School Science and Mathematics, 102*(7), 335–345.

Halpern-Felsher, B., & McLaughlin, S. (2016). The importance of scientific mentoring programs for underrepresented youth. *Journal of Health Disparities Research Practice, 9*(5), 87–89.

Health characteristics of the American Indian or Alaska Native adult population: U.S., 2004–08: National Health Statistics Reports; 2010 ASI 4146-16.19; National Health Statistics rpt. no. 20. (2010). Retrieved from https://www.ihs.gov/sdpi/includes/themes/responsive2017/display_objects/documents/factsheets/Fact_sheet_AIAN_508c.pdf

Helsper, E. (2008). *Digital inclusion: An analysis of social disadvantage and the information society.* Department for Communities and Local Government. Retrieved from http://eprints.lse.ac.uk/26938/

Horrigan, J. B. (2015). *The numbers behind the broadband "homework gap."* Retrieved from http://www.pewresearch.org/fact-tank/2015/04/20/the-numbers-behind-the-broadband-homework-gap/

Ibarra, R. A. (2001). *Beyond affirmative action: Reframing the context of higher education.* Madison, WI: University of Wisconsin Press.

Indian Health Service: Fact sheet: diabetes in American Indians and Alaska Natives [article online]. Available from http://www.ihs.gov/MedicalPrograms/Diabetes/index.cfm?module=resourcesFactSheets_AIANs08

McGee, R., Jr., Saran, S., & Krulwich, T. A. (2012). Diversity in the biomedical research workforce: Developing talent. *Mount Sinai Journal of Medicine: A Journal of Translational and Personalized Medicine, 79*(3), 397–411.

Moore, K., Dodge Francis, C., & DeBruyn, L. (2009). American Indian higher education consortium honoring our health grant program. In L. C. Liburd (Ed.), *Diabetes and health disparities: Community-based approaches for racial and ethnic populations* (pp. 257–274). New York, NY: Springer.

Mouza, C. (2008). Learning with laptops: Implementation and outcomes in an urban, under-privileged school. *Journal of Research on Technology in Education, 40*(4), 447–472.

National Research Council. (2005). *Assessment of NIH minority research and training programs: Phase 3.* Washington, DC: The National Academies Press.

Nesbitt, S., & Palomarez, R. E. (2016). Review: Increasing awareness and education on health disparities for health care providers. *Ethnicity & Disease, 26*(2), 181–190.

Norris, K. C., & Agodoa, L. Y. (2009). Expanding the minority biomedical pipeline: The NIDDK national high school summer research program. *Ethnicity & Disease, 16*(4 Suppl 5), 1. Retrieved from http://www.ncbi.nlm.nih.gov/pubmed/17186588

Norris, T., Vines L. P., & Hoeffel M. E. (2012). *American Indian and Alaska Native population: 2010.* Washington, DC: United States Census Bureau. Retrieved from https://www.census.gov/prod/cen2010/briefs/c2010br-10.pdf

Patterson Silver Wolf, D., Butler-Barnes, S. T., & Zile-Tamsen, C. V. (2015). American Indian/Alaskan Native college dropout: Recommendations for increasing retention and graduation. *Journal on Race, Inequity, and Social Mobility in America, 1*(1), 2–15.

Patterson Silver Wolf, D., & Carline, J. (2004). *Literature review on partnerships compiled for the health professions partnership initiative.* Washington, DC: Association of American Medical Colleges.

Rhodes, J., & DuBois, D. (2008). Mentoring relationships and programs for youth. *Current Directions in Psychological Science, 17*(4), 254–258. doi:10.1111/j.1467-8721.2008.00585.x

Sánchez, J. P., Poll-Hunter, N. I., & Acosta, D. (2015). Advancing the Latino physician workforce-population trends, persistent challenges, and new directions. *Academic Medicine Journal of the Association of American Medical Colleges, 90*(7), 849–853. doi:10.1097/ACM.0000000000000618

Seymour, E., Hunter, A., Laursen, S. L., & DeAntoni, T. (2004). Establishing the benefits of research experiences for undergraduates in the sciences: First findings from a three-year study. *Science Education, 88*(4), 493–534.

Shor, I., (1992). *Empowering education: Critical teaching for social change.* Chicago, IL: University of Chicago Press.

Simpkins, S. D., Little, P. M. D., Weiss, H. B., & Simpkins-Chaput, S. (2004). Understanding and measuring attendance in out-of-school programs. *Issues and Opportunities in Out-of-School Time Evaluation Briefs, 7.*

Sipe, C. L. (2002). Mentoring programs for adolescents: A research summary. *Journal of Adolescent Health, 31*(6), 251–260.

Smedley, B. D., & Mittman, I. S. (2011). The diversity benefit: How does diversity among health professionals address public needs? In R. A. Williams (Ed.), *Healthcare disparities at the crossroads with healthcare reform* (pp. 167–193). Boston, MA: Springer.

United States Census Bureau. (2016, November 2). *Facts for features: American Indian and Alaska Native heritage month: November 2016* (Release number: CB16-FF.22). Retrieved from https://www.census.gov/newsroom/facts-for-features/2016/cb16-ff22.html

Valway, S., Freeman, W., Kaufma, S., Welty, T., Helgerson, S. D., & Ghodes, D. (1993). Prevalence of diagnosed diabetes among American Indians and Alaska natives, 1987: Estimates from a national outpatient data base. *Diabetes Care, 16*(1), 271–276.

Villarejo, M., Barlow, A. E., Kogan, D., Veazey, B. D., & Sweeney, J. K. (2008). Encouraging minority undergraduates to choose science careers: Career paths survey results. *CBE-Life Sciences Education, 7*(4), 394–409.

Williams, R. A. (2008). *Eliminating nealthcare disparities in America: Beyond the IOM report.* Totowa, NJ: Humana Press.

Winkleby, M., Ned, J., Ahn, D., Koehler, A., & Kennedy, J. D. (2009). Increasing diversity in science and health professions: A 21-year longitudinal study documenting college and career success. *Journal of Science Education and Technology, 18*(6), 535–545.

CHAPTER 9

WELCOMING AFRICAN IMMIGRANT STUDENTS INTO U.S. K–12 STEAM CLASSROOMS THROUGH CULTURALLY RELEVANT TEACHING

Sherilynn Nidever-Jordan
Blue Mountain Community College

Michael Takafor Ndemanu
Ball State University

Teachers of African immigrant children in U.S. K–12 schools can better reach this growing population of students by incorporating culturally relevant pedagogy into their teaching contexts. In this chapter, we describe this growing diverse demographic in the United States and teachers' challenges welcoming African immigrant children in U.S. classrooms. We propose culturally responsive teaching as an asset-based pedagogy readily

Culturally and Linguistically Diverse Learners and STEAM, pages 189–209
Copyright © 2019 by Information Age Publishing

integrated into STEAM classrooms to tackle these challenges. We describe specific classroom-based challenges and offer culturally responsive teaching-informed solutions.

WHO ARE THESE "AFRICAN IMMIGRANTS"?

The numbers of recent immigrants to the United States from Africa and the Caribbean—and their children—are expanding rapidly. Between 1990 and 2009, the number of "foreign-born Blacks" in the United States rose from 1.4 million to 3.3 million (Capps & Fix, 2012, p. 1). In 2010 in New York City, 13,000 of the 70,000 foreign-born students in elementary and middle schools were Black (Doucet, Schwartz, & Debraggio, 2012). We refer to these children in K–12 classrooms as African immigrant students: first- and second-generation students whose families immigrated voluntarily or involuntarily (as refugees) into the United States to escape political, civil, and/or economic turmoil or to pursue further studies (Arthur, 2000; McHugh & Sugarman, 2015).

Although U.S. Census Bureau data have consistently ranked African immigrants as the most educated of all immigrants, their children in U.S. schools continue to suffer from discontinuity in academic culture, communication, and power relations (Adair, 2015; Anderson, 2015; Dryden-Peterson, 2015; McHugh & Sugarman, 2015; Ogbu & Simons, 1998). According to a 2014 U.S. Census Bureau report, 41% of foreign-born Africans had a bachelor's degree, which contrasts with 28% of all foreign-born in the United States (Gambino, Trevelyan, & Fitzwater, 2014). Although African immigrants are often welcomed to cities across the country (Takyi, 2002), their children frequently encounter cultural, linguistic, academic, and social challenges in public schools, which may lead to poor academic performance in school.

Teachers are often culturally and pedagogically ill-equipped to meet the needs of their immigrant students, either due to lack of training or due to lack of exposure to these populations (Samson & Collins, 2012; Suarez-Orosco & Suarez-Orosco, 2001). In one K–12 teacher education program at a Midwest university where we have taught, primarily White future teachers expressed their belief that they would not encounter students very different from themselves, hence their choice to pursue teaching careers close to home (Ndemanu, 2018). However, the reality is that teachers may be teaching students very different from themselves, and given culturally responsive teaching tools, these teachers can gain the confidence and skills to better meet the needs of these culturally diverse children in STEAM classrooms. This chapter analyzes some of the challenges facing African immigrant children—and their teachers—in schools and suggests culturally responsive solutions for STEAM classrooms.

WHAT IS CULTURALLY RESPONSIVE
(OR CULTURALLY RELEVANT) TEACHING?

Culturally responsive/relevant teaching is at its core an asset-based approach to teaching. Culturally responsive teaching is defined by Gay (2001) as "using the cultural characteristics, experiences, and perspectives of ethnically diverse students as conduits for teaching them more effectively" by reaching into the "lived experiences and frames of reference of students" to make the curriculum "more personally meaningful," accessible and engaging (p. 106). The goal is for students to succeed by engaging them on their own cultural terms (Gay, 2001). Culturally responsive teaching encompasses several important instructional elements. These elements include (a) teacher knowledge about students' cultures, (b) a pedagogy of care for students' wellbeing both in class and at home, (c) relevant cross-cultural communication skills, and (d) infusing a cultural lens in instruction. In this chapter, we focus primarily on (a) and (d)—with the assumption that all good teachers enact a pedagogy of care. To be more effective in teaching African immigrant children, culturally responsive teaching compels STEAM educators to acquire pre-immigration information about immigrant students and their families to understand why they may initially speak, read, write, learn, and engage differently—not deficiently—from other students. African immigrant children and their new classmates and teachers are then freed to mutually learn from each other.

Culturally responsive teaching enables students to see their realities reflected in a curriculum that otherwise tends to be predominantly "window" frames rather than "mirror" frames, to use Emily Style's (1988) terminology. Style calls for education in which students can both "look through window frames in order to see the realities of others" and gaze into "mirrors in order to see [their] own realit[ies] reflected" (p. 1). In this way, a healthy "dialogue between the self and the world" is promoted (Style, 1988, p. 1), rather than the invisibility of self that can lead to silencing for African immigrant children. A culturally responsive teacher enables other students, who might otherwise only see mirrors, to see both, as well.

What are some of the specific challenges these children face, and how can a culturally relevant teaching approach help STEAM teachers to help their African immigrant (and arguably, all) students to succeed? In the next section, we identify and offer solutions for five common classroom challenges: (a) linguistic challenges, (b) adaptation to a new education system, (c) differing expectations of student classroom behavior, (d) differing expectations of parental/family involvement, and (e) stereotypes and misunderstandings of African immigrant cultural identities.

CHALLENGES AND SOLUTIONS

Challenge 1: Linguistic Challenges

To start with, it is helpful for teachers to consider the significant contrasts between the school systems in African immigrants' home countries and in the United States. The education systems in Africa abound in both similarities and contrasts among each other and with the U.S. education system. More than 70% of the countries in Africa use either French or English as a medium of instruction in their school systems. Since its independence in the early 60s, for example, Cameroon has continued with both French and British education systems from the colonial era. In one system, the medium of instruction is French and in another, it is English. Both have different curricula and end-of-term exams. This means Cameroonian immigrants from both education systems experience education differently in the United States, depending on their prior medium of instruction and the kind of tracking system their education system practiced.

Other countries use Arabic, Spanish, Portuguese, and other African languages to a lesser degree. Most school-aged African children speak at least one European language plus one or more national languages. In addition to the many European languages used as official languages on the continent, the number of African languages is estimated at about 2,000 (Childs, 2003). In New York City schools alone, Black immigrants from non-Caribbean countries speak 79 different languages (Doucet, Schwartz, & Debraggio, 2012). A culturally responsive instructional practice would entail an understanding of this linguistic diversity, which is part of the culture in Africa. Because a good number of African immigrant students are either bilingual or multilingual, they bring these academic strengths and assets to our classrooms. On the other hand, because native African and European languages have had profound influence on the way English is spoken in all the English-speaking countries, this influence is highly noticeable at the level of vocabulary, syntax, semantics, and accent. These variations of "World Englishes" (Kachru, 1992) can lead to misunderstandings and ridicule in public schools (Kigamwa & Ndemanu, 2016)—when in fact, they bring the realities of English varieties right to our front door. English has almost become a global lingua franca (Bohórquez, 2013). However, it is impossible to homogenize the way people speak English because a large number of its diverse speakers are native speakers of other languages (Alptekin, 2002). Crystal (1997) estimates that the non-native English-speaking population is between 430 million and 1.35 billion. Teachers can become aware of this reality and learn to better serve students who are proficient in both spoken and written English, but who speak the language with a non-native accent.

With this backdrop of diverse linguistic backgrounds, African immigrant students' English language proficiency will vary depending on which language they used in their home countries and which they use with their parents at home. These learners need a range of linguistic supports, depending upon their linguistic backgrounds—for instance, newcomer English learner support for those who have not learned English previously, but instruction in academic American English as an additional language for those who have already learned another English dialect. Even learners who appear to speak and understand everyday English fluently may struggle with academic English (Migration Policy Institute, 2015), and require more time to learn, as Cummins (2005) postulates in his theory of second language acquisition. He differentiates between Basic Interpersonal Communication Skills (BICS), which takes learners 1–2 years to learn, and Cognitive Academic Language Proficiency (CALP), which can take 5–7 years to learn.

Solutions

STEAM instructors can offer the linguistic support African immigrant learners need in a number of ways. One way is by investing in and establishing a positive classroom climate, for example by structuring the way classroom learning is organized to include independent learning stations. Learning stations give students an opportunity to simultaneously develop content knowledge and academic English, develop a sense of autonomy over their learning, and interact with more proficient English-speaking peers, who are language models:

1. *Reading (and video) stations:* A reading station can be set up with a variety of reading materials (e.g., articles, books, magazines, graphic novels, etc.). These materials support students' STEAM content development and language learning by giving them repeated exposure to the important concepts they are studying, as well as to the language they are simultaneously learning (e.g., key scientific terms, grammatical structures typically found in science texts). Adding classroom opportunities for students to do close reading of STEAM texts also provides more practice with STEAM reading development. Reading stations can be used in a variety of ways, preferably with pairs or groups reading and discussing the same articles or books together and relating the content to the current unit. The stations open up opportunities to read and discuss complex science texts with a peer or in a small group, which can encourage immigrant students to participate when a larger class discussion might feel intimidating. Alternatively or additionally, this station might include video materials to add scaffolding.

2. *Writing and vocabulary stations:* A blended learning station approach is highly recommended for differentiating and providing additional scaffolding, as well as student engagement, in STEAM classrooms. (See the *Blended Learning* link in the Appendix.) At a writing and vocabulary station at the beginning of a unit, individuals or pairs can each be assigned a new word or concept for that unit—then use the resources available (particularly if a computer station is available) to research their assigned STEAM concept central to the unit of study (for example, photosynthesis or bioaccumulation) and teach it to the other members of the group or even the whole class. Later in the unit, students may write in response to an open prompt about what they discussed at the reading/video station (above) using the term(s) from the writing and vocabulary station. In this way, the reading/video station provides a bridge to academic science writing, with the support of vocabulary that is provided at this station, along with some helpful prompts and opportunities to write. At the writing/vocabulary station, students may even create some of the reading or video materials (possibly with illustrations) to be used at the reading/video station.

3. *Classroom climate:* A classroom climate that welcomes and celebrates linguistic diversity and does not tolerate ridicule should be established early on. Students can co-create "class rules" or a less authoritarian list (e.g., "classroom customs," "STEAM class norms") at the beginning of the school year, along with consequences for code violations, like laughing at others for their accent. Allowing the use of students' home languages in projects, activities, and independent learning stations creates an inclusive STEAM class climate, and if school policies do not currently allow this, advocating for it is critical. Students from similar linguistic backgrounds who have been in the United States longer can become class mentors or pair up with newer students less familiar with English. Home languages can be used in projects, whether in illustrations or in part of the written (or digitally created) work. Encouraging home language use allows African immigrant students to showcase their strengths, becoming the "teachers" of their classmates and teacher, and opens up their worlds and perspectives to other classroom members. It also welcomes and values the richness of diversity in the classroom.

Challenge 2: Adaptation to a New Education System

The home education systems of African-immigrant children and that of the United States typically differ dramatically, creating educational culture shock on top of societal and linguistic culture shock for the children of African immigrants. According to Ruiz-de-Velasco and Fix (2000), orientation to the U.S. school system is necessary for immigrant students and their parents, who are often unfamiliar with course requirements, types of assessments, and the school program in general. Many of these parents do not fully understand the academic progress of their children because of the differences in the education systems of their home countries and the United States. Standardized tests and authentic assessments used in U.S. school systems also differ from the academic assessments of the immigrants' home countries. For this reason, these assessment systems may not accurately measure the academic knowledge of African immigrants. Government immigrant services and some nonprofit organizations may provide some forms of orientations to refugees and individuals on academic and cultural exchange programs, but such orientations rarely provide relevant information for immigrant parents and families about the U.S. education system that their children will be attending.

One major difference between African and U.S. education systems that African immigrant parents and families need to understand stems from the fact that, because most African education systems are based on European models, specialization and tracking begin very early. Some education systems begin academic tracking at the end of the elementary education cycle, paving ways for students to take a vocational, general, or technical track as early as seventh grade. In general education, students must specialize by the time they are enrolled in high school or earlier. As a result, U.S. teachers may find newly arrived African immigrant children enrolled in high school STEAM classes either far more advanced than their American counterparts in the subjects of their specialization, or lagging considerably behind in the subjects that were not part of their specialties in their home countries. Many African students from the former British colonies who passed the General Certificate Examination Advanced Level in science subjects are often eligible for credit transfer in U.S. colleges because their high school courses have been evaluated to be equivalent to Advanced Placement and International Baccalaureate courses. Unlike higher education institutions, many U.S. K–12 schools are not familiar with education systems around the world and as a result, they may not identify the student's appropriate academic level until after a series of academic misdiagnoses and misinformed referrals to special needs and English as a second language programs. This process wastes valuable time for African immigrant students and limits their opportunities.

Furthermore, the timing of examinations in African countries varies from course to course, subject to subject, examination to examination, and education system to education system. For example, it takes 3–4 weeks to take the Cameroon General Certificate of Education Ordinary and Advanced levels examination. Students are given 45 minutes per essay question, so it can take a half day to take a General Certificate of Education exam in just one section of a history course. Similarly, on the Cameroon Baccalaureate examination, one essay question in French literature is four hours long, and one third of the students do not complete that one essay within the time frame because of the critical thinking skills required to respond fully. Multiple-choice exams are only beginning to appear in some African countries.

The examination culture in Africa influences the way African immigrant children approach test-taking in U.S. schools. These students fare better on essay questions than on multiple-choice questions partly because of limited time allocated for those exams, partly because of their home experiences with essay exams, and partly because of limited knowledge about test-taking strategies on multiple-choice test questions. If careful attention is not taken to study the immigrants' prior systems of education, teachers can easily conclude that these students have learning disabilities, when in fact, they are serious critical thinkers and already accustomed to explaining their thinking, skills that are highly valued in new state science, math, English language arts, and English language proficiency standards.

Solutions

Transitioning from different African systems of education, where neither breakfast nor lunch is served in schools, where the grade retention rates are very high (Cameroon Ministry of Education, 1995), and where there is no school bus system, African immigrant children easily thrive in American public schools when given an effective newcomer orientation and classroom learning experiences that are culturally responsive. Some solutions to help students and their families navigate the new pathways of the education system that they will encounter in U.S. schools and STEAM classrooms could include the following:

1. *Parents/families orientation to U.S. schools programs:* STEAM instructors may want to work with other school faculty and personnel to provide orientations for students and their parents on the U.S. education system. Ideally, the facilitators of these orientations would share the language and/or culture of the students' families in order to help quell their anxieties, worries, or discomfort with the vast differences they will face in U.S. schools. Alternatively, current students nearing graduation who have been in the school for some time might team with instructors or other personnel to provide an insider perspective on differences between schooling in the United States and families' home countries. In addition, immigrant fami-

lies, especially those who have children in high school, need to be advised on college admission criteria, which tend to encompass not only ACT or SAT test scores and grade point averages, but also volunteering service hours, essays, and Advanced Placement courses. These parent/family education programs should include printed materials that families can take home to consult and discuss. Materials might include checklists for ensuring access to and succeeding in various STEAM courses and levels, flow charts or maps of STEAM and post-graduation options, and so on. Ultimately, the goal should be to empower parents and families to advocate for their students' success in K–12 schooling and for students' opportunities to be competitive college applicants.

2. *Explore other education systems in STEAM:* Teachers, counselors, and administrators should educate themselves about students' prior experiences so that they can adapt current systems, such as the way counseling occurs or how students are assessed, to integrate students' cultural experiences into coursework. Particularly if there are a large number of students from a particular country or region of Africa, STEAM instructors might create a unit that explores some of the differences in other education systems, or more specifically, in STEAM subjects in those countries. Then, once again, African immigrant students become the experts in those units, community members can be invited in to contribute (e.g., university students, local services representing and serving these specific communities), and authentic learning of the richness of cultures within the classroom happens.

3. *Teach to a variety of learning preferences:* Rather than teaching to the primary learning preferences of mainstream American students (e.g., the emphasis on independent learning), explore and teach to a variety of learning preferences represented by the cultures of students in the classroom (e.g., more cooperative learning styles; see Nieto & Bode, 2008). Rather than separating children into groups based on learning styles, all children can be introduced to a variety of methods, which enriches everyone's ability to adapt and grow.

Challenge 3: Differing Expectations of Student Classroom Behavior

Cultural differences in expectations of classroom behavior can lead at best to misunderstanding and at worst to punishment or ridicule of students who do not behave in the culturally expected way. For example, in many U.S. classrooms, K–6 students sit on the floor for a specific activity such as a teacher read aloud. However, in many parts of Africa, students sit only on benches and chairs when classroom floors are cemented and cold or too dusty to sit on. Being aware of these cultural differences is key; otherwise, the teacher might unjustly penalize an immigrant student who is restless and consistently stretches his/her legs when seated on the carpet. A culturally responsive teacher will notice the discomfort and either assign the student a seat next to his/her peers sitting on the floor or ask the student to sit on the front row so that his/her stretched legs do not touch someone.

Another, much more insidious, peril is that teachers may have low expectations of new immigrant students based on deficit assumptions of what they see lacking (Nieto & Bode, 2008). Low expectations are more challenging to address because they may be rooted in cultural bias and unexamined notions of what schooling should be. (This issue is further addressed in Challenge 5 below.)

Solutions

The solutions for preventing cultural conflicts in the classroom are practices that STEAM teachers may already engage in. However, these practices are even more critical with African immigrant children who may come from vastly different home cultures than the ones teachers are accustomed to.

1. *Parental/family involvement:* Consistent and persistent communication and interaction with African immigrants' parents and families is key. Involving parents improves the quality of their child's education, in part, by adding to the technical know-how of teachers (Comer & Haynes, 1991). Immigrant children may lack the maturity or linguistic skills to provide constructive information to their teachers, which can be used to inform culturally responsive teaching, but their parents could provide this information if the channels of communication are opened by teachers. Parents can inform teachers of their children's present and past academic history, which is critical in helping students transition from the teacher-centered setting of African classrooms to the student-centered learning in U.S. classrooms. The more teachers know about their individual students' cultural backgrounds, the more they can tailor their pedagogic strategies to meet their students' diverse academic needs and interests.

2. *Home visits:* Teacher visits to immigrant children's homes is a vital element of culturally responsive teaching—this works in both directions: The teacher can gain a wealth of knowledge about a student's culture and "funds of knowledge" to inform classroom practices

(Moll, Amanti, & Gonzalez, 2005); the parents in turn can learn a great deal of information about how to work with their children on their school-related learning as they observe a teacher work with their children. (See Appendix references and Moll, Amanti, Neff, & González, 2005, for suggestions on how to conduct the home visit).

In addition, behavior issues are less likely to occur when students know their teachers are in communication with their parents and can contact them any time. As one Detroit teacher stated about home-visits, "When you have a kid walk into class, you just see the kid. But after a home visit, when that student walks into class you see his aunt, his uncle, the drawing pad that he brought to share with you—it's a whole picture. I get immeasurable data about what inspires them and motivates them" (Flannery, 2014, p.1).

3. *Oral history or digital storytelling projects:* Since conducting home visits may be impractical for some teachers, particularly for busy high school teachers, collecting oral histories as case studies may provide a good alternative. Nieto and Bode (2008) note that oral histories "are an excellent way to learn about your students' family histories, challenges, and triumphs" (p. 181) and can be integrated to all content areas, not just English or social science classes. See the International Society for Technology in Education website (among other rich resources online) in the Appendix for ideas of how to integrate digital storytelling into the STEAM curriculum.

4. *Cultural Sensitivity Professional Learning:* Nearly all accredited teacher education programs in the United States now require preservice teachers to take a course in multicultural education prior to the completion of the program. The rationale behind this requirement is to ensure that pre-service teachers are exposed to a variety of diversity-related literature and clinical experiences that help them understand and teach effectively students who are culturally, linguistically, and economically different from themselves. The course also helps preservice teachers learn about the sources of inequities and strategies to deconstruct privilege, institutional racism, linguicism, subtractive beliefs, and other forms of "isms" relative to human diversity. The course also addresses intercultural competence and communication, culturally informed pedagogy, high expectations, and promotion of social justice. In a nutshell, a course in multicultural education is important for preservice and in-service teachers of all diverse backgrounds so that they can acquire the cultural proficiency that is germane to understanding and meeting the academic needs of African immigrant students, as well as all students regardless of their race, ethnicity, nationality, language, religion, family dynamics, sexual orientation, and social class.

Challenge 4: Differing Expectations of Parental/Family Involvement

It is clear that parental involvement can play a key role in African immigrant children's success in the STEAM classroom. However, most immigrant parents do not initially become involved to the same extent as American parents due to a combination of factors, including language barriers, a lack of knowledge about the American system of education (Ruiz-de-Velasco & Fix, 2000), and conflicting work schedules. Like some Chinese parents in Canada who contested their roles in the education of their children (Li, 2005), many African immigrant parents who have not studied in the United States do not expect their involvement in their children's education to extend beyond the home onto school grounds. The parents do, however, tend to have very high expectations for their children, and attend parent teacher conferences and open house events at the beginning of the academic year when their schedules permit. Unbeknownst to them, many American educators expect more than open house participation from parents. School expectations of parents include volunteering in classrooms and assisting with fund-raising, field trips, and other school-related events. While some of these parents see these teachers' expectations as too demanding and others may not comply as a result of a language barrier, still other parents may be undocumented immigrants and avoid appearing in public places for fear of arrest and deportation (Capps et al., 2005).

In addition, schools have implicit expectations that parents will reinforce the learning children are doing in school. However, African immigrant parents may not be able to assist their children the same way that many U.S. parents do. Because of the differing education systems, African immigrant parents may have different patterns of reading and solving math problems with their children. They may have different frames of reference, levels of understanding, and communication styles with regard to scientific concepts. For instance, recently arrived immigrants may not have been exposed to the kind of education that promotes critical thinking skills through learner-centered pedagogy. They have often been exposed to the type of pedagogy Paulo Freire (1970) referred to as the banking concept, in which students sit quietly in class and consume uncritically the knowledge that the teacher dispenses. This teacher-centered pedagogic practice has contributed to many African immigrants' discomfort and unassertiveness in more democratic classrooms, as in the United States.

Solutions

The solutions here are essentially the same as for Challenges 2 and 3 above: The diversity of African immigrant students' experiences requires more culturally responsive teachers to infuse the frames of reference and lived experiences of these immigrant children into the school curricula and to be conscious of their own unintended implicit biases that may be affecting teaching and learning. As Howard (2006) argues, we can't teach what we don't know—so in order to teach what we know, we have to learn it. School–home connection involves teachers' visits to immigrant family homes and in turn, parents' volunteering in their children's classrooms to familiarize themselves with their new country's instructional culture (Dantas & Manyak, 2010). Frank conversations with the parents of African immigrant children, in addition to newcomer and college orientations, can orient parents to the expectations U.S. public schools have of them and hopefully allow STEAM teachers and parents to come to a mutual understanding of parental (and/or extended family) involvement. If families include undocumented family members, it may be important to meet with them in a "safe space," such as a community center, faith-based center, or the families' homes.

Challenge 5: Stereotypes and Misunderstandings of African Immigrant Cultural Identities

Stereotyping and misunderstanding African immigrant students are perhaps the most insidious of challenges that African immigrant children experience, because these experiences are so entangled with issues of race, class, and ethnocentrism in U.S. culture. The lack of exposure to accurate and balanced information about Africa has often led to overgeneralizations, stereotypes, and misinformation. Many of these misconceptions are propagated by Hollywood movies and television channels like Discovery Channel, Animal Planet, and National Geographic, and by popular movies or television series such as *Amistad* and *Roots* (Traore, 2004). Africans are commonly portrayed as "primitive, diseased, and uneducated," and when these images are brought into the classroom, they lead to the "sham[ing]" and ridiculing of African immigrant children, who may be unprepared to counter them (Harushimana & Awokoya, 2011).

In the absence of authentic knowledge about Africa, educators become influenced by this "societal curriculum." Cortes (1979) defines societal curriculum as "that massive, ongoing, informal, curriculum of family, peer groups, neighborhoods, mass media, and other socializing forces that educate us throughout our lives" (p. 476). Misrepresentations which emerge from societal curriculum can result in lower teacher expectations of African immigrant students; misunderstandings between teachers, students, and their parents; and even discrimination (Adair, 2015; Long & Brown, 2001). Long and Brown (2001) discuss the oppositional posture of immigrant youth who identify with U.S.-born African Americans, and how racism and discrimination factor into this posture. Adair (2015) examines how stereotypes and misunderstandings of immigrant youth and cultures can lead to "personal discrimination" by teachers and other members of the educational community, and how structural factors, like the settlement of immigrants and refugees into poor urban settings, can lead to reduced educational opportunities and resources through institutional discrimination.

In addition, even when an effort is made to incorporate African-friendly content into the curriculum, it can be superficial and misleading. Many educators attempting to be culturally inclusive in fact adopt "tourist-multicultural" (Derman-Sparks, 1992) and stereotyping curriculum, but a multicultural approach that truly addresses the needs of all learners, while tackling the challenges of standards and testing, is needed. A thorough vetting and critical analyses of ethnic content propagated in mass media is vital prior to dissemination in the school context, given that the unintended misrepresentation of people and their culture could be even more damaging than doing nothing.

Solution: Authentic Knowledge as a Tool Against Stereotypes

1. *Accurate information:* To practice culturally responsive teaching, STEAM teachers must grow their knowledge base with authentic information about their students' cultures and educational backgrounds. Without authentic information, teachers may subconsciously employ stereotypical information to inform instruction and decisions that impact ethnically different students. Teachers can begin by familiarizing themselves with at least the macro-history and cultures of Africa. Africa is made up of 53 independent countries with a vast diversity of ethnic groups, political and economic disparities, native and European languages, religious beliefs, cultures, races, and education systems. Based on the multiple levels of diversity, clearly, the experiences of two African immigrant students from two different countries is likely to differ considerably especially if, for instance, one comes from an urban area and the other from a rural area.

2. *Reading and/or Film groups:* STEAM teachers may want to form reading groups that meet regularly to discuss discoveries in their reading or viewing of African-created media (Harushimana & Awokoya, 2011). For example, students can read biographies of African scientists or other STEAM professions and compare notes on what they learned. See the Appendix for a list of recommended

readings, keeping in mind that researching the specific countries and cultural groups represented by the students in your classrooms is critical.

3. *Integration of Africans into the curriculum:* Similar to Challenge 2, Solution 2 above, STEAM teachers can create a unit that revolves around some of the cultures represented in the classroom (or around one, if there is a large minority). The unit can take a variety of forms—from children signing up to research and present (or create a product) on a STEAM project in a particular country, to researching a problem (e.g., lack of clean water) and designing a solution (which then enables African immigrant children to choose their own country, if they like), to incorporating special speakers from, and trips into, the community (e.g., a local engineer who is also an African immigrant, an ethnic community center showcasing art or projects benefiting the community). A focus on leaders in STEAM professions should also reflect the cultures of students in the classroom. Because African immigrant students may often be in the process of becoming American in their own right, and individual students' identities are constantly evolving, culturally relevant curriculum can in fact include African Americans in STEAM (see references in the Appendix). This option offers a greater range of role models for a very diverse group of students. These are some of the ways that STEAM teachers can design curriculum specifically to create "windows" for mainstream students and "mirrors" (Style, 1998) for minority students from a content lens.

4. *Pedagogical adaptation:* Once they have learned some of the strengths that African immigrant children bring into the classroom and some of the pedagogical styles from students' native classroom backgrounds, teachers can adapt these practices in their own teaching to make the STEAM classroom more "culturally congruent" (Nieto & Bode, 2008). For instance, project-based STEAM learning leverages the cooperative learning styles that are typical in many African cultures, and once teachers recognize this, they can adapt the way they teach to be more responsive to students. Even outside the STEAM classroom, the school can create a more welcoming environment for African immigrant (and other minority) students by incorporating signage and bulletin board postings and other visible acknowledgements and celebrations of the diversity of cultures represented in the school, and not limiting these to "international nights" or other once-a-year events (Harushimana & Awokoya, 2011; Nieto & Bode, 2008).

CONCLUSION

Culturally responsive teaching not only helps teachers to support the educational and cultural transition of African immigrant students in U.S. K–12 STEAM classrooms, but also advocates for understanding of cultural differences without essentializing students, since culture is dynamic (Nieto & Bode, 2008). This type of teaching also challenges ethnic and racial stereotypes. Stereotypes in such cases are often negative and tend to diminish not only teachers' expectations of their students, but also nonimmigrant students' expectations of the academic abilities of their immigrant classmates, not to mention African immigrant students' own perceptions of themselves as STEAM learners.

Depending on their academic levels and their countries of origin, African immigrant students bring into their classrooms diverse experiences that were valued in their home countries. These experiences must not be left outside the U.S. STEAM classroom door; instead, they can be used as to scaffold new knowledge (Johannessen, 2004). Just as first language acquisition aids in learning a second language (Andrew, 2007; Cummins, 2005), so too does previous knowledge aid in learning new knowledge.

All students in the United States are growing up in an environment that is becoming increasingly diverse. Engaging all students in multicultural education not only speeds up English acquisition for those African immigrant students not already fluent in American English, but also helps all students adapt positively to the increasing diversity in society. As Derman-Sparks (1992) intimated, "[W]hile we give [African immigrant children] the skills needed to participate in the dominant culture, we must also make their home culture, including their language, an integral part of the curriculum" (p. 21). Multicultural education and culturally responsive teaching benefits both immigrants and nonimmigrants as they both see themselves in the curriculum "mirror" and come to understand others through the curriculum "window" (Style, 1988).

Inquiry Questions

- What are schools and preservice teacher education programs currently doing to prepare teachers to understand and meet the needs of African immigrant students? In what ways do these current practices reflect or enact some of the topics presented in this chapter?
- In what ways are some of the perceptions about African immigrant students and implicit biases highlighted in this chapter reflected in current curricula, teacher attitudes, and classroom teaching prac-

tice? What are some ways to enact real change to counter misperceptions or biases?

Action Research Questions

- Which African countries are represented in your classroom, school, or district? What do you know about the country-of-origin education systems and cultures of your African immigrant students, as well as their prior educational backgrounds? How can you learn more, and how might what you learn influence your practice?
- What are some culturally responsive teaching strategies from this chapter you could incorporate right away? Which can you plan to incorporate over a longer time period?

APPENDIX: REFERENCES FOR TEACHERS

Africans in STEAM

- ACS Honors African Americans in the Chemical Sciences. (2018). *ACS (American Chemical Society) Chemistry for life.* https://www.acs. org/content/acs/en/education/whatischemistry/african-americans-in-sciences.html
- African American Scientists. (2018). *Biography.* https://www.biography.com/people/groups/famous-black-scientists
- Bracetti, A. (2012). The 25 Most Important Black Tech Pioneers. *Complex.* http://www.complex.com/pop-culture/2012/01/the-25-most-important-black-tech-pioneers/
- Fawcett, K. (2015). 11 African American Inventors Who Changed The World. *Mental Floss.* http://mentalfloss.com/article/86923/11-african-american-inventors-who-changed-world
- *Selected Internet Resources: African Americans in Science and Technology.* (2015). Library of Congress. https://www.loc.gov/rr/scitech/selected-internet/africanamericans.html

African-Created Representations of African Cultures, the African Experience, or the African Immigrant Experience

- African Film Festival (NYC): http://africanfilmny.org/ (African-made films)
- African Film Festival (Portland, Oregon): https://www.africanfilmfestival.org/ (African-made films)

- *Americanah* by Chimamanda Ngozi Adichie: Novel about a Nigerian woman's experience with race and other issues in the United States.
- *Brother I'm Dying* by Edwidge Danticat: Memoir of a Haitian girl's family's experience with the U.S. immigration system while migrating to New York.
- *Behold the Dreamers* by Imbolo Mbue: Novel of a Cameroonian family struggling with issues of race, class, and immigration in migrating to New York.
- *Hope and Other Dangerous Pursuits* by Lalai Lalami: Stories of undocumented Moroccan migrants in Spain.
- *Say You're One of Them* by Nigerian author Akpan, Uwem: Short stories from children's perspectives around Africa (adult content: prostitution, war, genocide, conflict between Christians and Muslims, slavery, violence, etc.).
- *Voice of America: Africa* news source at https://www.voanews.com/p/5749.html

Best Practices in Culturally Responsive Classrooms

- Blended Learning Models. *BLU—Blended Learning Universe.* https://www.blendedlearning.org/models/
- *Digital Storytelling.* 2018. ISTE (International Society for Technology in Education) https://www.iste.org/explore/categorylist?code=Digital+storytelling
- "Lessons from the Kitchen Table: Visiting With Families in Their Homes." (2007). *Teachers Teaching Teachers, 3(4).* https://learningforward.org/wp-content/uploads/2007/12/lessons-from-the-kitchen-table.pdf
- "Making Your First ELL Home Visit: A Guide for Classroom Teachers" by Gisela Ernst-Slavit and Michele Mason at http://www.colorincolorado.org/article/making-your-first-ell-home-visit-guide-classroom-teachers

REFERENCES

Adair, J. K. (2015). *The impact of discrimination on the early schooling of children from immigrant families.* Washington, DC: Migration Policy Institute.

Alptekin, C. (2002). Towards intercultural communicative competence in ELT. *ELT Journal, 56*(1), 57–64.

Anderson, M. (2015). Six key findings about Black immigration to the US. *Fact Tank: News in the Numbers.* Retrieved from http://www.pewresearch.org/fact-tank/2015/04/09/6-key-findings-about-black-immigration/

Andrew, A. J. (2007). Interlanguage variation and transfer of learning. *International Review of Applied Linguistics in Language Teaching, 45*(2), 95–118.

Arthur, J. A. (2000). *Invisible sojourners: African immigrant diaspora in the United States.* Westport, CT: Praeger.

Bohórquez, P. (2013). In-between languages: Translingual living and writing in the United States. In S. Pinder (Ed.), *American multicultural studies: Diversity of race, ethnicity, gender, and sexuality* (pp. 37–52). Los Angeles, CA: SAGE.

Cameroon Ministry of Education. (1995). *Etats generaux de l'education: Rapport general* [National meeting on education: General report]. Yaoundé, Cameroon: Author.

Capps, R., & Fix, M. (Eds.). (2012). *Young children of Black immigrants in America: Changing flows, changing faces.* Washington, DC: Migration Policy Institute.

Capps, R., Fix, M., Murray, J., Ost, J., Passel, J. S., & Herwantoro, S. (2005). *The new demography of America's schools: Immigration and the No Child Left Behind Act.* Washington, DC: The Urban Institute.

Childs, G. T. (2003). *An introduction to African languages.* Amsterdam, Netherlands: John Benjamin.

Comer, J. P., & Haynes, N. M. (1991). Parent involvement in schools: An ecological approach. *The Elementary School Journal, 91*(3), 271–277.

Cortes, E. C. (1979). The societal curriculum and the school curriculum: Allies or antagonists? *Educational Leadership, 36*(7), 475–479.

Crystal, D. (1997). *English as a global language.* Cambridge, England: Cambridge University Press.

Cummins, J. (2005). Teaching the language of academic success: A framework for school-based language policies. In C. Leyba (Ed.), *Schooling and language minority students: A theoretical framework* (3rd ed., pp. 3–32). Los Angeles, CA: LBD.

Dantas, M. L., & Manyak, P. C. (2010). *Home-school connections in a multicultural society.* New York, NY: Routledge.

Derman-Sparks, L. (1992). How well are we nurturing racial and ethnic diversity? In R. Lowe, R. Peterson, D. Levine, & R. Tenorio (Eds.), *Rethinking schools: An agenda for change* (pp. 17–22). New York, NY: The New Press.

Doucet, F., Schwarts, A. E., & Debraggio, E. (2012). Beyond Black: Diversity among Black immigrant students in New York City public schools. In R. Capps & M. Fix (Eds.), *Young children of Black immigrants in America: Changing flows, changing faces* (pp. 299–331). Washington, DC: Migration Policy Institute.

Dryden-Peterson, S. (2015). *The educational experiences of refugee children in countries of first asylum.* Washington, DC: Migration Policy Institute.

Flannery, M. E. (2014). All in the family: How teacher home visits can lead to school transformation. *neaToday.* Retrieved from http://neatoday.org/2014/10/28/all-in-the-family-how-teacher-home-visits-can-lead-to-school-transformation/

Freire, P. (1970). *Pedagogy of the oppressed.* New York, NY: Continuum.

Gambino, C. P., Trevelyan, E. N., & Fitzwater, J. T. (2014). *The foreign-born population from Africa: 2008–2012.* Washington, DC: United States Census Bureau.

Gay, G. (2001). Preparing for culturally responsive teaching. *Journal of Teacher Education, 53*(2), 106–116.

Harushimana, I., & Awokoya, J. (2011) African-born immigrants in U.S. Schools: An intercultural perspective on schooling and diversity. *Journal of Praxis in Multicultural Education, 6*(1), 34–48.

Howard, G. R. (2006). *We can't teach what we don't know*. New York, NY: Teachers College Press.

Johannessen, L. R. (2004). Helping "struggling" students achieve success. *Journal of Adolescent and Adult Literacy, 47*(8), 638–647.

Kachru, B. (1992). World Englishes: Approaches, issues and resources. *Language Teaching, 25*(1), 1–14.

Kigamwa, J., & Ndemanu, M. T. (2016). Translingual practice among African immigrants in the United States: Embracing the mosaicness of the English language. *Journal of Multilingual and Multicultural Development, 38*(5), 468–479.

Li, G. (2005). *Culturally contested pedagogy: Battles of literacy and schooling between mainstream teachers and Asian immigrant parents*. Albany, NY: State University of New York Press.

Long, X. L., & Brown, F. (2001). The effects of immigrant generation and ethnicity on educational attainment among young African and Caribbean Blacks in the United States. *Harvard Educational Review, 71*(3), 536–565.

McHugh, M., & Sugarman, J. (2015). *Transatlantic symposium report: Improving instruction for immigrant and refugee students in secondary schools*. Washington, DC: Migration Policy Institute.

Migration Policy Institute. (2015, October 27). *Young refugee children: Their schooling experiences in the United States and in countries of first asylum* [Webinar]. Retrieved from http://www.migrationpolicy.org/events/young-refugee -children-their-schooling-experiences-united-states-and-countries-first-asylum

Moll, L. C., Amanti, C., Neff, D., & González, N. E. (2005). Funds of knowledge for teaching: Using a qualitative approach to connect homes and classrooms. In N. E. González, L. C. Moll, & C. Amanti (Eds.), *Funds of knowledge: Theorizing practices in households, communities, and classrooms* (pp. 71–88). Mahwah, NJ: Erlbaum.

Ndemanu, M. T. (2018). Pre-service teachers' resistance to multicultural education courses: The binary fear of the familiar and the unfamiliar communities. *Multicultural Learning and Teaching, 13*(2). doi:10.1515/mlt-2017-0020

Nieto, N., & Bode, P. (2008). *Affirming diversity: The sociopolitical context of multicultural education* (5th ed.). New York, NY: Pearson.

Ogbu, J. U., & Simons, H. D. (1998).Voluntary and involuntary minorities: A cultural-ecological theory of school performance with some implications for education. *Anthropology & Education Quarterly, 29*(2), 155–188.

Ruiz-de-Velasco, J., & Fix, M. (2000). *Overlooked & underserved: Immigrant students in U.S. secondary schools*. Washington, DC: The Urban Institute.

Samson, J. F., & Collins, B. A. (2012). *Preparing all teachers to meet the needs of English language learners*. Washington, DC: Center for American Progress.

Style, E. (1988). *Curriculum as window and mirror*. Summit, NJ: Oak Knoll School.

Suarez-Orosco, C., & Suarez-Orosco, M. (2001). *The children of immigration*. Cambridge, MA: Harvard University Press.

Takyi, B. K. (2002). The making of the second diaspora: On the recent African immigrant community in the United States of America. *The Western Journal of Black Studies, 26*(1), 32–43.

Traore, R. L. (2004). Colonialism continued: African students in an urban high school in America. *Journal of Black Studies, 34*(3), 348–369.

CHAPTER 10

MAKING EVERYDAY PHENOMENA PHENOMENAL

Next Generation Science Standards-Aligned Instructional Materials Using Local Phenomena With Diverse Student Groups

Okhee Lee
New York University

Rita Januszyk
Retired

Marcelle Goggins
New York University

Lorena Llosa
New York University

Alison Haas
New York University

Scott Grapin
New York University

ABSTRACT

In collaboration with a teacher advisory board, our research team is currently developing yearlong Next Generation Science Standards-aligned instructional materials for fifth grade that address physical science, life science,

Culturally and Linguistically Diverse Learners and STEAM, pages 211–228
Copyright © 2019 by Information Age Publishing

Earth science with engineering embedded, and space science. For each of the four units, we select and use a local phenomenon that integrates place-based learning from an equity perspective and project-based learning from a science perspective. For the first unit, we use the phenomenon of garbage, which is collected from the school, home, and neighborhood and taken to a landfill in the local community. Over the course of the unit, students build their understanding of matter in physical science to explain what happens to their garbage. We illustrate how a local phenomenon like garbage promotes access to science and inclusion in the science classroom for diverse student groups. In this chapter, we offer guidance on how to select and use local phenomena in developing Next Generation Science Standards-aligned instructional materials. We also describe challenges and how we address those challenges.

With the release of *A Framework for K–12 Science Education* (National Research Council, 2012; shortened to the *Framework* hereafter) and the Next Generation Science Standards (Next Generation Science Standards Lead States, 2013), there is a general consensus in the science education community around three key instructional shifts. The first shift involves explaining phenomena in science or designing solutions to problems in engineering. As students use science knowledge to make sense of phenomena or design solutions to problems, they experience the work of scientists and engineers. The second shift involves three-dimensional learning by blending science and engineering practices, crosscutting concepts, and disciplinary core ideas. The third shift involves learning progressions of student understanding over time. Combining these three shifts, students in the Next Generation Science Standards-aligned classroom explain phenomena or design solutions to problems (Shift 1) by engaging in three-dimensional learning (Shift 2). As students refine their explanations of phenomena or solutions to problems, they develop deeper understandings over time (Shift 3). The Next Generation Science Standards are written as performance expectations that describe what students should be able to do by the end of a grade level or grade band in order to demonstrate their understanding.

Although three-dimensional learning and learning progressions are clearly delineated in the *Framework* and Next Generation Science Standards, the role of phenomena is not explicitly defined and requires further attention. In the past, when science instruction was guided by inquiry approaches (National Research Council, 2000), there was the danger of hands-on activities lacking purpose beyond being fun and engaging (referred to as "activitymania" by Moscovici & Nelson, 1998). With a shift toward explaining phenomena and designing solutions to problems, students in the Next Generation Science Standards-aligned classroom have a purpose for learning science and engineering. At the same time, a focus on explaining phenomena raises a new danger of "phenomenal phenomena" that are selected primarily because they pique students' interests (e.g., a visually striking yet rare natural disaster that students have not personally experienced). While phenomenal phenomena inspire wonder and awe (e.g., students ask, "How could that happen!?"), they may have little relevance to students' experiences in their everyday lives. Furthermore, phenomenal phenomena may not be robust enough with explanatory power to sustain a science unit around a targeted set of performance expectations.

While selection of phenomena is important for all students, it is especially important for students who have not experienced science or engineering as real or relevant to their lives or future careers. For these students, selection of phenomena could either provide access to science by relating science to their lives or exacerbate marginalization by alienating them further from science. Despite growing recognition of the importance of students explaining phenomena in Next Generation Science Standards-aligned instructional materials (Achieve, Inc., 2016, 2017; BSCS, 2017; Carnegie Corporation of New York, 2017; National Science Teachers Association, n.d.), this topic has not received comprehensive treatment, especially as it relates to student diversity.

The purpose of this chapter is two-fold. First, we offer guidance on how to select and use local phenomena in developing Next Generation Science Standards-aligned instructional materials with diverse student groups. Second, we describe challenges in selecting phenomena for instructional materials and how we address those challenges. As part of our Science and integrated language (SAIL) project in which we are developing yearlong Next Generation Science Standards-aligned instructional materials for fifth grade, we use local phenomena with diverse student groups and English learners (ELs) in particular. We aim to "make everyday phenomena phenomenal" because even the most quotidian things are phenomenal when looked at closely. In collaboration with a teacher advisory board, we are in the process of developing, field-testing, and revising four science instructional units that address physical science, life science, Earth science with engineering embedded, and space science.

LOCAL PHENOMENA WITH DIVERSE STUDENT GROUPS: INTEGRATING PLACE-BASED LEARNING AND PROJECT-BASED LEARNING

To make sense of phenomena or design solutions to problems, students engage in three-dimensional learning and develop more sophisticated understanding over time. Krajcik (2015) emphasizes that "three-dimensional learning involves establishing a culture of figuring out phenomena or designs to problems" (p. 51). He advises science teachers to "look for engaging phenomena or problems that build toward performance expectations" (p. 51). In this section, we describe how we develop our Next Generation Science Standards-aligned instructional materials with diverse student groups.

Phenomenon-Based Science Instruction

Some approaches to developing Next Generation Science Standards-aligned instructional materials consider student diversity as part of their criteria for selecting phenomena (Achieve, Inc., 2016, 2017; BSCS, 2017; Carnegie Corporation of New York, 2017; National Science Teachers Association, n.d.; Penuel & Bell, 2016). For example, the recently published *Primary Evaluation of Essential Criteria (PEEC) for Next Generation Science Standards Instructional Materials Design* (Achieve, Inc., 2017) highlights selecting phenomena in local contexts of homes and communities:

- Inclusion of phenomena and problems that are relevant and authentic to a range of student backgrounds and interests, with supports for modifying the context to meet local needs and opportunities for students to make meaningful connections to the context based on their current understanding and personal experiences.
- Teacher materials including suggestions for how to connect instruction to the students' home, neighborhood, community and/or culture as appropriate and providing opportunities for students to connect their explanation of a phenomenon and/or their design solution to a problem to questions from their own experience. (Achieve, Inc., 2017, p. 25)

In our work developing Next Generation Science Standards-aligned instructional materials in fifth grade for diverse student groups and ELs in particular, we use local phenomena that meet two criteria. First, they are compelling to figure out as students experience these phenomena in their homes and communities (i.e., place-based learning). Second, they are comprehensive enough to sustain a science unit that addresses multiple Next Generation Science Standards performance expectations within and across science disciplines over an extended period of instruction (i.e., project-based learning). In addition to these two criteria, our research team is also concerned with selecting and using local phenomena that are universal phenomena across school districts and states so that our instructional materials could be implemented at large scale. (This criterion is not addressed specifically in this chapter.)

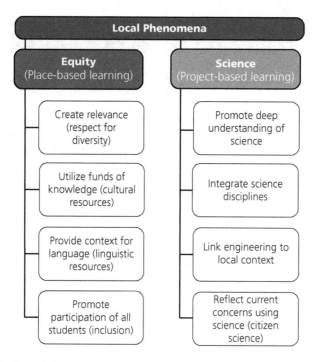

Figure 10.1 Local phenomena with diverse student groups.

Local phenomena integrate place-based learning from an equity perspective and project-based learning from a science perspective in mutually supportive ways (see Figure 10.1). By capitalizing on the cultural and linguistic resources that students from diverse backgrounds bring to the science classroom, local phenomena engage students in science and engineering. As students recognize the relevance of science and engineering to their lives or future careers, they are compelled to use their knowledge to solve problems in their communities and participate in citizen science.

Place-Based Learning From an Equity Perspective

From an equity perspective, through place-based learning, students apply science and engineering to their everyday lives in local contexts (Avery, 2013; Brehm, Eisenhauer, & Stedman, 2012; Endreny, 2010; Haywood, 2014; Semkin & Freeman, 2008; Smith, 2002; Tolbert & Knox, 2016). The goal of place-based learning is "ground learning in local phenomena and students' lived experience" (Smith, 2002, p. 586). Place-based science has been advocated for its relevance and potential to attract underrepresented

TABLE 10.1 Equity Components of Local Phenomena With Diverse Student Groups	
Equity Component 1: Create Relevance	Using local phenomena or problems makes science real by grounding experiences in students' everyday lives.
	As students figure out local phenomena, they realize how science is relevant to their lives, their communities, and their future careers.
Equity Component 2: Utilize Funds of Knowledge	Using local phenomena or problems allows students to use their funds of knowledge from their homes and communities.
	Students capitalize on their cultural resources by engaging in authentic tasks that build on their everyday experiences.
Equity Component 3: Provide Context for Language Use	Using local phenomena or problems generates language and facilitates communication.
	Students capitalize on their linguistic resources by engaging in meaningful discourse through all of the modes of communication at their disposal, including everyday language, home language, and multimodality.
Equity Component 4: Promote Participation of All Students	Using local phenomena or problems creates an inclusive learning environment by acknowledging the diversity of students, their families, and their communities.
	Students bring their cultural and linguistic resources into the science classroom, which are recruited as valued resources for learning science.

groups to science, particularly members of indigenous or historically inhabited communities, through place attachment (i.e., an emotional bond between a person and a place) and place meaning (i.e., the meanings that a person associates with a place; Brehm et al., 2012). Our instructional materials connect student diversity to science and engineering by capitalizing on equity components that local phenomena or problems present to diverse student groups (see Table 10.1; also see Figure 10.1).

Project-Based Learning From a Science Perspective

From a science perspective, through project-based learning, students integrate science disciplines as they explain phenomena or design solutions to problems through collaborative investigations (Harris et al., 2015; Krajcik & Czerniak, 2013; Krajcik, McNeill, & Reiser, 2008). Project-based learning is an approach to designing learning environments that promotes active construction of understanding through participation in authentic and meaningful experiences. According to the *Framework* and Next Generation Science Standards, phenomena or problems are central to science

TABLE 10.2 Science Components of Local Phenomena With Diverse Student Groups	
Science Component 1: Promote Deep Understanding of Science	Using local phenomena allows students to develop deep understandings of science as they try to make sense of the phenomena in personally meaningful ways.
	This is in contrast to the traditional approach of learning abstract science content without personal connection.
Science Component 2: Integrate Science Disciplines	Using local phenomena or problems allows students to make connections across science disciplines in order to explain phenomena or design solutions to problems.
	This is in contrast to the traditional approach of learning a particular science idea, topic, or concept without crossing disciplinary boundaries.
Science Component 3: Link Engineering to Local Contexts	Using local phenomena or problems connects science with engineering as students design solutions to problems in their communities.
	This is in contrast to the traditional approach of learning science and engineering in isolation from each other.
Science Component 4: Address Current Concerns Using Science	Using local phenomena or problems allows students to participate in citizen science by contributing to knowledge-building and effecting change in their communities (Bonney et al., 2009).
	This is in contrast to the traditional approach of learning science without reference to societal issues or concerns.

and science learning, as "the goal of science is to develop a set of coherent and mutually consistent theoretical descriptions of the world that can provide explanations over a wide range of phenomena" (National Research Council, 2012, p. 48). In the Next Generation Science Standards-aligned classroom, students make sense of phenomena as scientists do and design solutions to problems as engineers do. Our instructional materials make connections across science and engineering disciplines by capitalizing on science components that local phenomena or problems present to diverse student groups (see Table 10.2; also see Figure 10.1).

SELECTING AND USING LOCAL PHENOMENA IN THE SAIL INSTRUCTIONAL MATERIALS IN COLLABORATION WITH A TEACHER ADVISORY BOARD

We are currently developing yearlong Next Generation Science Standards-aligned instructional materials for diverse student groups in fifth grade and ELs in particular. The Next Generation Science Standards for fifth grade identify 16 performance expectations, including six physical science; two life science; five Earth and space science; and three engineering, technology, and applications of science. Our instructional materials bundle the Next Generation Science Standards performance expectations into four units addressing physical science, life science, Earth science with engineering embedded, and space science. Each unit is intended for approximately one marking period of 9 weeks, assuming 45–60 minutes of science instruction three times per week.

Unit 1: What happens to our garbage? (physical science)
Unit 2: Why did the tiger salamanders disappear? (life science)
Unit 3: Why does it matter if I drink tap water or bottled water? (Earth science with engineering embedded)
Unit 4: Why do falling stars fall? (space science)

Collaboration With Teacher Advisory Board

The initial versions of our instructional materials were field-tested in five fifth-grade classrooms from five elementary schools in an urban school district in a northeast state during the 2016–2017 school year. The district administrators in science education and ESL/bilingual education selected the teachers based on having large numbers of ELs in their classrooms and being willing to participate in the project. The teachers served as the teacher advisory board for the project and worked closely with the project personnel to implement and provide feedback on the draft instructional materials.

We held four teacher advisory board meetings over the course of the school year. Following each meeting, the teachers field-tested the science units in their classrooms. Multiple sources of data provided insights about the opportunities and challenges of implementing our phenomenon-based instructional materials with diverse student groups in the classrooms. First, the project personnel visited each teacher weekly, taking detailed notes about each lesson. For the majority of lessons, we made multiple observations. Second, teachers filled out a brief feedback form at the end of each class period and a more comprehensive online feedback form using both ratings and written responses at the end of each lesson. Teachers provided additional feedback about the unit that they had just implemented during the subsequent teacher advisory board meeting. Third, the project personnel held weekly debriefing meetings throughout the year to discuss strengths, areas for improvement, and suggestions for revision. We kept extensive notes for each of these debriefing meetings to guide subsequent revisions and field-testing. Through triangulation across multiple data sources, we were able to identify opportunities and challenges in selecting and using local phenomena with diverse student groups.

Selection and Use of Local Phenomena in SAIL Instructional Materials

We use the first unit on physical science and parts of life science to illustrate how we select and use local phenomena in SAIL instructional materials. Specifically, we attend to place-based learning from an equity perspective and project-based learning from a science perspective.

The Phenomenon of Garbage

For this first unit, we selected the phenomenon of garbage in the school, home, and neighborhood, which all goes to a landfill in the local community. The anchoring phenomenon for the unit is that the school, home, and neighborhood make large amounts of garbage every day. Then, we frame the driving question for the unit broadly, "What happens to our garbage?" In answering this driving question over the course of the unit, students investigate a series of questions about garbage (e.g., What is that smell? What causes changes in the properties of materials in garbage?) that address the targeted set of performance expectations across science disciplines. Over the course of the unit, students develop a coherent understanding of the structure and properties of matter to make sense of the anchoring phenomenon and to answer the driving question.

The garbage unit is comprehensive enough to fully address four fifth-grade physical science (PS) performance expectations and to introduce one life science (LS) performance expectation (see Figure 10.2).

5-PS1-1 Develop a model to describe that (SEP) matter is made of particles (DCI) too small to see (CCC).

5-PS1-2 Measure and graph quantities to provide evidence that (SEP), regardless of the type of change that occurs when heating, cooling, or mixing substances, the total weight of matter (CCC) is conserved (DCI).

5-PS1-3 Make observations and measurements (SEP) to identify materials (DCI) based on their properties (CCC).

5-PS1-4 Conduct an investigation to determine (SEP) whether the mixing of two or more substances results in (CCC) new substances (DCI).

5-LS2-1 Develop a model to describe (SEP) the movement of matter among (DCI) plants, animals, decomposers, and the environment (CCC). (This performance expectation is partially addressed in the unit.)

Note:
  SEPs: science and engineering practices
  CCCs: crosscutting concepts
  DCIs: disciplinary core ideas

Figure 10.2 Performance expectations for the Garbage Unit.

To answer the driving question of "What happens to our garbage?" students develop physical models of a landfill by creating "landfill bottles" as open systems and closed systems (see Figure 10.3).

As the unit progresses, students' understanding of science builds coherently as they investigate what happens to the garbage in the landfill bottle systems. Students begin by investigating what happens to garbage materials (5-PS1-3 on properties of materials in Figure 10.2). When the landfill bottles start to smell in the open system, students ask, "What is that smell?" (5-PS1-1 on particle nature of matter/gas). They also ask, "What causes changes in the properties of materials in the garbage?" and "What causes smell from the garbage?" (5-PS1-4 on chemical reactions). They obtain information about microbes causing food materials to decompose and produce smell (5-LS2-1 on decomposers in the environment). In addition, they make observations of the weight of the garbage materials when some materials (e.g., banana and orange) seem to have vanished (5-PS1-2 on conservation of weight of matter).

Moreover, our instructional materials promote learning progressions over the course of the year. Students learn that microbes cause food materials to decompose, which is also addressed in the subsequent ecosystems unit (5-LS2-1). Likewise, materials that do not decompose (e.g., plastic) are addressed in the Earth's systems unit, as students learn that plastic from

Figure 10.3 Open and closed landfill bottle systems for the Garbage Unit.

water bottles pollutes Earth's systems (5-ESS-2-1) and that individual communities can use science ideas to protect the Earth's resources and environment (5-ESS3-1).

Place-Based Learning From an Equity Perspective

We start the development of each unit by selecting a compelling phenomenon rooted in everyday experiences. First, the phenomenon of garbage creates relevance for all students in local contexts (Equity Component 1). As students enter the classroom and see in the center of the room a mound of garbage collected from their school cafeteria, including their own lunch garbage, they express a wide range of reactions from excitement to disgust. The everyday phenomenon of garbage becomes phenomenal.

Second, garbage from the school, home, and neighborhood that goes to a community landfill also capitalizes on students' funds of knowledge (Equity Component 2). For example, students make observations of garbage in their homes and communities, comparing the garbage materials and their properties (e.g., texture, color). They connect observations of their home garbage to the community garbage disposal system. They use their experiences with the components of the garbage disposal system (e.g., taking out the trash, seeing garbage trucks in the neighborhood) to connect the components in terms of the larger system of garbage in their community.

Third, the phenomenon of garbage provides a context for all students, and ELs in particular, to communicate their ideas using all of the meaning-making resources at their disposal, including everyday language, home language, and multimodality (Equity Component 3). The opportunity to use all of their meaning-making resources from the outset of instruction promotes participation of all students in the science classroom. For example, at the beginning of the garbage unit, students make observations of the mound of garbage using everyday language (e.g., students say, "It smells like when the garbage truck drives by my house!") and home language (e.g., students say, "¡Qué asco!"). Importantly, their observations are valued for their contribution to the discourse, not their linguistic accuracy. Students also use multiple modalities, including drawings, symbols, and text, to develop initial models of smell. Over the course of the unit, as students develop deeper understanding of science to make sense of the phenomenon of garbage, they adopt a more specialized register (e.g., students say, "Smell is a gas made of particles too small to see.") and use modalities more strategically (e.g., students use arrows to represent gas particles moving freely in space) to communicate the sophistication of their ideas.

Finally, the phenomenon of garbage promotes access and participation of all students in the science classroom (Equity Component 4). As a result, abstract ideas of matter (e.g., particle nature of matter, properties of matter, chemical reaction, and conservation of weight of matter) are made accessible and relevant to all students. Students' contributions are valued based on the merit of their ideas, not their social status or linguistic accuracy.

Project-Based Learning From a Science Perspective

We select a phenomenon that is comprehensive enough to address multiple performance expectations over an extended period of instruction (in our case, approximately a 9-week marking period) and allows students to develop their understanding coherently over the course of a unit (Science Component 1). In each unit, students develop a driving question board, which serves as a physical location in the classroom to organize their questions about the phenomenon. Students create the driving question board based on their initial experience with the phenomenon and then add to and reorganize the board as they progress through the unit. The phenomenon connects the student questions together and provides a context to investigate a series of subquestions. Every lesson starts with a subquestion that students decide based on previous investigations to help them explain the phenomenon. Over the course of the unit, each investigation contributes to progressively figuring out the phenomenon.

Designing a unit around the phenomenon of garbage allows students to understand science more broadly across science disciplines (Science Component 2). As students use science to make sense of the phenomenon, they experience the work of scientists who investigate questions that transcend disciplinary boundaries. For example, fifth-grade students explain the smell of garbage in terms of the particle nature of gas (i.e., a physical science idea) and the cause of the smell as microbes decomposing the banana and orange (i.e., a life science idea). In figuring out what happens to garbage, students meet performance expectations across physical and life science disciplines.

Moreover, the phenomenon of garbage leads to engineering in the subsequent Earth's systems unit, as students find out that plastic, which does not decompose, pollutes Earth's systems. Then, they design solutions to solve this problem by reducing the amount of plastic from water bottles in their classroom and school (Science Component 3). The Earth's systems unit addresses engineering performance expectations (3-5-ETS1-1, 3-5-ETS1-2). Students' experiences with societal concerns about garbage and plastic pollution could lead them to use science ideas to protect the Earth's resources and environment and to participate in citizen science (Science Component 4).

Challenges in Selecting and Using Local Phenomena With Diverse Student Groups

Through the development of initial instructional materials and field-testing, we gained insights into challenges in selecting and using local phenomena with diverse student groups. Below, we organize our insights in terms of challenges in promoting place-based learning from an equity perspective and project-based learning from a science perspective. Again, we use examples from the garbage unit to illustrate challenges and how we address these challenges.

Place-Based Learning From an Equity Perspective

As the concept of "local" is relative and interpreted variably, it is challenging to select a phenomenon that is perceived as relevant by all students. Phenomena are generally perceived as local if students have had experience in their school, home, or neighborhood. For our instructional materials, we do not begin the garbage unit with the phenomenon of a community landfill because not all students know a landfill or experience it daily. Instead, we use school lunch garbage as an entry point to talk about the larger garbage handling system, including a landfill in the community. As students figure out what happens in their landfill bottles in the classroom, this everyday phenomenon becomes phenomenal.

Furthermore, it is challenging to identify a local phenomenon that is engaging and relevant for students while also comprehensive enough to address multiple performance expectations. One candidate phenomenon may be engaging and relevant for students but may not address a targeted set of performance expectations or sustain a unit over several weeks. Another candidate phenomenon may be well matched with the performance expectations but have little relevance to students' everyday experiences in their homes and communities. Thus, it is necessary to consider each candidate phenomenon in terms of trade-offs (i.e., what is gained and what is lost) while keeping equity at the forefront. As described earlier, the phenomenon of garbage meets both criteria as it is compelling and relevant to students while addressing multiple performance expectations over a 9-week period. Garbage as a locally relevant phenomenon offers an entry point for all students to develop deep understanding of complex and abstract ideas in physical science over a sustained period of instruction.

Project-Based Learning From a Science Perspective

Selecting an anchoring phenomenon and a driving question that build toward a targeted set of performance expectations over a sustained period of time requires teachers to possess deep and extensive knowledge of the phenomenon, performance expectations, and their relationship. Implementing phenomenon-based instructional materials presents a challenge to teachers who need to have sufficient knowledge about the disciplinary core ideas and the phenomenon of a unit. For example, to implement the garbage unit, teachers must be familiar with the particle nature of matter, the process of rotting garbage materials producing a smell, and the causal relationship between microbes on garbage materials and the particles of smell in the air. These demands on content knowledge are especially acute for teachers who do not have a strong background in science. To address this challenge in our instructional materials, we embed just-in-time science background knowledge for teachers so that they can make connections (and, ultimately, help their students make connections) between the performance expectations and the phenomenon under study.

It is also unclear to what extent student learning transfers beyond the phenomenon to other contexts. An affordance of phenomena is that they create rich contexts for learning science ideas through engagement in science and engineering practices. However, students should also be able to apply what they have learned beyond the context of the phenomenon to new contexts. For example, as part of the garbage unit, students learn that materials in the landfill do not disappear or vanish since weight is conserved. In field-testing, however, students struggled to transfer their understanding of conservation of weight to other contexts. To address this challenge in our instructional materials, we embed assessments that probe students' understanding of key science ideas in less familiar contexts that are outside of the unit phenomenon. For example, after students come to understand conservation of matter in the context of garbage, they are asked to predict the weight of an ice cube in a plastic bag after the ice cube melts. Teachers use these assessments formatively to tailor subsequent instruction.

Bringing phenomena to the classroom presents logistical challenges. Students may understand how a phenomenon is real and relevant to their lives, but continued student interest and engagement in learning science requires multiple and varied experiences with the phenomenon over the course of a unit. Although a trip to the local landfill would be ideal in the garbage unit, schools cannot always afford these types of experiences. Instead, we substitute this experience with a video that simulates a virtual trip to the landfill. While students continue their study of the landfill bottles over the course of the unit, they also conduct related investigations to reinforce their understanding of core ideas (e.g., crushing and tearing everyday objects to learn about conservation of matter/weight; compressing air in a syringe to learn about the particle nature of gas). While necessary to address the targeted performance expectations, these related investigations could take the focus away from the phenomenon and the storyline of the unit. To address this challenge in our instructional materials, we select related investigations based on everyday occurrences and make explicit their purpose and connection to making sense of the phenomenon under study.

CONCLUSION

The Next Generation Science Standards present key instructional shifts that pose both opportunities and challenges to teachers and students. Providing these opportunities and meeting these challenges are particularly critical when working with students who have not experienced science and engineering as real and relevant to their lives or future careers. We argue for local phenomena or problems that compel students from diverse backgrounds to engage in three-dimensional learning and to build their science understanding over a sustained period of instruction. Local phenomena promote access and inclusion in the science classroom by grounding experiences in students' everyday lives.

In this chapter, we describe how we select and use local phenomena in developing Next Generation Science Standards-aligned instructional materials with diverse student groups. Specifically, we describe how our instructional materials integrate place-based learning from an equity perspective and project-based learning from a science perspective. We also describe both opportunities and challenges in selecting and using local phenomena with diverse student groups. In light of these opportunities and challenges, we propose inquiry questions for science education researchers and action research suggestions for practitioners in Appendices A and B, respectively.

As our work continues through an iterative process of field-testing in classrooms and subsequent revisions, we aim to capitalize on opportunities and address challenges. The insights we gain through our collaboration with the teacher advisory board will further improve our instructional materials specifically and the Next Generation Science Standards community broadly. By "making everyday phenomena phenomenal," we move a step closer to realizing the vision of the *Framework* and Next Generation Science Standards and to ensuring all students, especially those underserved in science education, have access to rigorous science learning that prepares them for college and careers.

Inquiry Questions for Science Education Researchers

This chapter describes both opportunities and challenges in selecting and using local phenomena with diverse student groups. For science education researchers concerned with issues of equity, it is important to address challenges while capitalizing on opportunities. We propose the following inquiry questions to examine the challenges discussed in the chapter.

Inquiry Question 1

Challenge: Phenomena are generally perceived as local if students have had experience in their school, home, or neighborhood. As the concept of "local" is relative and interpreted variably, it is challenging to select a phenomenon that is perceived as relevant by all students.

Question: How is a "local" phenomenon defined? What are key features of a local phenomenon?

Inquiry Question 2

Challenge: It is challenging to identify a local phenomenon that is engaging and relevant for students while also comprehensive enough to address multiple performance expectations. It is necessary to consider each candidate phenomenon in terms of trade-offs (i.e., what is gained and what is lost) while keeping equity at the forefront.

Question: What are design principles for instructional materials to address a phenomenon, a targeted set of performance expectations, and student diversity simultaneously in a science unit?

Inquiry Question 3

Challenge: Selecting an anchoring phenomenon and a driving question that builds toward a targeted set of performance expectations over a sustained period of time requires teachers to possess deep and extensive knowledge of the phenomenon, performance expectations, and their relationship.

Question: What are features of instructional materials so that teachers have sufficient knowledge to integrate a phenomenon, a targeted set of performance expectations, and student diversity in their teaching?

Inquiry Question 4

Challenge: It is unclear to what extent student learning transfers beyond the phenomenon to other contexts.

Question: How can science instructional materials be developed to promote transfer of science knowledge beyond the phenomenon under study to other contexts?

Inquiry Question 5

Question: For developers of instructional materials aimed at large-scale implementation, how can materials utilize local phenomena that are also universal phenomena across settings so that the materials could be implemented at large scale?

Action Research Suggestions for Practitioners

For practitioners who are interested in designing Next Generation Science Standards-aligned instructional materials based on local phenomena with diverse student groups, we offer the following action research. We emphasize that the process of designing such materials is iterative and nonlinear.

1. Identify the intended grade level for a science unit.
2. List Next Generation Science Standards performance expectations for the unit.
3. Identify a local phenomenon (for science) or a problem (for engineering) to serve as the anchoring phenomenon or problem for the unit.
4. Establish a driving question for the unit.
5. Give your reasoning of how the phenomenon or problem meets the following two criteria (see Figure 10.1, Table 10.1, and Table 10.2):
   - Criterion 1: Place-based learning from an equity perspective
   - Criterion 2: Project-based learning from a science perspective
6. Design an outline of the unit or revise an existing unit that enables your students to meet the targeted set of performance expectations by explaining the phenomenon or designing solutions to the problem.

REFERENCES

Achieve, Inc. (2016). *Using phenomena in NGSS-designed lessons and units*. Washington, DC: Author.

Achieve, Inc. (2017). *Primary evaluation of essential criteria (PEEC) for Next Generation Science Standards instructional materials design*. Washington, DC: Author.

Avery, L. M. (2013). Rural science education: Valuing local knowledge. *Theory Into Practice, 52*(1), 28–35.

Bonney, R., Cooper, C. B., Dickinson, J., Kelling, S., Phillips, T., Rosenberg, K. V., & Shirk, J. (2009). Citizen science: Developing a tool for expanding science knowledge and scientific literacy. *BioScience, 59*(11), 977–984.

Brehm, J., Eisenhauer, B. W., & Stedman, R. C. (2012). Environmental concern: Examining the role of place meaning and place attachment. *Society & Natural Resources: An International Journal, 26*(5), 522–538.

BSCS. (2017). *Guidelines for the evaluation of instructional materials in science*. Colorado Springs, CO: Author.

Carnegie Corporation of New York. (2017). *Instructional materials and implementation of NGSS: Demand, supply, and strategic opportunities*. New York, NY: Author.

Endreny, A. H. (2010). Urban 5th graders' conceptions during a place-based inquiry unit on watersheds. *Journal of Research in Science Teaching, 47*(5), 501–517.

Harris, C. J., Penuel, W. R., D'Angelo, C. M., DeBarger, A. H., Gallagher, L. P., Kennedy, C., . . . Krajcik, J. S. (2015). Impact of project-based curriculum materials on student learning in science: Results of a randomized controlled trial. *Journal of Research in Science Teaching, 52*(10), 1362–1385.

Haywood, B. K. (2014). A "sense of place" in public participation in scientific research. *Science Education, 98*(1), 64–83.

Krajcik, J. (2015). Three-dimensional instruction: Using a new type of teaching in the science classroom. *The Science Teacher, 82*(8), 50–52.

Krajcik, J. S., & Czerniak, C. (2013). *Teaching science in elementary and middle school classrooms: A project-based approach* (4th ed.). London, England: Routledge.

Krajcik, J., McNeill, K. L., & Reiser, B. J. (2008). Learning-goals-driven design model: Developing curriculum materials that align with national standards and incorporate project-based pedagogy. *Science Education, 92*(1), 1–32.

Moscovici, H., & Nelson, T. M. (1998). Shifting from activitymania to inquiry. *Science and Children, 35*(4), 14–17.

National Research Council. (2000). *Inquiry and the national science education standards: A guide for teaching and learning*. Washington, DC: National Academy Press.

National Research Council. (2012). *A framework for K–12 science education: Practices, crosscutting concepts, and core ideas*. Washington, DC: National Academies Press.

National Science Teachers Association. (n.d.). *Criteria for evaluating phenomena*. Arlington, VA: Author.

Next Generation Science Standards Lead States. (2013). *Next generation science standards: For states, by states*. Washington, DC: The National Academies Press.

Penuel, W. R., & Bell, P. (2016). Qualities of a good anchor phenomenon for a coherent sequence of science lessons. *STEM Teaching Tool, 28*. Retrieved from http://stemteachingtools.org/assets/landscapes/STEM-Teaching-Tool-28 -Qualities-of-Anchor-Phenomena.pdf

Semkin, S., & Freeman, C. B. (2008). Sense of place in the practice and assessment of place-based science teaching. *Science Education, 92*(6), 1042–1057.

Smith, G. A. (2002). Place-based education: Learning to be where we are. *Phi Delta Kappan, 83*(8), 584–594.

Tolbert, S., & Knox, C. (2016). "They might know a lot of things that I don't know": Investigating differences in preservice teachers' ideas about contextualizing science instruction in multilingual classrooms. *International Journal of Science Education, 38*(7), 1133–1149.

PART II

TECHNOLOGY, ENGINEERING, ARTS, AND MATHEMATICS FOR DIVERSE LEARNERS

CHAPTER 11

IMPROVING STUDENTS' MATHEMATICS DISPOSITIONS AND PARTICIPATION THROUGH CARING MATHEMATICS INSTRUCTION

Nancy Tseng
University of California at Davis

> *I'm kind of afraid to [share my math strategies out loud] because if I get it, like,
> wrong, I'm afraid the class would laugh at me. Because, uh, at school, a lot kids
> laugh at the other kids, and I'm just afraid they'll laugh at me for getting one of the
> answers wrong. Like once I said the wrong answer before and I got laughed at.*
> —Colin, Interview 1, January 8, 2013

Research indicates that caring teacher–student relationships influence mathematics learning (Hackenberg, 2010), support the development of positive mathematical identities and dispositions (Gresalfi, 2009; Martin, 2007), and can be leveraged to support more equitable learning opportunities for marginalized student populations (Bartell, 2011). Strong student–teacher relationships can be particularly transformative for student populations that have been traditionally underserved in education (Bartell,

Culturally and Linguistically Diverse Learners and STEAM, pages 231–248

2011; Rosiek, 2003; Valenzuela, 1999). Teachers themselves also readily identify care as a lens through which they view their teaching and rationalize their instructional decision-making process (Goldstein, 2002; McBee, 2007; Tarlow, 1996). Attending to who students are as individuals and being responsive to their personal and academic needs is part and parcel of the work teachers do on a daily basis (Kennedy, 2005; Rosiek, 2003). The quote above from Colin,[1] one of the fourth-grade students in this action research project, illustrates one of the "needs" that teachers strive to attend as they care for students through their mathematics instruction.

Although there is wide consensus in the field of mathematics education that teaching mathematics is a social and relational practice (Franke, Kazemi, & Battey, 2007), less attention has been paid to the role of student–teacher relationships in the mathematics classroom and how this relationship influences student learning. The theoretical assumption driving this study holds that mathematics teaching and learning is relational, and the quality of the constructed relationship between teacher and student influences how students learn and come to identify with the discipline. If caring teacher–student relationships matter for mathematics learning, then what happens when a teacher-researcher approaches her mathematics instruction from a theoretical lens of care? The purpose of this action research project was to explore how approaching mathematics teaching from a caring approach influenced the mathematical experiences and dispositions of a class of fourth-grade students. In this chapter, I address the following questions:

- How do fourth-grade students respond to a caring approach to mathematics instruction?
- In what ways do fourth-grade students' mathematical dispositions shift after their engagement with a caring approach to mathematics instruction?
- What factors do students report as influencing their mathematical participation?

THEORETICAL PERSPECTIVES ON CARE

Nel Noddings, whose foundational work on care has been most influential in the field, frames *caring* as "a way of being in relation with another, not as a specific set of behaviors" (1984, p. 17). A caring teacher, therefore, is not someone who possesses static, desirable characteristics but rather one who can establish relationships with students across different contexts. The notion of *care* consistently emerges as a theme in the literature related to the formation of productive teacher–student classroom relationships (Bartell, 2011; Battey, Neal, & Hunsdon, 2018; Noddings, 1984). Teachers frequently identify care as an essential component of their work, indicating they care deeply for their students as individuals and the content they teach them (McBee, 2007). Students similarly note the importance of caring teachers and report that they feel cared for when teachers are sensitive to their needs and interests, show concern for learning outcomes, and provide a safe learning environment (Stipek, 2006). Seen this way, social and emotional aspects of learning are not peripheral to the learning process, but rather centrally located in and inextricably related to learning (Goldstein, 2002; Gresalfi, 2009; Hargreaves, 2000; Rosiek, 2003). Rosiek (2003), for example, argues that the ways in which teachers attend to and influence students' emotional responses to subject matter critically shapes student engagement and learning. Specifically, caring teachers engage in *emotional scaffolding* where they seek to foster students' constructive emotional responses to content and reduce their unconstructive emotional responses in order to provide more enriching classroom experiences.

In recent years, scholars have built upon and refined Noddings' (1984) description of care to detail what care looks like specifically in mathematics instruction (Bartell, 2011; Hackenberg, 2010). For example, Hackenberg's (2005a, 2005b, 2010) model of *mathematical caring relations* demonstrates how teachers can "conjoin affective and cognitive realms in the process of aiming for mathematical learning" (2010, p. 237). She argues that although mathematics teachers can act as carers in a general sense, caring becomes distinctly mathematical when teachers "work to harmonize themselves with and open new possibilities for students' mathematical thinking, while maintaining focus on students' feelings of depletion and stimulation" (Hackenberg, 2005a, p. 45). Establishing mathematical caring relations with students requires teachers to remain attuned and responsive to how students are engaging with the mathematics and interact with students in ways that sustain their engagement. Hackenberg's research (2005b, 2010) further illustrates that the mathematical activities students engage in play a salient role in whether and how caring relations are formed. That is, teachers care for students by posing challenging yet appropriate tasks within a student's zone of proximal development (Vygotsky, 1978).

Bartell's (2011) notion of *caring with awareness* moves the field towards a crystallized vision of how teachers can explicitly attend to students' cultural, racial, and linguistic identities through their mathematics instruction. Because definitions and expectations of "appropriate" classroom behavior are culturally influenced, conflicts and misunderstandings occur when teachers and students come from different cultural, racial, and socioeconomic backgrounds (Weinstein, Tomlinson-Clarke, & Curran, 2004). Teachers must know their students well mathematically, racially, culturally, and politically and use this knowledge to create learning opportunities that support equitable classroom participation. Specifically, teachers build authentic and respectful relationships with their students by confirming who they are, assigning competence to the mathematical contributions of "lower status" students, and explicitly rejecting deficit-based narratives associated with students of color. Teachers also work to ensure that mathematics instruction is *equi*table for all students by supporting students' participation throughout a mathematics lesson; for example, by making explicit the underlying assumptions in a task scenario that may be unfamiliar to some students, and by ensuring that students have an understanding of key mathematical relationships described in the task, and access to necessary language (Jackson & Cobb, 2010).

Taken together, a synthesis of the research literature (Table 11.1) reveals that caring mathematics instruction in the classroom can be parsed into three related dimensions: caring for students' social-emotional responses as they engage in mathematics (personal caring), providing students opportunities to engage in mathematical sensemaking (mathematical caring), and approaching racially, culturally, linguistically diverse students from a strengths-based approach, validating the multiple ways students come to know mathematics, and ensuring they have equitable access and opportunities to learn mathematics (political caring).

LEARNING ABOUT CARING IN MATHEMATICS

The inquiry project I describe in this chapter took place in the school district where I taught elementary school for 9 years prior to becoming a teacher educator. There were 34 students in my fourth-grade class, and the 12-week action research project took place in a culturally, racially, and linguistically diverse Title I school in Northern California. Of the 34 students, 10 children were identified as Latino, 10 as White, eight as Asian-American, four as African American, and two students were identified as biracial (African American and Latino). Fourteen students were designated as English learners, and the variety of languages spoken among the children (i.e., Spanish, Hmong, Hindi, Russian, and Samoan) reflected the rich diversity of our classroom. According to students' scores on the state's standardized English language proficiency test, three students were categorized as being in the early to beginning phases of their English language development, six in the intermediate phase, and five students in the early advanced to advanced phases. Two students had individualized education plans (IEPs), and they received math and reading instruction daily from the special education teacher at the school.

TABLE 11.1 Framework for a Caring Approach to Mathematics Instruction		
Dimension of Care	Description	Examples in Practice
Personal Care	Caring for students' social-emotional responses as they are learning mathematics.	Attending to student emotional responses and (a) fostering constructive emotions by offering reasons why the content is worthwhile to learn, or (b) mediating unconstructive emotional responses by drawing attention to these emotions and assuring students it is "not as bad as it seems" (Rosiek, 2003, p. 407). Leading discussions in ways to gain student interest—connecting with the personal lives of students and giving students a sense of purpose for how mathematics can be used in their own lives (Bartell, 2011).
Mathematical Care	Providing students with opportunities to engage in mathematical sensemaking.	Posing a cognitively demanding task (Henningsen & Stein, 1997). Selecting problems to pose based on students' previously demonstrated mathematical reasoning (Hackenberg, 2010) and interests.
Political Care	Approaching racially, culturally, linguistically diverse students from a strengths-based approach, validating the multiple ways students come to know mathematics, and providing access to mathematical concepts.	Assigning competence, for example, by publicly highlighting a contribution made by students who may be typically quiet or marginalized (Boaler & Staples, 2008). Validating student contributions when they use informal language to explain their reasoning and revoicing student explanations using formal mathematics language to provide access to academic language (Moschkovich, 2002). Unpacking and discussing key contextual features and mathematical ideas and language within a task to enable all students to engage productively in a mathematical task (Jackson & Cobb, 2010).

Student surveys, interviews with focal students, and my reflective journal served as the primary sources of data for this analysis. An open-coding technique (Strauss & Corbin, 1990) of highlighting, labeling, and categorizing was used as the overarching method of analysis. To conceptualize students' mathematical dispositions and experiences, I identified general themes in students' survey responses by engaging in iterative cycles of open coding (see Table 11.2 for sample survey questions). I reviewed transcripts

TABLE 11.2 Sample Student Survey Questions				
	Statement of Prompt	Type of Response	Time of Administration	Analyzed for
Question 1	What does it mean to be good at math?	Open-ended	Beginning/end of intervention	Emerging mathematical dispositions
Question 2	I like to share my math strategies in class.	Multiple choice	Beginning/end of intervention	Emerging mathematical dispositions
Question 3	What do you like about learning math through discussions?	Open-ended	End of intervention	Mathematical experiences
Question 4	What do you dislike about learning math through discussions?	Open-ended	End of intervention	Mathematical experiences

of student interview data to affirm and elaborate the themes that emerged from students' responses to survey questions. I also referenced relevant literature throughout the process to understand, label, and inform my analysis of students' responses.

Students' Initial Dispositions

Before starting the 12-week inquiry project, I administered student surveys to get a sense of students' current mathematical dispositions and conceptions of mathematics. I also conducted individual student interviews with 10 students who reflected the student diversity within the classroom. My students' initial perspectives prior to the start of the intervention indicated that many held traditional and narrow conceptions of mathematical competence. According to them, competent mathematics learners achieved high scores, did a "great" job, followed specific behaviors, or were adept with numbers and arithmetic. To a lesser degree, students' conceptions of mathematical competence aligned with characteristics of a productive mathematical disposition (National Research Council, 2001), specifically the notions of effort and persistence and problem-solving. Half of the responses of the fourth-grade students (14 out of 28) revealed a view of mathematical competence linked to achieving high scores, not making mistakes, or learning mathematics easily and quickly. Students expressed that strong learners do well on their tests and assignments, and do not make mistakes. For example, Sean wrote that, "being good at math means having a great grade" and Jason wrote that it meant "to not get 50%. To get 100%." Anisa suggested it was okay to make some mistakes, but that someone who was good at math would "know most of the answers." Like his classmates,

Rohan believed good math learners made few mistakes, and he identified this as one of the reasons for his competence in mathematics:

> **NT:** Can you give me some reasons why you are good at math?
> **R:** Because like my mom always checks it and sometimes I only get a little wrong. Sometimes I get a lot right, [but] then most of the time, I always get them right. (Interview 1, January 8, 2013).

Rohan conceptualized himself as a good learner because he performed well (i.e., "most of the time, I always get them right") and made few errors (i.e., "sometimes I only get a little wrong"). In his response, Rohan also positioned himself in a passive learning role compared to a more mathematically knowledgeable other (i.e., "my mom always checks it"). Rohan's response suggests that he did not appear to recognize that he could be a source of mathematical knowledge for himself.

According to nine students, students who are good at mathematics demonstrate specific behaviors. These students identified specific actions that good learners exhibit, for example, they "pay attention," "listen," or "show [their] work." Students also indicated that good mathematics learners could be identified not only by visible actions, but also by their non-actions. That is, mathematically capable students solved problems on their own and did not seek input from others. For example, Cindy explained that "[being good at math] is like when you do it and you don't asked [*sic*] for help." Her response intimates that those who ask for help are less capable than those who work on their own, while simultaneously portraying the process of learning mathematics as a solitary activity that one engages in individually. Four students reported that good math learners had strong knowledge of numbers and operations and arithmetic. Emanuel suggested that "counting really good [and] knowing how much money you have" indicated that someone was good at math. Edward, wrote that knowing how "to multiply, divide, add and subtract" demonstrated one's competence. Angela confirmed his statement by stating that strong mathematics learners "really know [their] math facts."

To a lesser degree, my students identified two characteristics of mathematically competent students that aligned with the notion of a productive mathematical disposition (National Research Council, 2001). Five students recognized that good mathematics learners exercised effort and persistence in the face of challenge. In particular, good learners "always try [their] best" or "never stop." Libby responded that "[being good at math] means to try to do the one you don't get," and her response suggests that good mathematics learners not only persevere in the face of challenging problems, they specifically seek them out. Four students linked mathematical competence with solving problems and understanding. Specifically, these students indicated that it was important "to understand math" or be "a good solver."

Sharing one's mathematical ideas publicly is an important aspect of learning and doing mathematics in classrooms that aim to implement ambitious mathematical practices (Franke et al., 2007; Hiebert & Grouws, 2007). Student survey responses revealed that the majority of the class preferred not to share their mathematical ideas with the class. Specifically, 10 of the 28 students indicated they *never* liked to share their strategies, 11 students liked doing it *a little*, four students *sometimes* liked sharing, and only three students indicated they were willing to share their strategies *most of the time* (See Figure 11.1).

My interviews with individual students confirmed the patterns I found among students' survey responses, and students offered important reasons to explain their reluctance to participate in discussions. Specifically, their concerns revolved around three interrelated issues: sharing in front of a large group of people, making a mathematical mistake in front of the class, and the nature of their relationships with their classmates.

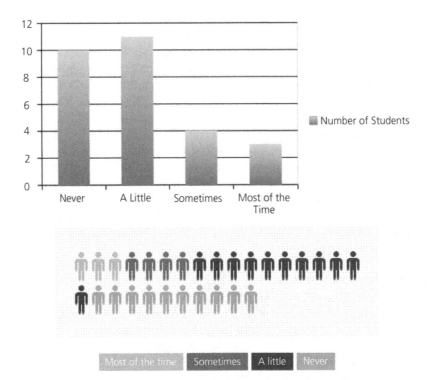

Figure 11.1 Students' initial willingness to participate in mathematical discussions.

Jewel shared that the public aspect of sharing strategies in front of the whole class inhibited her desire to participate. She noted that sharing her solution with the class would draw attention to her and this appeared to make her uncomfortable. She explained that "[sharing my strategy] makes me nervous because I know other people are watching me, so I don't like to do it" (Interview 1, January 9, 2013). Rohan was also aware that being a strategy-sharer meant there would be an audience watching and listening. In addition, he recognized that making his mathematical ideas visible meant that his ideas would be open for critique by others. He described his strategy-sharing experiences in this way: "It's like... I feel like I'm on a stage with, like, a lot of people watching me. And then if you're wrong, maybe people will laugh at you." (Interview 2, March 14, 2013). Rohan recognized that sharing his mathematical ideas with the class meant that he was placing himself in a vulnerable position, particularly if his ideas were not considered thoughtfully or respectfully by his classmates.

The knowledge I gained from student surveys and interviews served as a window into the perspectives of my students and to understand their classroom experiences as mathematics learners. These insights illuminated a path for how I could modify instruction and interact with students in ways that would be more responsive to their individual needs and support their mathematics participation in more productive ways.

Caring Mathematics Instruction in Action

As care theory suggests, pedagogical relationships emerge in the interactional space between student and teacher in the teaching and learning process (Goldstein, 1999; Hackenberg, 2005a). As a teacher-researcher interested in better understanding the impact that intentional acts of care can have on student mathematics learning, I designed and implemented an organized pedagogical approach guided by the theoretical perspectives discussed earlier (see Table 11.1). I intentionally aimed to influence students' mathematics learning through the design of my lessons, and the framework served as a tool for guiding and making sense of my choices and actions as I planned and implemented lessons. I theorized the key to sustaining student mathematical engagement involved presenting students with mathematically rich tasks, providing opportunities to engage in mathematical sensemaking, monitoring student affective and socio-emotional responses as they engaged with the task, and embracing and validating the multiple ways students from diverse backgrounds come to know mathematics as they shared their strategies during whole-class discussions.

The district used a state-adopted, mathematics program called *envision-MATH* (2009) that aligned with the curriculum focal points suggested by the National Council for Teachers of Mathematics (2000) standards and the California state standards. The intended goals of the curriculum were "centered around interactive and visual learning and differentiated instruction to address the specific needs of all students" (p. xxi). The curriculum was organized around 20 topics, and each topic focused on a particular content strand. Lessons organized under each topic were aimed to address key aspects of each mathematical topic. Based on the curriculum guide, the format of each lesson progressed through three main components: the first part, the "interactive learning" activity was a "problem-based" introductory activity to the lesson, followed by guided problem sets, and closing with independent student practice. The structure of the interactive learning activity loosely resembled three phases: posing of a mathematical task, students working on solving the task, and the teacher orchestrating a whole-class discussion where student mathematical strategies are presented and discussed. The dimension of mathematical care aims to support students in conceptualizing mathematics as a process of sensemaking and reasoning, and the interactive learning activity presented me with the greatest opportunity to approach mathematics instruction as a sensemaking activity. Therefore, instead of the 15–20 minutes suggested by the curriculum, I extended the interactive learning activity to 45 minutes and shortened the amount of time for guided and independent practice. I closed each day's lesson with a facilitated discussion where students shared the strategies they used to solve problems.

Prior to each math lesson, I began by examining the given "problem of the day" in each textbook lesson to see if the task aligned with the mathematical concepts and objectives of the lesson and engaged students in learning mathematics through problem-solving. If the provided task did not suffice, I substituted tasks using outside curricular resources. I also made decorative and non-mathematical "tweaks" to some of the mathematical tasks, for example, by changing the names of individuals in the problem to names of students in our class. Other times, drawing on my knowledge of students and the school community, I modified the original problem situation to a context that would be familiar to students' experiences (e.g., using the school or classroom as a context, using the everyday context of dividing brownies or buying pencils at the student store). These choices illustrated examples of the mathematical and personal dimensions of care in my lesson planning. I hypothesized that making tasks more familiar to students could potentially serve as a mechanism to facilitate student interest and engagement and potentially enable constructive emotional responses (Rosiek & Beghetto, 2009). Doing this also enabled students to see their cultures, ethnicities, and communities reflected in the curriculum, which reflected aspects of the dimension of political care (Bartell, 2011).

My lessons throughout the 12 weeks followed the iterative cycle of practitioner research, and therefore my instructional approach was constantly evolving. As working hypotheses emerged from my ongoing analyses, I refined lessons as well as my interactions with students during mathematics activities.

Students' Shifting Mathematical Dispositions

Students' views at the end of the intervention revealed a broader perception of what it meant to be a doer and learner of mathematics as evidenced through the emergence of several new themes (see Table 11.3). Importantly, students' responses shifted to reflect dimensions in alignment with those of a productive disposition (National Research Council, 2001). As outlined in Table 11.3, in contrast to their collective views at the beginning of the intervention, students prioritized the importance of effort and persistence, problem-solving and understanding, and collaboration.

An increased number of students recognized the importance of effort and perseverance when learning mathematics. Eight students suggested that characteristics such as "trying hard" and "giving [math] your best try" were indicators of mathematical competence. Anthony pointed out that good learners "don't get distriecked [*sic*]" and "never give up when [they're] doing math." Alex reasoned that "if you keep trying, then it is not so hard for you to learn math." Libby's response linked the notions of effort and reasoning together. In her words, "[being good at math means] trying new ideas when the first idea doesn't make sence [*sic*]." Therefore,

TABLE 11.3 Comparison of Student Views of Mathematical Competence			
Initial Views	**Students**	**Shifting Views**	**Students**
High performance	14	Effort and persistence	8
Exhibiting classroom behaviors	9	Problem-solving & understanding	7
Effort and persistence	5	Collaboration*	7
Numbers and operations	4	High performance	6
Problem-solving & understanding	4	Exhibiting classroom behaviors	5
		Numbers & operations	3
		Mathematician*	3
		Smartness*	2
		Resources*	2
		Nervousness*	1

* Indicates emergence of new theme.

in her view, a mathematically competent learner spent time and effort re-strategizing based upon one's initial reasoning.

Seven students reported that learning strategies, problem-solving, or sense-making were characteristics aligned with competent mathematics learners. Rohan, for example, developed an appreciation for making mistakes. Specifically, he viewed them as a learning opportunity and a way to increase one's mathematical competence. In his words, "the thing that makes you good at math is to make some mistakes because you learn from your mistakes." He went on to add, "Getting anserws [*sic*] right is good, but getting anserws [*sic*] right dosen't [*sic*] mean you are good at math. Its [*sic*] about what you think."

Seven students' responses revealed that their conceptions of the discipline had shifted from viewing the discipline as a solitary activity to a collaborative one. These students indicated that competent learners work with and learn from others. Specifically, good learners "talk to people" or "ask other people about their ideas." Daniel articulated that good learners "share [their] strategies with others [because] you learn together." Emanuel indicated that part of being a good mathematics learner involved "listening to other students' math strategies because it can help you." Turning Emanuel's response on its head, Kamari suggested that being a good math learner meant "help[ing] others fix their mistakes." Jewel explained how hearing other students' ideas afforded the opportunity to strengthen her own mathematical understandings:

> **J:** If someone has a different idea than you, then somebody else's idea can connect to yours.
> **NT:** Oh, can you say more about that?
> **J:** Ideas can connect even if you learn it a different way. Because you could be doing different things but you could get the same answer. That's how they connect. (Interview 2, March 12, 2013)

Jewel's response reflects an understanding that students could approach a mathematics problem in multiple ways (i.e., "if someone has a different idea than you," "you could be doing different things but you could get the same answer") and that it was possible to make connections between the different approaches students used (i.e., "ideas can connect even if you learn it a different way").

Students also developed an expanded conception of mathematical competence as evidenced by the emergence of several new themes in their post-intervention responses. Three students positioned a "mathmatishun [*sic*]" or someone who could "solve problems like a mathmatition [*sic*]" as an indicator of someone who was good at math. Two students linked a sense of competence with the notion of smartness or, as Carol put it, "being good at math [means] to be smart at it and know everything." Likely thinking of the public risks of strategy-sharing, Kyler associated feelings of apprehension with competence and suggested that being good at math meant "you get nervus [*sic*] sometimes." Two students referenced the use of strategies and tools as indicators of a competent learner. Specifically, Justin and Anthony expressed that "draw[ing] models to help you" and using "a math chart to help your thinking," respectively, reflected characteristics of mathematical competence.

Although students developed a more nuanced conception of what it meant to be good at mathematics, students' post-intervention responses indicated that half of them (14 out of 28) held on to views of mathematical competence related to high performance, exhibiting particular classroom behaviors, or being adept with numbers and operations.

Students also developed more positive orientations towards sharing their mathematical ideas with their classmates compared to the beginning of the intervention (see Figure 11.2). In particular, students' willingness to participate in mathematical discussions increased during the intervention. Of the

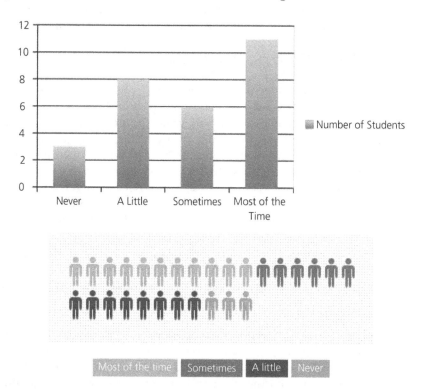

Figure 11.2 Students' willingness to participate in mathematical discussions post-intervention.

28 students, 11 suggested they liked sharing their mathematical strategies *most of the time*, six students *sometimes* liked sharing their strategies, eight students indicated they only liked doing it *a little*, and three students revealed that they *never* liked to share their strategies.

During our interviews, students cited several reasons for their increased willingness to participate in mathematical discussions. Students named stronger relationships with peers, overcoming shyness, or desires to help other students as influential factors. Jewel, for example, moved from liking to share *sometimes* to *most of the time*. When I asked her what accounted for this shift, she explained that her increased familiarity with the class, or more specifically, getting "used to" the other students supported her inclination to participate. She explained:

> **J:** Because every day I've been in the classroom longer and, like, I know them better. Some of the kids I didn't know before, 'cause they were in a different class last year or they were new to [this school], and I'm used to them now.
> **NT:** So it sounds like you're saying that spending time together and being more familiar with the kids in our class has made a difference?
> **J:** Yeah. (Interview 2, March 12, 2013)

Students also shared specific strategies they developed that supported them in overcoming their fears of sharing in front of the whole class. Colin, who moved from liking to share his strategies *a little bit* to *most of the time* noted that a useful strategy for him was to rehearse what he would say in front of the class before going up to the board. He described that "if I practice what I'm going to say first, like it got easier to say in front of everyone because I knew what I was going to say" (Interview 2, March 13, 2013). Melissa explained that pretending other people were not around was useful for her, and her openness in sharing her perspective helped me make sense of some of her actions I had observed in the classroom. Other students were motivated to share their mathematical thinking out loud with others for altruistic reasons, namely, in order to help their classmates learn mathematics. For example, Rohan indicated that "if people don't understand things and if I do, I can share my idea to help other people understand" (Interview 2, March 14, 2013).

All students' views of participating in mathematical discussions, however, did not shift. Justin remained willing to share his strategies with the class only *a little bit*. As he did during our first interview, Justin referenced the notion of mathematical correctness and responded that he "might get the answer wrong in front of everyone." Thus, because learning mathematics was about getting the answer right or wrong, sharing his strategies publicly remained a risky move for Justin. Specifically, the risks of making a mathematical mistake in front of his classmates continued to limit his inclination to participate publicly, and his perspective did not change during the course of the intervention. Like Justin, Leena's willingness to participate in classroom discussions also did not shift, and she remained at liking to share her strategies only *a little bit.* Early on in the intervention, Leena described herself as a "shy" student to explain her reluctance to participate in our classroom discussions. Unlike Melissa, however, she did not come to see herself as a "strategy-sharer" despite her recurrent opportunities to publicly share her strategies. As she explained, "I just don't really like to say what I think in front of everyone out loud" (Interview 2, March 12, 2013). Leena also clarified that her willingness to share her strategies with the class had nothing to do with making a public mistake in front of the class.

> **N:** Would you be more willing to share your strategy if you
>   knew your answer was correct?
> **L:** No. It doesn't matter. I wouldn't care if I got my answer right
>   or wrong. It's just math (Interview 2, March 12, 2013).

For Leena, the repeated opportunities to contribute to our classroom discussions did not appear to motivate her to participate in whole-class discussions more often.

REFLECTIONS AND RECOMMENDATIONS

In this chapter, I have described a framework for understanding how teachers can care for their students through their mathematics instruction. In closing, I end with some lessons learned and offer strategies teachers can use to establish caring student–teacher relationships through their mathematics instruction. My first point of insight is that caring for students involves taking on students' perspectives. The insights I gained from my analysis of student surveys and interviews during the intervention served as an essential window that allowed me to understand students' classroom experiences as mathematics learners. For example, I came to recognize that students' minimal participation during whole-class discussions was not necessarily a sign of disengagement, but rather that students were reluctant to participate due to social and public aspects of learning mathematics. This knowledge, in turn, enabled me to be more responsive to students' individual needs and consider ways to support their mathematics participation through my instruction. As Cook-Sather (2002) suggests, understanding classroom experiences from students' perspectives "is more than simply an interesting experience [for teachers], it can help teachers make what they teach more accessible to students" (p. 3).

To this end, I argue that paying attention to students' social and emotional responses as they are learning mathematics is as critical as attending to how students making sense of the content academically. Providing emotional scaffolding (Rosiek & Beghetto, 2009), or monitoring and influencing students' emotional responses to mathematics, can positively or negatively shape student engagement and learning. For example, embedding the content of a math problem in the context in which students are familiar, promoting a growth mindset (Dweck, 2010), creating shared classroom norms and a safe environment for learning to promote intellectual risk-taking among students are all ways that teachers can work towards facilitating productive engagement and ensuring that students feel they can take the risks necessary to learn.

Last, I leave with the notion that the caring approach to mathematics framework I implemented in this study should be revised and strengthened to better attend to the needs of second language learners, particularly those in the early stages of English language acquisition. While there is evidence that the approach did support the emergence of positive mathematical dispositions and increase students' willingness to participate, the framework did not appear to enable all students to participate and learn in equitable ways. More specifically, several of the students who remained at *never* liking to share their mathematical strategies were second language learners who, according to the school's English language proficiency test scores, were in the early phases of their English language development. I did not interview these students, thus I do not know precisely what may have accounted for their continued reluctance to participate. Although the framework did note the importance of "validating student contributions when they use informal language to explain their reasoning and revoicing student explanations using formal mathematics language to provide access to academic language," this was insufficient to encourage the participation of these students. Identifying and incorporating additional strategies to leverage the linguistic resources second language learners bring with them to the classroom (e.g., by encouraging them to share their mathematical understandings in their native language) would be beneficial.

Some future inquiry questions and action research ideas that educational researchers and teacher-researchers could explore follow.

Inquiry Questions

- How does the framework of caring mathematics instruction differ across subject-specific content areas? How is it similar across subject-specific content areas?

- How do the racial, cultural, and ethnic backgrounds of teachers and students influence the formation of caring student–teacher relationships in classrooms?
- How does the framework of caring mathematics instruction affect students' peer relationships and willingness to participate in mathematics discussions?

Action Research Questions

- Which specific actions can teachers take to create a classroom culture in which all students are willing participants and view themselves as mathematically competent?
- How can teachers scaffold the framework of caring mathematics instruction to more specifically support second language learners?

NOTES

1. All student names are pseudonyms.

REFERENCES

Bartell, T. G. (2011). Caring, race, culture, and power: A research synthesis toward supporting mathematics teachers in caring with awareness. *Journal of Urban Mathematics Education, 4*(1), 50–74.

Battey, D., Neal, R., & Hunsdon, J. (2018). Strategies for caring mathematical interactions. *Teaching Children Mathematics, 24*(7), 432–440.

Cook-Sather, A. (2002). Authorizing students' perspectives: Toward trust, dialogue, and change in education. *Educational Researcher, 31*(4), 3–14.

Dweck, C. (2010). Even geniuses work hard. *Educational Leadership, 68*(1), 16–20.

enVisionMATH. (2009). Toronto, Canada: Pearson Education.

Franke, M. L., Kazemi, E., & Battey, D. (2007). Mathematics teaching and classroom practice. In F. K. Lester (Ed.), *Second handbook of research on mathematics teaching and learning* (pp. 225–256). Charlotte, NC: Information Age.

Goldstein, L. S. (2002). *Reclaiming caring in teaching and teacher education.* New York, NY: Peter Lang.

Gresalfi, M. (2009). Taking up opportunities to learn: Constructing dispositions in mathematics classrooms. *Journal of the Learning Sciences, 18*(3), 327–369.

Hackenberg, A. (2005a). A model of mathematical learning and caring relations. *For the Learning of Mathematics, 25*(1), 45–51.

Hackenberg, A. (2005b). Mathematical caring relations as a framework for supporting research and learning. In G. M. Lloyd, M. Wilson, J. L. M. Wilkins, & S. L. Behm (Eds.), *Proceedings of the 27th annual meeting of the North*

American Chapter of the International Group for the Psychology of Mathematics Education (pp. 639–646). Roanoke, VA: Virginia Polytechnic Institute and State University.

Hackenberg, A. (2010). Mathematical caring relations in action. *Journal for Research in Mathematics Education, 41*(3), 236–273.

Hargreaves, A. (2000). Mixed emotions: Teachers' perceptions of their interactions with students. *Teaching and Teacher Education, 16*(8), 811–826.

Hiebert, J., & Grouws, D. A. (2007). The effects of classroom mathematics teaching on students' learning. In F. K. Lester (Ed.), *Second handbook of research on mathematics teaching and learning* (pp. 371–404). Charlotte, NC: Information Age.

Jackson, K., & Cobb, P. (2010, May). *Refining a vision of ambitious mathematics instruction to address issues of equity.* Paper presented at the annual conference of the American Educational Research Association, San Diego, CA.

Kennedy, M. M. (2005). *Inside teaching: How classroom life undermines reform.* Cambridge, MA: Harvard University Press.

Martin, D. (2007). Mathematics learning and participation in African American context: The coconstruction of identity in two intersecting realms of experience. In N. S. Nasir & P. Cobb (Eds.), *Improving access to mathematics: Diversity and equity in the classroom* (pp. 146–158). New York, NY: Teachers College Press.

McBee, R. (2007). What it means to care: How educators conceptualize and actualize caring. *Action in Teacher Education, 29*(3), 33–42.

National Council of Teachers of Mathematics. (2000). *Principles and standards for school mathematics.* Reston, VA: Author.

National Research Council. (2001). *Adding it up: Helping children learn mathematics.* Washington, DC: National Academy Press.

Noddings, N. (1984). *Caring: A feminine approach to ethics and moral education.* Berkeley, CA: University of California Press.

Rosiek, J. (2003). Emotional scaffolding: An exploration of the teacher knowledge at the intersection of student emotion and the subject matter. *Journal of Teacher Education, 54*(5), 399–412.

Rosiek, J., & Beghetto, R. A. (2009). Emotional scaffolding: The emotional and imaginative dimensions of teaching and learning. In P. A. Schutz & M. Zembylas (Eds.), *Advances in teacher emotion research: The impact on teachers' lives* (pp. 175–194). New York, NY: Springer.

Stipek, D. (2006). Relationships matter. *Educational Leadership, 64*(1), 46–49.

Strauss, A., & Corbin, J. (1990). *Basics of qualitative research: Grounded theory procedures and techniques.* Newbury Park, CA: SAGE.

Tarlow, B. (1996). Caring: A negotiated practice that varies. In S. Gordon, P. Benner, & N. Noddings (Eds.), *Caregiving* (pp. 56–82). Philadelphia, PA: University of Pennsylvania Press.

Valenzuela, A. (1999). *Subtractive schooling: U.S.-Mexican youth and the politics of caring.* New York, NY: State University of New York Press.

Vygotsky, L. S. (1978). *Mind in society: The development of higher psychological processes.* Cambridge, MA: Harvard University Press.

Weinstein, C., Tomlinson-Clarke, S., & Curran M. (2004). Toward a conception of culturally responsive classroom management. *Journal of Teacher Education, 55*(1), 25–38.

CHAPTER 12

ENGAGING NEW AMERICANS IN STEAM

Project-Based Learning Using Genre-Based Pedagogy

James Nagle
Saint Michael's College

Will Andrews
Winooski Middle and High School

ABSTRACT

This chapter describes how the iLab academic program at Winooski High School integrates genre-based pedagogy in a project-based learning environment for students to investigate STEAM topics. The iLab is a high school course that allows students to explore their interests in STEAM related projects, work with community experts, and share their learning. While topics focus on STEAM related projects, the work involves literacy instruction in all four domains: speaking, listening, reading, and writing. Using a genre-based pedagogy approach, we examine student work of new Americans, who are English learners, to understand how authentic learning opportunities in a

Culturally and Linguistically Diverse Learners and STEAM, pages 249–266
Copyright © 2019 by Information Age Publishing
249

project-based learning environment allow students to become conversant in the language of STEAM while learning the professional skills needed to become career and college ready.

The iLab academic program at Winooski High School is a technology-rich space in which students explore their own areas of interest, work with community experts, and take ownership of their learning. First started in 2013, the iLab was created as a response to decreasing student engagement at Winooski High School and to address a recent Vermont educational policy reform; Act 77—The Flexible Pathways Initiative (2013), which mandated proficiency-based education, promoted expanded learning opportunities in and out of school, and created personal pathways for students that lead to high school graduation and college and career readiness. Students enroll in iLab just like any other course in Winooski High School and can receive elective credit or credit for a particular discipline. However, unlike content specific courses, such as Algebra II or World Civilizations, in which the curriculum is teacher-driven, in the iLab students choose to investigate topics important to them which revolve around authentic, real-world issues. Students then follow a project-based learning (PBL) process which allows them to create projects like building a drone, designing and making a clothing line, or developing skills and knowledge to become an electrician.

In this chapter we, an academic advisor and coordinator of internships at iLab (Andrews) and a professor of a teacher educator program at a local college (Nagle), examine the work of students who are new Americans as they progress through the PBL framework called *Think It–Learn It–Make It–Share It* during the Fall 2016 semester while pursuing science, technology, engineering, arts, or mathematics (STEAM) projects. The iLab is situated within the Winooski High School building but it is not a typical classroom. It looks like a makerspace meets tech lab (see Figure 12.1). There are computers, laptops, other technical equipment and materials depending on the products in development, but also comfortable areas for reading and rooms for interviews or small group discussions.

The approximately 80 students who enroll in iLab from Grades 9 through 12 represent the demographics of the high school in which 56% of students are White, and the remainder represent over 25 ethnic and cultural backgrounds—Somali, Sudanese, Nepalese, Iraqi, Afghani, and other ethnicities. Forty-two percent of these students receive instruction as English learners (ELs). Also, 76 % of the students are eligible for free and reduced lunch, and 20% receive learning support services through individual education plans (IEPs). Of the students who enroll in iLab, about 20 take it for math or science credit. And of those 20 students, about half are new Americans who are also English learners. This action research study follows these 11 students as they take iLab for math or science credit and create a

Figure 12.1 The Winooski High School iLab.

STEAM project. To provide a sense of the types of projects students investigate, Table 12.1 lists each of the research questions and project products developed by the 11 English learners.

We were specifically curious about how the components of the *Think It–Learn It–Make It–Share It* framework affected student literacy skills while students worked through their STEAM projects. Specifically, we asked the question: How are literacy skills addressed by students who are new Americans while developing their iLab projects using the *Think It–Learn It–Make It–Share It* framework?

To answer this question, we sifted through a mountain of data.[1] As students worked through their projects over the Fall 2016 semester, we collected a variety of student and program data to better understand the *Think It–Learn It–Make It–Share It* framework and to better respond to the academic needs of new Americans (Loughran, 2004). The data for this chapter come from a data set of interviews, observations, student work, and program documents collected during the 2016–2017 academic year.

Of particular importance were the data saved on each student's Google Drive. These data were a treasure trove of how students interacted and responded to iLab program protocols and prompts and provided in-depth details of how students used academic language in the development of their projects and approached the process of contacting personnel resources and finding textual resources for their projects. The data collected from Google

TABLE 12.1 STEAM Projects by Research Question and Product		
Student[a] and *Country*	Student Research Question	Student Project
Amin *Congo*	What are the fundamental skills and knowledge to be an electrician?	Assist in wiring a house.
Amir *Somalia*	How can I use what I learned about photography to show what Vermont looks like today?	Produce Vermont Sideways, a collection of photos and voice overs about my Vermont.
Anwar *Somalia*	How can I improve my reaction time as a soccer goalie?	Develop training workout to improve reaction time.
Astur *Somalia*	Does learning two languages affect the way the brain develops?	Continue learning my native language, Mayy-Mayy, and also English.
Lutfiya *Sudan*	What is the role of a director in a play?	Produce a play.
Dilek *Sudan*	How do you make a drone?	Fly a drone.
Devnand *Nepal*	How can you use the Art of Deduction in real life, and is it actually effective?	Teach a lesson on deduction and how it is useful in everyday life.
Darmaan *Somalia*	How can I learn Python to program my phone to lock?	Make a smart lock for my phone.
Kwina *Nepal*	How do I start a clothing line and fashion business?	Sketch out a clothing line.
Marie *France*	How do telescopes work?	Build a reflecting telescope.
Mire *Somalia*	How do computers work?	Take apart and build a computer.

[a] All student names are pseudonyms.

Drive accounts allowed for a combination of narrative and thematic analysis. In reviewing the data, we were able to construct a narrative of how students developed academic language and professional dispositions (how one acts and converses among like-minded professionals) as they progressed through the *Think It–Learn It–Make It–Share It* framework to complete their projects (Gubrium & Holstein, 2009). We then reviewed the data and organized them using categories based on themes such as academic language, professional dispositions, engagement, and collaboration (Corbin & Strauss, 2008). We finally re-examined the data generated by student interviews, observations of students, and student work products, to triangulate and confirm these categories to ensure validity and reliability (Gibbs, 2007).

To address our findings from our analysis of the data from the iLab, we first provide an in-depth instructional context of the *Think It–Learn It–Make It–Share It* framework as students move through their projects over the course of one semester. We share how the specific protocols of the *Think*

It–Learn It–Make It–Share It framework borrow from genre-based pedagogy and lend themselves to scaffold learning as students delve deeper and deeper into their projects. Next, we present examples of students working through the *Think It–Learn It–Make It–Share It* framework. In doing so, we explain how this framework can shine a light on specific literacy genres that allow students to work through project-based learning while developing literacy skills. Finally, we discuss implications that this framework has on honoring the learning of students who are new Americans.

THE THINK IT–LEARN IT–MAKE IT–SHARE IT FRAMEWORK

The iLab is an innovative program that allows students to choose and investigate one topic or issue in-depth during one semester. It follows the *Think It–Learn It–Make It–Share It* framework which has its origins in project-based learning and proficiency-based education. Project-based learning allows for student voice and choice in their learning. The framework roughly follows the common criteria for project-based learning by: (a) requiring a research question about a specific topic or issue; (b) mandating an action plan to complete the project within a particular time frame; (c) identifying specific skills that will be learned or practiced; and (d) expecting that the project drives the learning (Larmer & Mergendoller, 2015). To engage students in creating projects, the academic advisors of iLab developed the *Think It–Learn It–Make It–Share It* framework. In this framework there are no tests, quizzes, or final examinations. Rather, students follow the process of:

> *Think It:* setting goals and creating an action plan to investigate a semester-long project;
> *Learn It:* learning about their project based on the action plan;
> *Make It:* creating a final product; and
> *Share It:* writing a paper about the learning process and presenting the product and the learning process to the school community in a multimedia format.

The purpose of this framework is to prepare new Americans and other students for the rigors of college, career, and civic engagement while developing the most important skills required for 21st century education: critical thinking, communication, collaboration, and creativity.

Academic advisors monitor and support this learning process throughout the semester to hold students accountable to their project goals, action steps, and learnings. Students complete projects within one semester but they are responsible for creating a timeline for each stage of the project. Many projects generally follow the sequence shown in Table 12.2.

TABLE 12.2 Timeframe for Think It–Learn It–Make It–Share It Framework			
Phase	Performance Tasks	Collaboration	Time
Think It	Research question Project goals & action steps	Conference with peers for critiques and feedback.	2 weeks
Learn It	Annotations Community connection Interviews	Share notes of articles, observations, and interviews.	4–6 weeks
Make It	Project development	Conference with peers on stages of product development.	4–6 weeks
Share It	Presentation Reflective essay	Practice presentation in front of peers, peer review of essay drafts.	2–4 weeks

Each phase of the *Think It–Learn It–Make It–Share It* framework follows an iterative learning cycle in which students take on the roles of researchers and collaborators. Students investigate topics and create products for their own project but also provide constructive critiques on other students' projects. For instance, in the *Think It* stage, once students have formed a research question they will conference with two other students to present and receive feedback on the question. Afterward, the student revises the question and then presents it to the advisor for final review and evaluation. This iterative process occurs multiple times in each phase of the *Think It–Learn It–Make It–Share It* framework.

Since its inception in 2013, iLab has undergone some changes in its program to better address the needs of new Americans who enroll in the program. During that time, the academic advisors of iLab have refined the *Think It–Learn It–Make It–Share It* framework to make the PBL process more transparent for students and address gaps in student learning that are not necessarily addressed in traditional PBL. They have done this by creating a set of literacy tasks that requires students to work on all four literacy domains—listening, reading, speaking, and writing—through a genre-based approach. This emphasis on literacy identifies the genres of each part of the *Think It–Learn It–Make It–Share It* framework and uses a functional approach to language to make these genres explicit for students.

PERFORMANCE TASKS AS SCHOOL-BASED SCIENCE GENRES

There are specific performance tasks built into each phase of the *Think It–Learn It–Make It–Share It* framework that assist students to learn or practice specific literacy skills in each domain—listening, speaking, reading, and writing. While each phase may emphasize a particular domain, within each phase, advisors and peers consult with students as they work through their project so that all domains are practiced on a continual basis. These performance tasks guide students through the different phases of the framework to afford students the opportunities to learn and practice everyday literacy as they investigate and learn about their project.

While iLab requires certain performance tasks in its *Think It–Learn It–Make It–Share It* framework, it is essentially taking a functional approach to language, what Derewianka describe as "how language enables us to do things—to share information, to enquire, to express attitudes, to entertain, to argue, to get our needs met, to reflect, to construct ideas, to order our experiences, and make sense of the world. It is concerned with how people use real language for real purposes" (1990, pp. 3–4). Accordingly, the iLab advisors identified different performance tasks for students to learn and practice in each phase of the framework. They use a functional language approach to inform the writing instruction by being "proactive in focusing on language structure that students may not already be using in their writing" (Fang & Schleppegrell, 2008, pp. 112–113).

For each performance task the advisors model, co-construct, and provide feedback to students, as students work through those tasks in their project. For instance, in the *Learn It* phase, advisors model what an effective research question and goal look like; work with students on identifying the specific literacy structures of a research question, project goals, and action steps; and assist students in developing their own research question and project goals. Students then independently create their research question, project goals, and action steps, and share them with other students for additional feedback. This process is similar to the Derewianka's (1990) curriculum cycle of preparation, modeling, joint construction, and independent construction, which provides a way to explore the different language components and structures of the performance tasks so that students can understand how these performance tasks can create real-world authentic meaning in the context of their project (Derewianka & Jones, 2010).

Table 12.3 depicts each phase of the *Think It–Learn It–Make It–Share It* framework as it aligns with school-based science genres,[2] and iLab performance tasks with specific examples from one student's project.

MAKING SCHOOL-BASED SCIENCE GENRES WORK FOR THE *THINK IT–LEARN IT–MAKE IT–SHARE IT* FRAMEWORK

In taking a genre-specific perspective, iLab follows the thinking of Schleppegrell, Moore, Al-Adeimi, O'Hallaron, Palincsar, and Symons (2014) who state "Genres are ever evolving and not static, and, in work with teachers,

			TABLE 12.3 School-Based Science Genres and iLab Performance Tasks
Phase	**School-Based Science Genres**	**iLab Performance Task**	**Excerpt From Online Journals & Reflective Essays**
Think It	Procedure	Research question Project goals & action steps	What are the fundamental skills and knowledge to be an electrician? • Explain what electricity is and the properties of electricity • Meet with an electrician to teach me the basics of being an electrician. • Read and watch videos about electrical engineering. • Experiment with basic electrical circuits. • Assist an electrician while working on a house or remodel.
Learn It	Explanation	Annotations	"Electricity, Magnets, & Circuits"— PhET Simulations This source helped me learn about circuits and how to make parallel and series circuits. Also it provided the basics about how electricity works.
	Procedural Recount	Community Connection Reflection	Jan Ruta—Electrician—Kitchen Remodel She taught me why electricians use the ground fault circuit interrupter (GFCI). We used it for safety reasons so if the water touches a plug the electricity will go back to the ground and the GFCI will break the circuit and shut down the outlet. That's why we put it in places like bathrooms and kitchens— kitchens use the most electricity of any other room in the house.
	Procedure Procedural Recount	Interview Questions Note taking during the Interview	Myron Dorfman—Creative Carpentry & Construction What electrical work is needed on this house remodel? What materials do you use? Where do you buy these materials? How do you make this house more energy efficient? Why is it important to build houses this way?

(continued)

	School-Based		Excerpt From Online Journals
Phase	Science Genres	iLab Performance Task	& Reflective Essays
Make It	Procedure	Product Development	Designed and constructed parallel and series circuits based on chapters in physics text books and PhET Interactive Simulations website by developing instructions for the circuits
Share It	Report	PowerPoint presentation	{In a 20-minute presentation using ppt the student discussed the sources of electricity, alternating and direct circuits, and skills and knowledge needed to become an electrician.
	Exposition	Reflective essay	I really enjoyed working hands-on when helping the electrician, Jan Ruta… I had to research about ohm's law, circuits, and understood the math before building circuits. I wish I had more time working with Jan and Myron because I learned skills from wiring the house that I didn't get from reading or watching a video about being a electrician.

TABLE 12.3   School-Based Science Genres and iLab Performance Tasks (continued)

genre descriptions need to be adapted to local contexts so that they serve larger curricular purposes and are discipline-specific" (p. 38). As stated previously the academic advisors reviewed each performance task of the *Think It–Learn It–Make It–Share It* framework and the descriptions of school-based science genres. The advisors then adapted these school-based science genres to the "local contexts" of the iLab. This connection allowed advisors to explicitly teach these genres to students as the students worked through their projects so that they could make sense of their learning and communicate that learning to others.

In each phase of the *Think It–Learn It–Make It–Share It* framework, students are practicing a version of school-based science genres as described by Fang, Lamme, and Pringle (2010). As indicated on Table 12.4, these school-based science genres are procedure, procedural recount, explanation, report, and exposition. To make these genres serve the curricular purposes of the iLab, advisors adapted them to address the specific performance tasks

TABLE 12.4 Adapting School-Based Science Genres to Meet the Learning Context of iLab

School-Based Science Genre	iLab Genre Adaptation	What Students Did...
Procedure *Step by step instructions to perform an activity.*	Project Goals & Action Steps	Goals and action steps follow a step by step progression.
	Interview	The questions are ordered in a progression of most concrete to more abstract (what, where, when–to how and why).
	Product Development	Writing out and then using step by step instructions to build the product.
Personal or Procedural Recount *Records the specific steps or observations of an activity.*	Note Taking during an Interview	The notes accurately record what the interviewee said.
	Community connection reflection	The reflection accurately describes what was observed and discussed when visiting a community expert at their place of employment.
Explanation *Explains how something works or occurs.*	Annotation	In a paragraph the annotation explains how a particular phenomenon occurs from a reading or a video on their topic.
Report *Describes the traits, properties, behaviors of a particular phenomenon.*	PowerPoint presentation	In a 20-minute presentation using Google Slides, students describe their project topic, answer their research question, and share their project product.
Exposition *Argues a particular perspective with supportive evidence.*	Reflective essay	In a three-page essay, students reflect on what they learned during the projects and how they met their learning goals by providing specific evidence of their learning.

of creating a research question, goal setting and developing action steps, writing annotations from print text and multimedia, reflecting on a community partner visit, developing interview question protocols and taking notes while interviewing a community partner, designing and creating of a product, and presenting learning through a multimedia presentation and in writing a reflective essay.

Each of these performance tasks can be categorized within broader school-based science genres but are specific to the *Think It–Learn It–Make It–Share It* framework. Also, the prototypical school-based science genres tend to be limited to texts, specifically textbooks, while the performance tasks of the *Think It–Learn It–Make It–Share It* framework expand the notion of school-based science genres to include literacy practices of reading websites, viewing YouTube videos, observing experiences, conversing with experts, and making products. For instance, a procedural recount as a school-based science genre records the purpose, steps, and conclusion of a scientific event, while a procedural recount in the *Think It–Learn It–Make It–Share It* framework similarly accurately records the purpose, steps, and conclusions of a conversation that a student may have had with his/her community partner. Here, the difference is *the source of information* for the recount. These sources are authentic to the professional experience of that STEAM discipline. While iLab students may write or voice over (use audio or video recording) to create a recount similar in social purpose, text structure, and language features of a school-based recount, they are using different sources for that information (e.g., a website, a conversation, an experience) that allow students to make meaning from these authentic experiences of learning.

LESSONS LEARNED

New Americans, enrolled in the iLab during the Fall 2016 who were investigating STEAM projects, progressed in two ways that were consequential in their learning of STEAM fields and their learning of being part of a professional community: First, they became more conversant in the language of their STEAM discipline; and second, they became more aware of the professional dispositions of their STEAM field. The *Think It–Learn It–Make It–Share It* framework afforded students opportunities that they would not have experienced in a traditional science or math classroom. These opportunities provided the structure for students to become conversant in the language of their chosen professional field while providing a space for students to make connections and "try on" what it is like to be a part of that profession. The combination of affording students the opportunity to become conversant in the language of STEAM and learn dispositions of their professional field gave new Americans the social tools to maneuver in a community beyond high school. Such a trajectory provided students new opportunities to become participants of a wider community and develop skills and dispositions for independent learning after high school (Lave & Wenger, 1991; Wenger, 1998), while simultaneously sustaining the cultural and linguistic competence of their family heritage (Nagle & Andrews, forthcoming; Paris, 2012).

New Americans Becoming More Conversant in the Language of STEAM

The *Think It–Learn It–Make It–Share It* framework allowed new Americans varied and different opportunities to acquire and practice the academic language of STEAM while they researched, investigated, designed, and built their projects. Most commonly we witnessed students using academic language in the *Learn It* phase of the framework. As part of the *Learn It* phase, students were required to write annotations of texts, video, or websites about their project topic. In these annotations students used academic language of their STEAM field. For instance, Marie, who chose to build a reflecting telescope as her project, tapped into the school-based science genre of explanation to describe the difference between a reflecting telescope and a refracting telescope:

> The refracting telescope works differently than the reflecting telescope. For one, it uses lenses instead of mirrors. A lens is a curved piece of glass that forms an image by gathering light and focusing it. There is a lens on the front of the tube that allows light to pass through it which refracts the light and sends it toward the eyepiece lens. Refraction is when light is bent because it experiences a change in media. The light rays enter through the lens and are focused and sent to the eyepiece lens where it's seen as an image.

Here, Marie provides a technical explanation of how a refracting telescope works. Next, is another example of a technical explanation but from a project that would appear at first glance to be solely an art project comes from Kwina, who is focused on creating a clothing line (shirts and jeans for teenagers). In this excerpt she discusses the technical aspects of sketching clothing on models based on her reading of a series of fashion blogs.

> For example, a fashion figure is usually long-legged and taller than the average human. The average human has a proportion figure of six to seven heads tall but for a fashion figure, the proportions are eight to nine heads. When sketching clothing on a fashion model you will need to use the larger proportion, but remember to use the smaller proportion when making measurements for the clothing line (jeans) for regular teens.

The use of academic language also commonly appeared when students reflected on interviews or field experiences with their community expert in their community connection reflection.

Anwar, who was the high school soccer goalie when enrolled in iLab, wanted to improve his reaction time as a soccer goalie, so his project involved creating a workout regime to improve. However, as Anwar learned from his community expert, a professor of physical education and exercise science at a local university, improving as a goalie is more than reaction time. In this excerpt taken from a community connection reflection of the interview, Anwar writes a personal recount that summarizes the difference between reaction time and processing time in athletics:

> Meeting with Declan was great. He told me about reaction time and processing time and the difference. From the interview with Declan, "We give you a trigger, a light switch comes on and you hit a button and that's very simple. That's called simple reaction time." The meaning of processing time is different. Declan explained, "Tom Brady is a quarterback and what he does is great, but it is processing time." According to Declan, Brady takes all the irrelevant information and cancels that out and finds the relevant information and uses it during a game. So basically, what Declan is trying to say is reaction time is how fast you can react to a stimulus and processing time is how fast you process information and come out with a solution.

An example of using technical academic language through the use of a procedural recount in a community connection reflection comes from Amin's visit to a construction job site. Amin, whose project was to learn to be an electrician, describes the importance of using a ground fault circuit interrupter (GFCI) in kitchens and bathrooms.

> I met Myron Dorfman and Jan Ruta. He is the owner of a company named Creative Carpentry and Construction, and Jan Ruta, she is a master electrician. She owns Jan Ruta Electric. This was a good opportunity for me to learn more about wiring. Jan taught me why electricians use a ground fault circuit interrupter (GFCI). We used it for safety reasons so if the water touches a plug the electricity will go back to the ground and the GFCI will break the circuit and shut down the outlet. That's why we put it in places like the bathrooms and the kitchens. Kitchens use the most electricity of any other room in the house.

These examples of academic language used in specific STEAM projects allow students to access more advanced language for a higher purpose—to understand technical components and knowledge so that they can design and build the products of their projects and further investigate these topics. In some ways, the writing by students in iLab, such as annotations, is similar to that in typical science classrooms; however, the community connection reflections from the field experiences and the interviews allow students to go beyond traditional disciplinary learning from texts and begin to access professional knowledge and dispositions through authentic participation and interaction. This next step in writing requires students to access learning in real-world authentic settings and apply that learning using the academic as well as professional language of the discipline.

New Americans Becoming More Conversant in Professional Dispositions

Professional dispositions can take students to another level of understanding their project, their role as someone entering a STEAM field, and the type of interactions that reflective adults exhibit in a society. The evidence of these types of learning come primarily from the *Share It* phase when students write a reflective essay that discusses their learning during the project. The purpose of the reflective essay is not necessarily to re-summarize content or disciplinary knowledge but to critically reflect on evidence of how students met their initial project goals. In many cases students discussed professional dispositions, which they learned over the course of the project, specifically through interactions with their community connection partner, whether in the field, through an interview, or in the process of setting up that connection and exploring that professional community. In Marie's reflective essay she described professional dispositions she learned while preparing to interview and then work with her community expert:

> Throughout my experience, I worked closely with Bob Horton. He is a part of the Vermont Astronomical Society.... In order to set up an interview with him, I reached out through email. I had to write an email that was professional, grammatically correct, and made sense. This process was very successful for me and I was able to set up an interview with him. Before the interview, I created a list of 15 questions that I would ask. Through this interview I was able to not only gain a lot of basic knowledge on how telescopes work, but I also gained an amazing resource who helped me physically construct a telescope. This project made me become more of an independent person. It pushed me to go outside of my comfort zone and contact strangers. My social skills and comfort level of being around new people increased majorly....

Like Marie, other students discussed dispositions needed to gain entry into a profession of their choosing. Kwina, whose project goal is to design a line of clothing, also explained what it would take to become a fashion designer after working with her community partner. In her reflective essay Kwina summarized the next steps to move from making a clothing line to fashion designer:

> Fashion designers should at least, have bachelor's degree in fashion design or fashion merchandising. During these programs, a designer learns about textiles and fabrics. They also learn how to use a computer aided design (CAD) technology. Other qualities that I'll need for a fashion business career are: practicing my drawing skills, communicating with others, improving my computer skills, and being detail oriented.

Figure 12.2   Amin wiring a kitchen outlet.

Amin, the future electrician (Figure 12.2), saw that what he was learning was part of a vocation. Reflecting back on the reasons for selecting the career of electrician, he discussed the needs he witnessed in his native country of the Democratic Republic of the Congo.

> I think electricians have a very important job in our communities. It important to me because where I was born in Congo, there were always power problems and I want to be able to fix electric problems. My main goals are to learn how to put in a light switch and I will learn how to fix other electrical things like computers, fans, or other objects that need fixing.

In his reflective essay he discusses how the skills he learned in the field with the contractor and the electrician can make him more independent as a learner and can help his community.

CONCLUSION: NEW AMERICANS ENTERING A COMMUNITY OF PRACTICE

Etienne Wenger (1998) described a community of practice as a group of individuals who come together voluntarily to share knowledge with respect to a particular topic, concern, or problem. Wenger with Jean Lave (1991) also discuss how individuals enter a community of practice and how that trajectory can transform an individual's identity. They characterized this trajectory as "legitimate peripheral participation." Their point was that learning does not occur in the vacuum of a classroom curriculum, but through the context of participation in a community of practice and that this participation is both legitimate and peripheral. It is legitimate because the newcomer is given a sense of authenticity about their participation within the community of practice. Here, students of the iLab through the community connection experience were given legitimacy to participate as apprentices. Each student, discussed above, was taken in by a community partner to apply their learning to the facets of that profession. Their participation was also peripheral in that students were given exposure to the profession to "try on" the profession.

This legitimate peripheral participation perhaps would not have been as successful for these students if the iLab did not have structures in place for students to become conversant in the language of their chosen profession. "Literacy is a form of social action where language and context co-participate in making meaning" (Halliday, as cited in Schleppegrell, 2004, p. 5; Lemke, 1989). While it was not the explicit purpose of iLab's *Think It–Learn It–Make It–Share It* framework to create literacy as a form of social action, it did afford new Americans to learn and apply academic language to the context of their projects to make meaning and to begin to look beyond the rigors of high school schooling and toward possible participation in their careers and community.

INQUIRY QUESTIONS AND ACTION RESEARCH SUGGESTIONS

Inquiry Questions

1. How can project-based learning (PBL) sustain the cultural and linguistic competence of diverse students while simultaneously offering access to dominant cultural capital of society?
2. As many schools move to PBL as a primary pedagogical mode of instruction, what inquiry methods are available for educational researchers to investigate how effective teachers can be in addressing literacy needs of English learners and new Americans?
3. What literary genres are used in a PBL curriculum and how can they be taught in a PBL curriculum to assist English learners and new Americans in navigating the content knowledge and career disposition of STEAM related fields?

Action Research Questions

1. When developing a PBL unit of study in a STEAM classroom, what type of literacy practices (text and multi-modal) am I providing for my students to use to complete their projects?
2. When developing a PBL unit of study in a STEAM classroom, how can I explicitly teach those literacy practices?
3. When allowing my students to select a topic for a PBL unit of study in a STEAM classroom, what activities can I practice with my students for them to explore their cultural heritage that will lead them to choose a project that draws from and builds on that cultural heritage while addressing a current societal issue?

NOTES

1. While this action research project was part of a larger investigation of project-based learning at three different high schools in Vermont, the work of iLab academic advisors to scaffold learning for students, including new Americans in the iLab, was unique.
2. See Fang, Lamme, and Pringle (2010, pp. 105–109) for a discussion of school-based science genres.

REFERENCES

Corbin, J., & Strauss, A. (2008). *Basics of qualitative research: Techniques and procedures for developing grounded theory* (3rd ed.). Thousand Oaks, CA: SAGE.

Derewianka, B. (1990). *Exploring how texts work*. Victoria, Australia: Primary English Teacher Association.

Derewianka, B., & Jones, P. (2010). (2nd ed.). *Teaching language in context*. New York, NY: Oxford University Press.

Fang, Z., Lamme, L. L., & Pringle, R. M. (2010). *Language and literacy in inquiry-based science classroom, grades 3–8*. Thousand Oaks, CA: Corwin.

Fang, Z., & Schleppegrell, M. J. (2008). *Reading in secondary content areas: A language-based pedagogy*. Ann Arbor: University of Michigan Press.

Flexible pathways initiative. (2013). Dual enrollment. Vermont Statutes Annotated Title 16, §§ 941–945.

Gibbs, G. R. (2007). *Analyzing qualitative data*. Thousand Oaks, CA: SAGE.

Gubrium, J. F., & Holstein, J. A. (2009). *Analyzing narrative reality*. Thousand Oaks, CA: SAGE.

Larmer, J., & Mergendoller, J. R. (2015). *Gold standard PBL: Essential project design elements*. Buck Institute for Education. Retrieved http://www.bie.org/blog/gold_standard_pbl_essential_project_design_elements

Lave, J., & Wenger, E. (1991). *Situated learning: Legitimate peripheral participation.* New York, NY: Cambridge University Press.

Lemke, J. L. (1989). Semantic and social values. *Word, 40*(1–2), 37–50.

Loughran, J. J. (2004). A history and context of self-study of teaching and teacher education practices. In J. J. Loughran, M. L. Hamilton, V. K. LaBoskey, & T. Russell (Eds.), *International handbook of self study of teaching and teacher education practices* (pp. 7–39). Dordrecht, Netherlands: Kluwer.

Nagle, J. F., & Andrews, W. (in press). Creating a space for culturally sustaining pedagogy. In K. Brinegar, L. Harrison, & E. Hurd (Eds.), *Equity and cultural responsiveness in the middle grades.* Charlotte, NC: Information Age.

Paris, D. (2012). Culturally sustaining pedagogy: A needed change in stance, terminology, and practice. *Educational Researcher. 41*(3), 93–97. doi:10.3102/0013189X12441244

Schleppegrell, M. J. (2004). *The language of schooling.* Mahwah, NJ: Erlbaum.

Schleppegrell, M. J., Moore J., Al-Adeimi, S., O'Hallaron, C. L., Palincsar, A. S., & Symons, C. (2014). Tackling a genre: Situating SFL genre pedagogy in a new context. In L. C. de Oliveira & J. Iddings (Eds.), *Genre pedagogy across the curriculum: Theory and application in U.S. classrooms and contexts.* Sheffield, England: Equinox.

Wenger, E. (1998). *Communities of practice: Learning, meaning, and identity.* New York, NY: Cambridge University Press.

CHAPTER 13

FULL STEAM AHEAD!

Secondary Teachers' Artful Support of ELs Through Science Photography

Alandeom W. Oliveira
State University of New York

Luciana C. de Oliveira
University of Miami

ABSTRACT

Growing numbers of science, technology, engineering, and mathematics (STEM) instructors have resorted to artful pedagogies (aesthetically rich instructional approaches) in an effort to make content instruction more accessible to English learners (ELs). By strategically designing and facilitating content learning experiences at the intersection of art and science, educators have sought to enrich and transform students' classroom experiences in STEM. One major premise of this science, technology, engineering, *arts*, and mathematics (STEAM) educational approach is that infusing art can help ELs experience STEM more positively, and hence broaden the participation of culturally and linguistically diverse students in STEM fields. Consistent with this educational approach, the present chapter identifies important insights

Culturally and Linguistically Diverse Learners and STEAM, pages 267–290
Copyright © 2019 by Information Age Publishing

from the literature on STEAM and suggests ways that these insights can be translated into actionable research agendas. Attention is given specifically to how teachers can provide ELs with aesthetically rich learning experiences in STEM through implementation of photography-based science inquiries (discovery activities wherein students make a photographic record of their experiment and data) and whole-class critique of science photographs.

The "STEM to STEAM" movement to integrate the arts with science, technology, engineering, and mathematics has been steadily gathering currency (Maeda, 2013; Radziwill, Benton, & Moellers, 2015). In the last several years, growing numbers of educators have come to recognize the transformative and enriching potential of integrating art into the teaching and learning of STEM disciplines. In science education, such a trend is particularly evident in the increased popularity of classroom projects that combine scientific inquiry and discovery with artwork production and artistic expression. A good example is student creation of science *infographics* or information graphics (Fowler, 2015; Lamb, Polman, Newman, & Smith, 2014). Commonly used by science journalists in popular science articles, infographics take the form of highly imaginative visual representations that combine images, numbers, and words. As Davidson (2014) writes, "infographics incorporate art into the normally staid world of numerical information ... [and] are beautiful and engaging" (p. 35). In this type of STEAM project, students investigate a scientific question, gather data/evidence to answer it, and then creatively communicate their results as an infographic. Creative data visualization is used in lieu of the more traditional essay-style science report.

Despite its growing popularity, STEAM-based teaching approaches have received little scrutiny from educational researchers. Little attention has been given to essential questions such as: "What is science?"; "What is art?"; "To what extent are these two intellectual endeavors compatible and mutually supportive?"; "What might the infusion of scientific and artistic processes look like in practice?"; or "How can STEAM be effectively approached to support ELs?" We begin this chapter by addressing these complex and important questions, and then suggesting ways that they can be translated into pedagogical action. By examining theoretical work and empirical research that can inform STEAM curriculum design and implementation, we seek to help educators articulate actionable research agendas.

ART AS EXPERIENCE

Science states meanings: art expresses them.

—Dewey, 1934, p. 87

Only the psychology that has separated things which in reality belong together holds that scientists and philosophers think while poets and painters follow their feelings. In both [science and art], there is emotionalized thinking, and there are feelings whose substance consists of appreciated meanings or ideas.

—Dewey, 1934, p. 76

As illustrated in the above quotations, the famous progressive educator John Dewey dedicated a considerable amount of theoretical work to the question of what art is and how the artistic process compares to other intellectual endeavors like science. In his classic book *Art as Experience*, Dewey puts forward a theory of art as a type of activity that, despite its unique emphasis on personal expression, shares many similarities with other human endeavors such as science. For Dewey, art is a process that entails not only *artistic production* (imaginative creation of expressive objects like paintings or sculptures) but also *aesthetic experience*—a refined and intensified experience of everyday events. The artist carefully expresses his or her personal experience living in an environment based on long periods of observation, activity, and reflection. More than simply producing a material object whose artistic standing is contingent upon its public display in a venue such as a museum or gallery, the crafting of a "work of art" involves carefully performing an expressive act that is experienced by others aesthetically (as a source of emotional meanings such as enjoyment, inspiration, and appreciation). Further, rather than being the exclusive province of those endowed with rare skill in artistic expression, anyone who approaches an activity with great care and imagination, such as a scientist or an engineer, is artistically engaged. Like art objects, scientific artifacts can also have artistic qualities and can be experienced aesthetically or emotionally.

Dewey's experiential conception of art and artwork as aesthetic provides theoretical support for STEAM efforts. By conceiving of science and art as processes/activities that share many similarities, Dewey highlights the compatibility of these two human endeavors. This point is reinforced by art educators like Marshall (2010) who argue that "art is a form of inquiry with some processes and goals that are similar to those of other areas of study" (p. 14) like science. Instead of being completely distinct activities characterized by idiosyncratic attributes, art and science differ mainly in terms of degree or relative emphasis on features such as focus on expressive/stated meanings, implicit emotionality/explicit rationality, and literalness/*metaphoricity*. Therefore, it stands to reason that the two activities can harmoniously co-exist and be mutually supportive in classroom settings. Adopting a STEAM approach is nothing more than shifting one's teaching practices to a more intermediary position along the art–science continuum.

THE CREATIVE NATURE OF SCIENCE

The nature of science has been a prominent topic in the field of science education for the last few decades. Informed by philosophical and historical traditions, a large number of theorists and researchers have focused their work on issues such as what science is, how science works, what science can and cannot do, how scientific knowledge is constructed, and how scientific knowledge comes to be accepted (e.g., Carey & Smith, 1993; Clough, 2006; McComas, 2008). A prominent point in this literature is that creativity is a central and defining aspect of the nature science. Scientific inquiry is not an entirely objective and rational endeavor as creativity plays an important role in the development of scientific knowledge. Scientific processes such as generation of hypotheses, design of procedures, interpretation of data, and derivation of conclusions all require a degree of imagination and creativity on the scientist's part. Rather than simply following a fixed, and failure-proof scientific method, scientists have to creatively adapt and imaginatively make sense as they tackle procedural complications and unexpected results. Furthermore, scientific illustration is often done by professional artists like botanical illustrators who "bring an artist's eye to science" by producing visual renditions/interpretations of plant specimens that have artistic beauty as well as biological accuracy (Binns, Smith, & Milligan, 2011). In botany as well as other scientific fields, artists collaborate with scientists in publishing the scientific description of newly identified organisms. Therefore, scientific knowledge production can be said to be inherently creative, imaginative, and artful.

Nonetheless, research shows that misconceptions about the nature of science are pervasive (Akerson, Abd-El-Khalick, & Lederman, 2000; Lederman, Abd-El-Khalick, Bell, & Schwartz, 2002). When questioned whether scientists use their creativity and imagination during investigations, students and teachers typically provide responses such as, "No, they [scientists] just have to give the facts, not imagine the stuff," "[you] can't pretend things in science, so you can't imagine stuff," and "logic plays a large role in the scientific process" (Akerson & Abd-El-Khalick, 2005). Creativity is commonly viewed as an essential feature of artistic work, whereas logic and reason are the defining attributes of scientific inquiry; they are perceived as two mutually exclusive activities. Such misconceptions about the nature of science are typically the result of exposure to traditional science textbooks, verification labs, lectures, and the media—all of which portray the scientific endeavor as simply an objective pursuit of absolute truths or facts (Abd-El-Khalick, Waters, & Le, 2008; Ford, 2006).

Both the experiential nature of art and the creative nature of science underscore our present need for STEAM teaching approaches. By infusing art into STEM instruction and providing students with aesthetically rich learning experiences, secondary teachers can help counter prevalent student misconceptions of science as an intellectual endeavor devoid of creativity and imagination. By engaging in STEAM, students are more likely to begin to realize that scientific knowledge production has a creative and imaginative dimension, and eventually recognize how, to a certain extent, there is an "art" to doing science. In the next section, we provide a rationale for the use of photography as a particularly effective way of infusing art with STEM, followed by a description of lessons in which photography is integrated into scientific inquiry for high school students.

PHOTOGRAPHY AS STEAM PLATFORM

Integrating photography with scientific content instruction as a pedagogical platform for enacting STEAM is consistent with current literature in both fields of science education and art education. There is increasing recognition among science educators of the visual nature of science (Lemke, 1998; Oliveira & Cook, 2017; Oliveira et al., 2013). It is widely accepted that science entails visual modes of communication and that scientists commonly make truth claims based on visual evidence. Typically characterized by high degrees of realism and naturalism, the types of photographs favored by scientists make literal references to a particular aspect of the physical world with reduced levels of symbolism or metaphoricity (Kress & van Leeuwen, 2006; Sturken & Cartwright, 2009). Scientific photographs have the highest level of similarity with reality, serving as "prima facie evidence" of the truth (Myers, 1990), that is, as self-evident truthful images of natural phenomena (Pozzer & Roth, 2003). Scientists' highly specialized photographic representations of the world reflect their preferred ways of seeing the world—objectively, literally, and impersonally. These are values central to the scientific visual culture.

Similarly, there is now general consensus among art educators and art historians that photographic production is an art form. More than simply capturing reality with the push of a button, creation of photographic imagery invariably involves decision-making and aesthetic choice (i.e., artistic composition). In making the photographic record of a particular object or event, the photographer decides (often intuitively) on a particular part of a space to shoot (i.e., selects a focus) and chooses a particular framing (e.g., decides how to frame that space). Other decisions in photographic production include composition, lighting, color, shade, tone, contrast, depth, perspective contextual display, and captioning. These decisions reflect personal beliefs, ideologies (shared values), social norms, and accepted standards and conventions of visual representation. Photographic artifacts are undoubtedly objects of personal expression and aesthetic appreciation as evidenced by the extensive photographic collections of most current art museums. Barrett (2012), a scholar of art photography, emphasized,

> All photographs connote; and without some understanding that photographs connote or imply or suggest, viewers will not get beyond the obvious and will see photographs as reality rather than pictures of reality. (p. 50)

Photography is thus an important part of both art and science. Photographic artifacts hold a dual status as works of personal expression and objective reproductions of reality. All photos can be simultaneously appreciated for their aesthetic/artistic value as well as their evidential/epistemic value for advancing scientific claims. As such, this visual mode of communication can provide practitioners with a very effective platform for designing and delivering STEAM curriculum spaces that are inclusive and supportive of ELs. Visuals have been a major part of EL instruction for a long time (de Oliveira & Wilcox, 2017). As demonstrated by Jones (2010), photography can be used to support ELs during a content-language integrated lesson on natural habitats, animal adaptation, and biodiversity.

The growing literature on discipline integration corroborates further the use of STEAM approaches with ELs and other culturally and linguistically diverse students. Honey, Pearson, and Schweingruber's (2014) comprehensive review of research on integrated STEM education indicates potential for increased student engagement, motivation, and perseverance. For ELs in particular, a STEAM focus provides opportunities for promoting inquiry, using various modalities, and connecting concepts to the real world. Learning across disciplines can help better prepare students to tackle more realistic, complex situations. However, as English (2016) writes, "the interdisciplinary nature of the world in which we live demands a broadening of STEM education" (p. 2). This, we believe, can be accomplished through STEAM learning. Integration of art as a fifth discipline has the added benefit of cultural relevance/responsiveness and inclusiveness. Described next is how we sought to capitalize on the pedagogical potential and affordances of photography as part of our STEAM-oriented teaching efforts.

OUR STEAM APPROACH

Consistent with Dewey's theoretical work, we have adopted a STEAM approach that incorporates artistic production as well as aesthetic reception of science photography. These photography-based activities were implemented as part of an afterschool program in Upstate New York, wherein students in urban high schools with a large population of ELs photographed as well as critiqued photographic records of science inquiries. Our photograph-based approach was informed by a number of practitioner articles describing photography-based pedagogies and strategies previously adopted by science educators, including the after-school photography club (McMahon, 2002), the community photography project (Trimarchi, 2003), the photographic scavenger hunt (Gilbert, Brungardt, Dorr, & Balgopal, 2010), and photographic case studies (Krauss, Salame, & Goodwyn, 2010). This practitioner literature provided a practical foundation to our efforts, informing the design of the photography-based STEAM curriculum presented below.

Photography Production During Science Inquiry

As part of our efforts to provide ELs with access to STEAM curriculum spaces, we have used aesthetically rich discovery activities wherein students first make a photographic record of a science experiment and use photography as visual evidence (the main source of data) for their scientific inquiries. Taking digital pictures is meant to afford students opportunities to engage in and experience artistic production as they conduct a scientific investigation.

Working in small groups of three or four, students designed hands-on science experiments and investigations on various chemistry topics (described in Table 13.1). During these STEAM lessons, students typically brainstormed, selected a research question, came up with a procedure for

TABLE 13.1   Photography-Based Science Inquiry Lessons
Dissolving M&M
Students examined how placing an M&M in plates of water at varied temperatures led to the dissolution of the colored sugar coating, but not the fatty chocolate interior. Simultaneously, the plate of water could also be used by students like a white canvas onto which colored pigment(s) could be applied and manipulated. The brightly colored M&Ms could be used as paints, the edges of the plates as a picture frame, and the pigment dissolution in water as painting. Students had the opportunity to experience contemporary forms of art creation while simultaneously making a photographic record of scientific phenomena such as dissolution and molecular polarity.
Dissolving Solids in Liquids
Students investigated how temperature affects the solubility of salt and sugar and determined whether these substances dissolve better in hot or cold water. To this end, students attempted to fully dissolve the same amount of each substance in containers filled with water, and then compared how much (if any) of each substance remained at the bottom of each cylinder. Like art photographers, students could also compose photographs with varied levels of realism or abstraction, representation of human action or state of being, placement of objects against neutral or detailed backgrounds, color contrast or blending, etc.

(continued)

TABLE 13.1 Photography-Based Science Inquiry Lessons (cont.)
Soda Exploration
Students examined how the carbonation of carbonated drinks was affected by the presence of solid objects and substances. Students poured soda into small cups and then added various solids (sugar, M&Ms, Mentos, a pipe cleaner, etc.). These solids increased the amount of dissolved carbon dioxide gas coming out of solution (fizzing) at different rates. Solids with irregular surfaces experienced more adherence of gas, increasing the amount of gas coming out of solution through the formation of bubbles. Abstract artistic expression could be accomplished through aesthetic use of colors and/or basic geometrical shapes like circles.
Color Explosion
Students investigated how the varied content of fat in different types of milk (skim, whole, and half & half) affected the dispersion of food coloring. To this end, students poured samples of milk onto plates, added a few drops of food coloring, and then touched the center of the food coloring drops with a toothpick that had been dipped into dishwashing soap. This caused the food coloring to spread outwards and form various shapes and patterns depending on the chosen colors, type of milk used, etc. This "explosion of color" against a white background afforded students artistic opportunities. The plate of milk could be used by students like a white canvas onto which colored pigment(s) could be applied and manipulated. Their set of food colorings could be used as a palette, the edges of the plates as a picture frame, and the toothpick as a paintbrush. Students had an opportunity to experience abstract painting and contemporary art as they explored scientific phenomena such as surface tension, surfactants, and emulsions.

data collection that involved collecting photographic evidence, identified necessary materials, conducted their experiments, and proposed answers to their research questions based on photographic evidence. Students typically took a large number of pictures with their cell phones and used them as visual data for their science inquiries. Student-generated photography was shared through a computer projector during informal whole-class discussions at the end of each lesson.

Our Action Research

Examination of the photographic artifacts produced by our students revealed interesting patterns in students' perceptions of the nature of science (NOS). For instance, we noticed that most students favored impersonal photographs devoid of any form of human presence (see Figure 13.1a). Only in few instances did they include the human agents behind the science experiments being reported. For the most part, humans were systematically erased from the photographic records of the science activities conducted. This exclusion of people is consistent with pervasive views of science as a highly impersonal and objective endeavor. Inclusion of human agents can create the impression of subjectivity which is inconsistent with how science is typically seen.

Though devoid of human presence, students' impersonal photographs were aesthetically pleasing (Figure 13.1a). The highly saturated and

(a)

(b)

Figure 13.1 Students' (a) Impersonal Photographs of Dissolving M&M; and, (b) Personalized Photographs of Dissolving Solids in Liquids (left), Dissolving M&M (center), and Soda Exploration (right)

unmodulated use of primary colors (blue, red, and yellow) suggests an attempt to create pleasure through hyper-realism and strategic deployment of the affective values of individual colors. Students' photographs of the dissolving M&Ms came across as somewhat "un-naturalistic" (surreal) and pleasurably colorful, giving the impression that color was being used more for the sake of pleasure than naturalistic representation (like in abstract piece of modern art). On the other hand, students' personal photographs evoked a sense of presence of the body. The fingers, hands, and arms served as "visual synecdoches"—visual tropes wherein body parts stood for full bodies. In addition to literally illustrating procedural setups and findings, these photographs symbolically evoked the "hands-on" nature of science (the meaning of hand as a symbol of science).

Other students composed analytical photographs that combined naturalistic and graphical features (Figure 13.2). Usually in the form of highly realistic and detailed close-up images, these pictures mixed real entities (cylinder, paper plate, and M&M) with symbolic entities (arrows and numerical scales). Further, these photographs integrated verbal elements (e.g., captions) and visual elements (e.g., photographic images). Use of these highly specialized illustrative techniques suggests a high degree of familiarity with scientific visual conventions of symbolism and notation. As previous studies have shown, arrows and scales are an important part of the visual culture of science (Ametller & Pinto, 2002; Colin, Chauvet, & Vinnot,

Figure 13.2 Students' analytical photographs of dissolving solids in liquids (left and center) and dissolving M&M (right).

2002; Stylianidou, Ormerod, & Ogborn, 2002). Like scientists, students resorted to these visual devices strategically to enhance the accuracy of their photographic references. Their pictures were closer to the scientific end of the art–science continuum.

In sharp contrast, many other students produced photographs with a stronger artistic orientation (more closely situated toward the artistic end of the art–science continuum). This was particularly common during classroom implementation of the Color Explosion investigation.

Some groups demonstrated what could be considered a moderate level of artistic engagement by carefully selecting materials with matching colors to conduct their experimental tests. For instance, two groups selected plates with blue edges (floral and solid line patterns) that closely matched the blue food coloring (Figure 13.3). As a result, their photographs shared some resemblance with Delftblue ceramic design. Like a Dutch potter painting blue and white porcelain, students created a visual artifact with a degree of visual harmony. This aesthetic concern (attention to color composition) indicates that their work can be considered artistic as well as scientific.

A remarkably different artistic approach was taken by another group of students when making pictures of Color Explosion. Unlike the students who resorted to single and unmixed (pure) color to create photos with a high degree of color coordination and visual cohesion, this last group used a wide spectrum of brightly colored food colorings, mixing many colors imaginatively and creatively (Figure 13.4). Such an approach led to the production of photos with a usually high degree of diversity and exuberance in colors. These colorful photos shared some resemblance with action painting, a technique commonly used in contemporary forms of art making such as abstract expressionism. Rather than the traditional brushwork, action painters resort to spontaneous types of movement wherein paint is thrown, splashed, stained, or dripped directly from the tube or can. Their work of art takes the form of very colorful abstractions. Students' photos of

Figure 13.3 Students' Delftblue photographs of color explosion.

Figure 13.4 Abstract expressionist photographs of color explosion.

Color Explosion shared many stylistic similarities with the sort of creative achievement.

Elevated levels of artistic engagement among students was also evident during the Soda Exploration. Their photographic record of this investigation often took the form of abstract and otherworldly imagery (Figure 13.5).

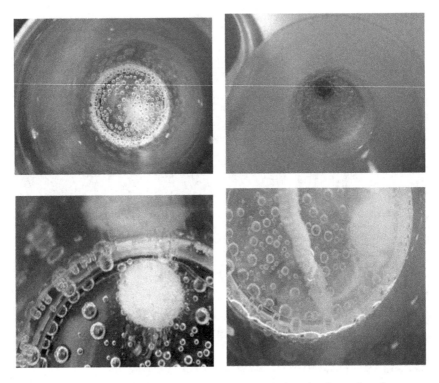

Figure 13.5 Students' geometric symbolic photographs of soda exploration.

Like geometrical abstractionists, some students seemed to resort to geometric symbolism, a contemporary art form wherein artistic expression is accomplished through use of basic geometrical shapes like circles (gas bubbles, M&Ms, and plastic cup). The predominance of circular shapes is reminiscent of biomorphic abstractionism, an artistic style that favors rounded abstract forms to create a more organic sense of mystery and surrealism.

Critiquing Science Photographs

To ensure that students experienced aesthetic reception as well as artistic production, every STEAM lesson ended with a teacher-led critique of the photographic record of their science investigations. Students shared their digital pictures through a computer projector and participated in informal whole-class discussions about these photographs. This activity reflected our belief that critique is a central component to any rigorous analysis of a work of visual art as well as science. Moreover, critiquing photographs requires visual literacy skills that often need to be scaffolded by the teacher.

As Vasquez, Comer, and Troutman, (2010) write, "[Science] teachers often assume that photographs are easy for students to understand, requiring little skill on the students' part and minimal instruction from the teacher... [however] looking at an image is only the first step in a much more complex process" (p. 16). Rather than simply presuming that photographs speak for themselves (i.e., are transparent and self-evident), teachers need to guide students' critique of photographs by explicitly prompting observations (What I see on this picture...), inferences (What I think this picture means...), and emotions (How this picture makes me feel...).

Like science educators, art educators have also underscored the importance of clearly defining what it means to critique a photograph. In his book *Criticizing Photographs*, Terry Barrett (2012) emphasizes that criticism involves much more than the simple act of judging—of determining whether one "likes" or "dislikes" a piece. Rather, it is a means toward the end of understanding a photographic composition. Further, critical consideration usually consists of at least three main activities:

1. *Describing* the work (What does it look like? What is it made of?): In this type of critique, the student simply identifies the formal qualities/stylistic attributes of a photographic piece to the audience.
2. *Interpreting* the work (What does it mean?): Here the student articulates his or her own subjective interpretation of the work's significance by inferring meanings, providing contextual or biographical information, etc.
3. *Evaluating* the work (Is it art? Is it interesting? Does it "work"?): This type of critique involves attributing value to a photographic piece. The student judges, assesses the quality, etc. This is the most difficult critical task, one that most viewers skip when criticizing a work of art. To thoughtfully evaluate a work of art, the student must determine what the criteria are for judging its relative worth or effectiveness.

By encouraging students to apply these principles of critique to accessible visual works, teachers can help them develop those critical skills necessary to also analyze scientific concepts and learn to systematically describe, interpret, and evaluate them—taking into account their personal (or internal) and cultural, historical, and scientific (or external) contexts.

Through engaging in spirited debate on relatively benign subjects such as formal elements of a work of art (line, shape, form, texture, value, color, space, etc.), students can have an opportunity to practice similar evaluative skills necessary to thoughtfully engage in evidence-based science argumentation. This possibility is underscored by Hunston (1994) who writes,

> To evaluate something [like a photograph] is to have an opinion about it, particularly in terms of how good or bad it is. The terms of reference for the judgment may be essentially personal... or they may occur within an institutionalized framework [like Toulmin's model of argument structure]. (p. 191)

When framed in a Toulminian manner, critiquing a photograph entails using it as a source of visual evidence or grounds for advancing scientific interpretations (claims) and articulating justifications (warrants) based on scientific principles (backings). As such, personal judgement based on emotion (How does the picture make me feel?) can be supplemented/paralleled by appraisal of rhetorical soundness (How well does the available photographic evidence support my claim?).

Engaging in such photography-focused dialogues can provide students, particularly ELs, with valuable opportunities not only to learn to argue like a scientist/artist but also to acquire the communicative resources used by English speakers to express different types of evaluation (scientific, artistic, etc.) through discourse (Martin & White, 2003). As a result, ELs may become more familiar with the range of linguistic forms (evaluative words and constructions) that English speakers have at their disposal as well as practice communicating from varied evaluative stances such as expressing personal opinion, emotional judgement, and scientific evaluation.

Informed by the above principles, we encouraged students to collaboratively reflect about descriptive, interpretive, and evaluative aspects of photographs. Working in the same groups where they had conducted the science inquiries, students selected and shared a few photographs that best represented what they did and what they found out during their investigation. Their peers were asked to first observe carefully and describe in detail the photographic record of an inquiry; as much as possible, this was to be done in their own words and without any inference or judgement. After thoroughly describing what they could observe, students were encouraged to interpret the photographs (ascribe meaning to what they saw). Lastly, students would collectively evaluate the pictures (assign scientific, artistic, and personal value). Members of the audience could comment, provide feedback, or ask questions to the student-photographers. Rather than a formal presentation, students engaged in a dialogue about the photographs they produced.

Our Action Research

The classroom discussion that ensued as a result of our critique protocol was both rich and diverse. Unlike in traditional science classrooms where student talk tends to be too narrowly focused on inauthentic use of isolated key terms (science vocabulary), our students had an opportunity to make more extensive and authentic use of oral language. While describing the pictures on Figure 13.3, students made comments such as:

> The color spread out in what looked like a *cross pattern*. *Spots of color* collected on the top, bottom, left and right of the plate.

> This time the coloring spread out evenly and formed a *ring of color* around the edge of the milk with a *spot of color* remaining in the middle.

> Immediately the coloring spread into what looked like a *star pattern*. The coloring did not spread as much as it did on the skim and whole milk.

As can be seen above, students initially described in their own words what they saw. Rather than trying to use the "right" scientific term, students had the freedom to use words that were personally meaningful for them such as *cross pattern, spot of color, ring of color,* and *star pattern*. This is in sharp contrast to more traditional science classroom talk wherein students tend to simply parrot back scientific jargon to the teacher (Lemke, 1990). To disrupt this trend and at the same time validate our students' prior vocabulary and knowledge, we encouraged them to use their own words first. This pedagogical approach also served to promote extended discourse and student thinking.

In contrast, interpretive critique of photographs tended to be more jargonized. Because this second discussion phase was focused on making sense (i.e., drawing inferences) from the science photographs, students usually relied more heavily on scientific vocabulary. Their main focus was on providing scientific explanations for the photographs which required use of specialized terms. For instance, while explaining the same pictures on Figure 13.3, students uttered statements such as:

> The half and half was *thickest*, so the food coloring drops stuck much more closely together, unlike the skim milk which was *thinnest*.

> I believe that the fat content of the milks *hindered* the spreading of the coloring. The skim has the least *fat content* so it spread out the most.

> Milk is an *emulsion* which is a *mixture* of two liquids that usually don't mix, water and fat.

Providing a scientific explanation for the pictures requires students to "talk science," that is, to use scientific terminology such as *mixture, emulsion, fat content, hindered,* and so forth. Students now use scientific terms as they articulate inferential meanings from the available photographic evidence. Photographs were explained in terms of standards scientific concepts.

Lastly, evaluative critique of the science photographs was much more open-ended, often characterized by a greater degree of personal informality. During this final discussion phase, students usually shared their personal reactions to the pictures and provided the student-photographers with evaluative feedback (comments on perceived strengths and weaknesses of the photos). The students who produced the photos also had a chance to reply to others' criticism, provide their rationale for their compositional decisions, and share their experiences making a photographic record of the science investigations (Table 13.2).

Interestingly, evaluative critique of the photography was predominantly artistic/aesthetic in nature. Evidence of such can be found in students use of emotive language (e.g., awesome, great) and subjective expressions (e.g., I felt, beautiful to look at). Put differently, scientific explanation gave way to artistic evaluation. As can be seen in Table 13.2, students refrained from judging the photographs scientifically—students did not evaluate whether the photographs provided strong or weak evidence for the scientific claims put forward by their peers (i.e., their value with regard to

TABLE 13.2 Students' Evaluative Critique of Science Photographs		
	Peer Critiques	**Replies to Critiques**
Dissolving M&M	Wow, these pics look great!	I inserted the pictures into a PowerPoint slide so you can see them all side by side.
Dissolving Solids in Liquids	The pictures are *awesome* and the way you organized the information is very clear. I liked how you provided us with different angles of the cups, so we could see it from other *viewpoints*.	I decided to include the bird's eye view pictures because I felt it was the easiest way to see the amount of sugar or salt. It was challenging to just look from the side to determine which had more or less. I know the pictures don't do a very good job of showing the sediment left in the containers.
Soda Exploration	The photos came out really well for this experiment, *great* job! I think the pictures you took were quite helpful to better visualize the experiment. I found it's hard to see the result with pictures. I can see the carbon dioxide in the pictures but I can't see the speed.	I do not think plastic cups would properly display the carbon bubbles. Graduated cylinder is the better option.
Color Explosion	You dropped food coloring drops in a *pretty design* in the center of each of these plates. It had a firework effect when you used all three colors, *great* job! The colors are *beautiful* to look at.	When making decisions about what color of food coloring to use, I chose to use blue food coloring because I *felt* it would show up more clearly in the milk.

scientific argumentation). Instead, students' evaluative comments centered on the aesthetic quality of the photos (i.e., beautiful colors, pretty design, very clear, firework effect) as well as particular elements of their photographic composition (i.e., viewpoint, angle, focus, ground/background, etc.)—much like a group of photographers discussing their techniques.

Areas of Improvement and Next Steps

Overall, we were very pleased with the results of our efforts to engage linguistically and culturally diverse students through STEAM. Not only did we see a substantial improvement in ELs' participation but also a drastic transformation in their learning experiences. Nonetheless, a couple of areas of needed improvement were apparent to us. One improvement that we would like to make moving forward is to incorporate explicit art instruction into our STEAM lessons. To prepare them for the investigations, our students were explicitly taught key science concepts like dissolution, molecular polarity, solute, solvent, surface tension, surfactants, and emulsions. This science instruction was given at the beginning or during the lessons as the need for conceptual knowledge arose. In contrast, no explicit instruction was provided about photography. We simply assumed that students already had sufficient prior knowledge and experience taking pictures with their cell phones. The problem, however, was that such familiarity with the photographic features of cell phones did not guarantee informed production and critique of digital photographs. Their photo-taking practices were often naïve rather than based on informed understandings of artistic visual expression.

To address this shortcoming, we plan to include explicit art instruction in future iterations of our STEAM lesson. Following Marshall's (2010) recommendation that effective art integration with other disciplines requires both "teaching *through* art and *about* art," we plan to teach conceptual strategies and approaches adopted by contemporary artists to make meaning, such as depiction, extension/projection, reformatting, mimicry, and metaphor. Providing students with such background knowledge in art concepts is essential if students are indeed to engage in "...informed discourse about art to increase understanding and appreciation..." (Barrett, 2012) when critiquing photographs of science investigations.

In addition to providing students with background knowledge about artistic concepts, it is also important to integrate instruction about art composition and about art history so that students can understand their creations in the context of other artists. A pedagogical approach likely to be productive is the guided study of representations of natural phenomena (e.g., animals, rain) in artwork from different historical periods. A particularly interesting example of this approach is Dicke's (2000) comprehensive database of representations of insects in 13th–18th century paintings from Europe and North America. This historical database reveals a wide variety of symbolic references (butterflies and dragonflies as symbols for the soul, caterpillars as symbols for the body, flies as symbols for the brevity of life), ways of artistically depicting insects (cultural entomological representations), and cultural perceptions (e.g., aversion to insects, association to pests) throughout many centuries of art. While emphasizing the educational value of such an approach, Dicke (2000) writes, "By studying the representation of insects in art from a historical perspective one can gain an appreciation of how the perceptions of insects has changed overtime" (p. 235). Such guided study of artistic representations of natural phenomena seems to have great potential to enrich STEAM lessons and should be capitalized upon by teachers.

We also believe that students might benefit from explicit instruction about scientific argumentation. As emphasized by national reform documents such as the Next Generation Science Standards (NGSS Lead States, 2013), students need instruction and guidance on evidence-based argumentation. However, developing such a skill requires explicit instruction about the structure, nature, and quality (i.e., soundness and logical coherence) of scientific argumentation. In particular, students need guidance on the rhetorical nature of argument components such as data, claim, warrants, backing, and rebuttal (Erduran & Jimenez-Aleixandre, 2008). In hindsight, we think the absence of this instructional component from our STEAM curriculum was a major factor behind our students' evaluative critique of photographs mostly on artistic grounds. Without a clear and solid understanding of scientific argumentation, students are unlikely to evaluate photographs on rhetorical grounds (i.e., in terms of their value as visual grounds from scientific claims).

Incorporation of explicit instruction on science argumentation can be informed by a growing number of articles recently published in practitioner journals. Much of this practical literature emphasizes the need for teachers to scaffold students' understanding of argumentation by providing them with guiding frameworks with explicit definitions for each individual argument component (Sampson, Enderle, & Grooms, 2013); by having students agree or disagree with a statement (e.g., "Frequent use of cell phones can cause brain cancer") or a text (Llewellyn, 2013); by analyzing videos of debates (Taylor, 2013); and by providing them with prompts (e.g., "My claim is . . . ," "A counter argument against my claim could be . . . ," "My evidence to refute the counter argument would be . . .") and starter sentences (e.g., "The statement contends that _____; however, I disagree with the statement because _____"; Llewellyn, 2013).

In addition to the curricular improvements outlined above, we have also included a few specific next steps in our action research agenda. One such step is increased attention to cultural relevance in our STEAM lessons. Members of particular social groups and communities often have *visual cultures* (Sturken & Cartwright, 2009), that is preferred ways of looking at and representing the natural world. Their visual representations of the world (for example, drawings and paintings) are cultural manifestations of larger societal developments and carry unique cultural meanings. A good example is the traditional woodcut illustrations of *cordel books*—string books popular in Latin American countries (Figure 13.6a). Another example is the *Adinkra* symbols of the Asante people commonly found in traditional clothing and jewelry in West African countries. One particularly well-known Adinkra symbol is Sankofa (Figure 13.6b), wherein a bird with its head turned backwards metaphorically represents the need to reflect on the past to build a successful future (a cultural representation of time). Likewise, artwork by master painters in Europe commonly make metaphoric references to insects as symbols of death and brevity of life (Dicke, 2000). A guided exploration of the unique visual features of such cultural artifacts could provide linguistically and culturally diverse students with examples that are both familiar and relatable.

We believe that exploring such cultural differences in the accepted ways of pictorially portraying the natural world, and communicating visually can make STEAM lessons more inclusive of linguistically and culturally diverse

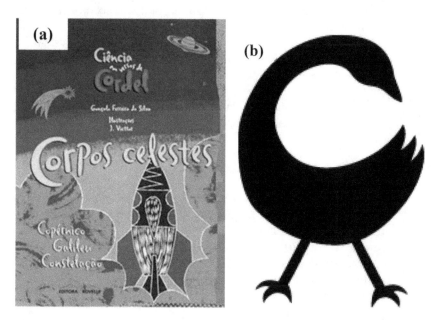

Figure 13.6 (a) Cover of Brazilian Cordel Book on Celestial Bodies; and (b) Sankofa, a Cultural Icon Used in Ghana to Symbolize "Learning from the Past"

students and at the same time help strengthen their knowledge of art concepts. An exploration of visual culture would also potentially validate ELs' diverse cultural backgrounds and ultimately help all students better understand that science and art photography are essentially visual cultures, two of a multitude of possible ways of representing and seeing the world.

FUTURE ACTION RESEARCH

We would like to conclude by identifying what we consider to be important open questions that should figure prominently in the agenda of anyone interested in doing further action research on photography-based STEAM pedagogy.

Action Research Questions

1. What are some ways that teachers can approach STEAM investigations to effectively foster artistic interpretation during whole-class critique of science photographs?
2. What strategies can we use to engage students in informed artistic discourse (e.g., artistic metaphors, context of production, emotional impact) when interpreting the photographic record of classroom science inquiries?
3. What are some ways that we can approach our STEAM investigations to effectively foster scientific evaluation during whole-class critique of science photographs?
4. What strategies can we use to encourage students to consider science argumentation (e.g., claim, evidence, reasoning) when evaluating the photographic record of classroom science inquiries?

Inquiry Questions

1. How can secondary teachers coherently integrate the study of visual cultures with photography-based science inquiries in ways that effectively support ELs?
2. How can secondary teachers effectively address the cultural aspects of science and art during STEAM lessons?
3. In what ways does the incorporation of art enhance language or academic outcomes for ELs?

REFERENCES

Abd-El-Khalick, F., Waters, M., & Le, A. (2008). Representations of nature of science in high school chemistry textbooks over the past four decades. *Journal of Research in Science Teaching, 45*(7), 835–855.

Akerson, V. L., & Abd-El-Khalick, F. S. (2005). "How should I know what scientists do—I am just a kid": Fourth grade students' conceptions of Nature of Science. *Journal of Elementary Science Education, 17*(1), 1–11.

Akerson, V. L., Abd-El-Khalick, F., & Lederman, N. G. (2000). Influence of a reflective explicit activity-based approach on elementary teachers' conceptions of nature of science. *Journal of Research in Science Teaching, 37*(4), 295–317.

Ametller, J., & Pinto, R. (2002). Students' reading of innovative images of energy at secondary school level. *International Journal of Science Education, 24*(3), 285–312.

Barrett, T. (2012). *Criticizing photographs: An introduction to understanding images* (5th ed.). New York, NY: McGraw-Hill.

Binns, S., Smith, M. K., & Milligan, D. (2011). *Smithsonian in your classroom: Botany and art and their roles in conservation.* Retrieved from the Smithsonian Institution website: https://learninglab.si.edu/collections/botany-and-art-and-their-roles-in-conservation/cAoin2jFwq9Ux7oJ#r/38802

Carey, S., & Smith, C. (1993). On understanding the nature of scientific knowledge. *Educational Psychologist, 28*(3), 235–251.

Clough, M. P. (2006). Learners' responses to the demands of conceptual change: Considerations for effective nature of science instruction. *Science & Education, 15*(5), 463–494.

Colin, P., Chauvet, F., & Vinnot, L. (2002). Reading images in optics: Students' difficulties and teachers' views. *International Journal of Science Education, 24*, 313–332.

Davidson, R. (2014). Using infographics in the science classroom: Three investigations in which students present their results as infographics. *The Science Teacher, 81*(3), 34–39.

de Oliveira, L. C., & Wilcox, K. C. (Eds). (2017). *Teaching science to English language learners: Preparing pre-service and in-service teachers.* New York, NY: Palgrave Macmillan.

Dewey, J. (1934). *Art as experience.* New York, NY: Perigee Books.

Dicke, M. (2000). Insects in western art. *American Entomologist, 46*(4), 228–236.

English, L. D. (2016). STEM education k–12: Perspectives on integration. *International Journal of STEM Education, 3*(3), 1–8.

Erduran, S., & Jimenez-Aleixandre, M. P. (2008). *Argumentation in science education: Perspectives from classroom-based research.* New York, NY: Springer.

Ford, D. J. (2006). Representations of science within children's trade books. *Journal of Research in Science Teaching, 43*(2), 214–235.

Fowler, K. (2015). For the love of infographics. *Science Scope*, March, 25–30.

Gilbert, P. B., Brungardt, M., Dorr, C., & Balgopal, M. (2010). The view at the zoo: Using a photographic scavenger hunt as the basis for an interdisciplinary field trip. *Science Scope*, February, 52–55.

Honey, M., Pearson, G., & Schweingruber, H. (2014). *STEM integration in K–12 education: Status, prospects, and an agenda for research.* Washington, DC: National Academy of Sciences.

Hunston, S. (1994). Evaluation and organization in a sample of written academic discourse. In M. Coulthard (Ed.), *Advances in written text analysis* (pp. 191–218). London, England: Routledge.

Jones, A. D. (2010). Science via photography: Using digital media to enhance animal adaptation and diversity lessons. *Science and Children, 47*(5), 26–30.

Krauss, D. A., Salame, I. I., & Goodwyn, L. N. (2010). Using photographs as case studies to promote active learning in biology. *Journal of College Science Teaching, 40*(1), 72–76.

Kress, G., & van Leeuwen, T. (2006). *Reading images: The grammar of visual design* (2nd ed.). New York, NY: Routledge.

Lamb, G., Polman, J. L., Newman, A., & Smith, C. G. (2014). Science news infographics: Teaching students to gather, interpret, and present information graphically. *The Science Teacher*, March, 25–30.

Lederman, N. G., Abd-El-Khalick, F., Bell, R. L., & Schwartz, R. S. (2002). Views of nature of science questionnaire (VNOS): Toward valid and meaningful assessment of learners' conceptions of nature of science. *Journal of Research in Science Teaching, 39*(6), 497–521.

Lemke, J. L. (1990). *Talking science: Language, learning, and values.* Westport, CT: Ablex.

Lemke, J. (1998). Multiplying meaning: Visual and verbal semiotics in scientific text. In J. R. Martin & R. Veel (Eds.), *Reading science* (pp. 87–113). London, England: Routledge.

Llewellyn, D. (2013). Making and defending scientific arguments: Strategies to prepare your students for the new wave of curricula reform. *The Science Teacher, 80*(5), 34–38.

Maeda, J. (2013). STEM + Art = STEAM. *The STEAM Journal, 1*(1), 1–3.

Marshall, J. (2010). Five ways to integrate: Using strategies from contemporary art. *Art Education, 63*(3), 13–19.

Martin, J. R., & White, P. R. R. (2003). *Language of evaluation: Appraisal in English.* New York, NY: Palgrave Macmillan.

McComas, W. F. (2008). Seeking historical examples to illustrate key aspects of the nature of science. *Science & Education, 17*(2–3), 249–263.

McMahon, M. M. (2002). Picture this! *Science and Children*, April, 42–45.

Myers, G. (1990). Every picture tells a story: Illustrations in E. O. Wilson's sociobiology. In M. Lynch & S. Woolgar (Eds.), *Representation in scientific practice* (pp. 231–265). Cambridge, MA: MIT Press.

NGSS Lead States. (2013). *Next generation science standards: For states, by states.* Washington, DC: The National Academies Press.

Oliveira, A. W., & Cook, K. (2017). Student visual communication of evolution. *Research in Science Education, 47*(3), 519–538.

Oliveira, A. W., Rivera, S., Glass, R., Mastroianni, M., Wizner, F., & Amodeo, V. (2013). Teaching science through pictorial models during read-alouds. *Journal of Science Teacher Education, 24*(2), 367–389.

Pozzer, L. A., & Roth, W.-M. (2003). Prevalence, function, and structure of photographs in high school biology textbooks. *Journal of Research in Science Teaching*, *40*(10), 1089–1114.

Radziwill, N. M., Benton, M. C., & Moellers, C. (2015). From STEM to STEAM: Reframing what it means to learn. *The STEAM Journal*, *2*(1), 3.

Sampson, V., Enderle, P., & Grooms, J. (2013). Argumentation in science education. *The Science Teacher*, Summer, *80*(5), 30–33.

Stylianidou, F., Ormerod, F., & Ogborn, J. (2002). Analysis of science textbook pictures about energy and pupils' reading of them. *International Journal of Science Education*, *24*(3), 257–283.

Sturken, M., & Cartwright, L. (2009). *Practices of looking: An introduction to visual culture*. New York, NY: Oxford University Press.

Taylor, L. (2013). The language of argumentation: Using debate to spark interest and learning in science. *The Science Teacher*, *80*(5), 44–49.

Trimarchi, R. (2003). Life is change: A community project captures life processes and fosters K-12 curriculum collaboration. *The Science Teacher*, May, 28–31.

Vasquez, J., Comer, M., & Troutman, F. (2010). *Developing visual literacy in science, K–8*. Arlington, VA: NSTA Press.

CHAPTER 14

FACILITATING DIVERSE STUDENTS' DISCOURSE DURING MATHEMATICS DISCUSSIONS

What Do Teacher Questions Have to Do With It?

Mary A. Avalos
University of Miami

Loren Jones
University of Maryland, College Park

TALK AND INTERACTION IN MATHEMATICS CLASSROOMS

Although meaningful mathematical talk, or discourse, has long been valued by mathematics educators (e.g., National Council of Teachers of Mathematics, 1989, 1991, 2001), current learning standards and mathematical practices expect teachers to engage students in discourse to develop deep

Culturally and Linguistically Diverse Learners and STEAM, pages 291–312
Copyright © 2019 by Information Age Publishing

content knowledge, problem-solving abilities, and reasoning skills (National Governors Association Center for Best Practices, Council of Chief State School Officers, 2010). Teaching to these new rigorous standards can be especially challenging for mathematics teachers serving English learners (ELs), who are simultaneously acquiring a new language and novel content (Bailey, 2015). Moreover, not only is implementing such an approach to teaching and learning mathematics a challenge, but sustaining a discussion-based approach can also be challenging for teachers and students (Avalos & Secada, 2019).

Focusing on specific talk moves may be helpful for teachers who wish to implement math talk. Talk moves are essentially a repertoire of responses to promote dialogic input; teachers can use talk moves to encourage clarification and expansion of thinking, encourage careful listening, press for deeper reasoning, and encourage application of students' reasoning to that of their peers (Michaels & O'Connor, 2012). Students may also learn to use these talk moves to respond to their peers during mathematics discussions. Talk moves should be seen as a scaffold for math talk in the classroom so that as the teacher becomes more adept at facilitating dialogic talk (i.e., adopting a dialogic stance), and as students become more proficient in responding to and initiating questions that foster deeper reasoning, the scripted talk moves can be replaced with more natural language that captures the same ideas or goals of dialogic talk. In sum, talk moves can facilitate the habits of mind needed by teachers and students to think more deeply about mathematics concepts and solutions while implementing quality math talk in classrooms; however, they should be seen as a scaffold so that as students become accustomed to dialogic talk, they can become more free to explore similar ways of expressing themselves.

In this chapter, we present a middle school teacher's talk moves and her linguistically diverse students' responses during mathematics discussions, as part of a 2-year professional development intervention project with the teacher. Although initially challenging to implement, results indicate a shift in teacher discourse and classroom interaction patterns with specific talk moves facilitating student participation, positively changing the dynamics of the classroom and learning environment.

BACKGROUND

Studies involving teacher discourse practices and classroom interaction patterns have helped to highlight the importance of language use during classroom instruction. Moschkovich (2007) examined mathematical discourse practices through a framework that involves conjecturing, explaining, justifying, and evaluating solutions during discussions. Other studies have analyzed talk in mathematics classrooms to better understand what teachers can do to facilitate students' extended thinking (Cengiz, Kline, & Grant, 2011); to push students to use higher-level knowledge structures (Huang, Normandia, & Greer, 2005); to foster argumentation, debate, and critique concerning important mathematical ideas (Drageset, 2015); and to elicit longer and more thoughtful responses from students (McConney & Perry, 2011). An overarching goal of these studies was to explore teacher–student discourse to discern how teachers' language choices might help students develop deeper reasoning skills and improve communication for mathematics learning.

Although discourse is important for mathematics instruction, as noted previously, it poses a challenge for both students and teachers, especially for ELs. A dialogic teaching approach may help to facilitate EL and diverse students' talk during mathematics and other STEAM-related subject discussions. According to Wegerif (2007), a dialogic approach to teaching includes a space for interactive negotiation of shared meaning in the classroom. The teacher orchestrates space for students to share, challenge, or build on others' ideas, and to interact in order to develop and construct shared meaning (Van der Veen, van Kruistum, & Michaels, 2015). In previous studies, dialogic teaching was found to benefit young children's oral communicative competence (Van der Veen, de Mey, Van Kruistum, & Van Oers, 2017), increase student engagement (Forman, Ramirez-DelToro, Brown, & Passmore, 2017), and positively impact student learning (Nystrand & Gamoran, 1991; O'Connor, Michaels, Chapin, & Harbaugh, 2017; Sherry, 2014).

As pointed out by Boyd and Markarian (2015), true dialogic teaching requires a *dialogic stance* on the part of the teacher to "model and support cognitive activity and inquiry and supportive classroom relations, to engage multiple voices and perspectives across time, and to animate student ideas and contributions" (p. 273). When teachers adopt a dialogic stance for their instruction, patterns of classroom interaction change. Namely, teachers release control of, as well as interpretive power about, the topic discussed and actively seek to include students' ideas as contributions to drive the discussion. Additionally, teachers vary their patterns of talk, sometimes using recitation and asking questions with known answers (i.e., the teacher initiates a question with an answer in mind, a student responds, and the teacher evaluates based on the expected answer; IRE, Mehan, 1979), and sometimes using open-ended questions to open the floor for exploring the content of the discussion to put the responsibility for thinking and reasoning on the students (Boyd & Markarian, 2015). While all students benefit from explaining their thinking and contributing to discussions, this is especially important for ELs, as they need multiple opportunities to speak in academic contexts, which may only be accessible during the school day, to improve communicative competence (van der Wilt, van Kruistum, van der Veen, & van Oers, 2016) and be success-ful in school (Díaz-Rico, 2004; Foorman, Koon, Petscher, Mitchell, & Truck-enmiller, 2015; Weber & Longhi-Chirlin, 2001). Importantly, it is the teach-er's ability to implement, orchestrate (to include all students), and sustain dialogic teaching that determines how successful dialogic teaching can be (Kumpulainen & Rajala, 2017); however, using a dialogic teaching approach is not easy due to the unfamiliar nature of using dialogic teaching, not only for teachers, but also for students.

Challenges for teachers implementing mathematics discussions with diverse populations include establishing appropriate classroom norms in which all students feel comfortable to participate, re-creating students' identities from passive receivers of formulae and content knowledge to do-ers of mathematics, and being consistent with this approach over time to apprentice student reasoning and critical thinking skills (Avalos & Secada, 2019). Another challenge for leading mathematics discussions is know-ing when to "step in" to guide students' thinking and when to "step out" (Rittenhouse, 1998, p. 173) to provide information that may be needed to support students' learning (Edwards & Mercer, 1987). Other challenges arise from factors that teachers typically cannot control, including strict district pacing guides that determine how much time should be spent on each learning standard, or student placement, resulting in homogeneous classroom environments (i.e., tracking that separates those who achieve at or above proficient levels on state tests from those who do not, disabling heterogeneous classroom grouping). These factors are especially common in today's accountability climate. School districts enrolling ELs and other diverse populations often require teachers to focus on content coverage (or follow pacing guides) over students' learning needs or mastery of the con-tent in order to prepare for high stakes assessments (Achinstein & Ogawa, 2006; Au, 2011), despite learning standards' expectations of the deep learn-ing outcomes that can be derived from dialogic teaching.

This chapter describes results of a small case study that evolved from a larger intervention project, which focused on the integration of mathemati-cal practices with discipline-specific literacy teaching, or mathematical liter-acies. The larger study, known as *Language in Math* (LiM; Secada & Avalos, 2010–2013), included both a comprehensive professional development component for participating teachers serving ELs (Avalos, Zisselsberger, Langer-Osuna, & Secada, 2014), and a classroom intervention aligned with national standards (National Council of Teachers of Mathematics, 1989, 1991, 2001). The intervention emphasized reading, writing, listening, speaking, and viewing mathematical semiotics (e.g., signs, symbols, graph-ics) during problem-solving via explicit language instruction (Avalos, Me-dina, & Secada, 2015). In this smaller case study, we examine a focal teach-er's classroom discourse to better understand how the use of language and student–teacher interactions during math discussions changed over time, and which talk moves (i.e., responses to promote dialogic input) facilitated more language and interaction from students. Accordingly, our research questions are: "How does the use of teacher language during math discussions change over time?" and "Which teacher talk moves facilitated more student language and interaction?"

A STUDY OF A FOCAL TEACHER AND HER CLASSROOM

The context for this case study was a culturally and linguistically diverse science, technology, engineering, and mathematics (STEM) magnet middle school in the Southeastern United States. At the time of data collection, the school population was 45% Hispanic and 44% African American, with approximately 85% of students participating in the free/reduced price lunch program (i.e., an indication of low socioeconomic status). Data were collected in two classes of students over 2 academic years in an "intensive math class" in which the students scored a 1 or 2 (below proficient) on the state's annual exam for mathematics in sixth grade and were therefore receiving a "double dose," or 1.5 hours, of daily math instruction. Ms. Roosevelt,[1] the focal teacher in this study, agreed to participate in the LiM project. At the time of this study, Ms. Roosevelt was considered a veteran teacher with more than 22 years of teaching experience; she had multiple subject certification to teach elementary grades and mathematics (Grades 5–9), and had earned a master's degree in mathematics education.

Throughout the LiM project, Ms. Roosevelt participated in the LiM professional development sessions. The majority of these sessions focused on developing ELs' mathematical literacies, including strategies that teachers could draw on in order to facilitate student participation in mathematics discussions. Additionally, LiM project personnel modeled instruction using mathematics discussions in Ms. Roosevelt's classroom, and coached her to implement the LiM intervention, which included mathematics discussions. In conjunction with these professional development sessions, Ms. Roosevelt's teaching was video-recorded at three different time points over the 2 years she participated in the project. The initial observation occurred when she started attending the professional development, the second took place mid-way through the project, and the last observation was completed in the final stages of the project. Each of the video recorded lessons was approximately 45 minutes in length. For purposes of this analysis, we elected to focus on whole-class, teacher-led discussions surrounding mathematics problem-solving.

During the first video-recorded lesson, Ms. Roosevelt reviewed equations with fractions with her students. As a whole class, they talked through numerous homework problems that students had completed earlier in the week. The second video-recorded lesson focused on the difference between direct variation and inverse variation. To address these concepts, Ms. Roosevelt led students through the completion of an activity in which they were challenged to solve a multi-step word problem. In the third and final video-recorded lesson, Ms. Roosevelt worked with students as they completed a word problem on linear equations for their warm-up activity. This particular activity required students to progress through multiple stages of problem solving, ultimately using either a table or graph to find the correct solution.

Discourse Analysis

To closely examine the classroom discourse from each of these video-recorded lessons, we utilized a coding process that was both inductive and deductive (Miles, Huberman, & Saldaña, 2014). We began the iterative coding process (Merriam, 2001; Strauss & Corbin, 1998) by first conducting a detailed reading of the verbatim transcripts from each of the video-recorded lessons. This reading allowed us to familiarize ourselves with the context and content of the discourse. We completed two phases of coding—the first focused on teacher talk and the second on student talk; however, we integrated and used both teacher and student talk holistically during the analysis to code the transcripts (e.g., to determine the function of talk).

The coding for teacher talk began as a deductive process in which we applied the *a priori* codes established in the Drageset (2015) framework to describe teacher and student interactions. As we progressed through our coding process, a theme began to emerge from the data that did not coincide with the original framework: *Teacher revoicing* was incorporated into additional inductive coding as a new code, and is described below in the adapted framework (Table 14.1). The resulting framework for teacher talk consisted of 12 categories, grouped according to three different actions: redirecting, progressing, and focusing actions (Drageset, 2015).

TABLE 14.1 Categories and Definitions of Teacher Discourse	
Teacher Talk	
Code	**Definition and Example**
Progressing actions: Used to move problem-solving progress forward	
Teacher demonstration	Teacher models to solve the task. For example: We take the rate from here [points at the bottom of the board] and we put it in the equation.

(continued)

TABLE 14.1   Categories and Definitions of Teacher Discourse (continued)

Teacher Talk	
Code	Definition and Example
Redirecting actions: Used to change student approaches to solving problem	
Correcting question	Teacher asks a question to redirect student to a different approach. For example: I borrow from the 1? Can I borrow from the 1?
Simplification	Adding information or altering the task to make it simpler. For example: But before you change anything remember what you want to do first. Get it to the point where you're going to add or subtract.
Requesting closed process details	Teacher asks for one detail at a time, moving along one step at a time (possibly to ensure all students are following and comprehending problem-solving process). For example: Which one would be x and which one would be y?
Initiating open process	Teacher seeks progress, but leaves it to the student to choose his/her own method. For example: What do I do next?
Focusing actions: Used to stop progress in order to look into details or reasons behind an answer or approach	
^Requesting student(s) to enlighten detail	Stop solution process to notice details or reasons behind an answer or approach from one or more students. For example: Can you elaborate on that? Can you be more specific? In between what?
^Requesting student(s) to justify	Makes details of problem-solving pathway explicit. For example: And how do we know?
^Requesting student(s) to apply to similar task/problems	Provides students with practice for a similar task that was just covered. For example: So, I have 12 dollars…and I'm going to share it with 3 people. How much is each person going to get?
^Requesting student(s) to make an assessment	Puts students in the teacher's position to evaluate the solution and/or process. For example: 2.4? Everybody agrees with that? Think about it a little bit more.
Pointing out something for student(s) to notice	Teacher wants students to notice something important during task problem-solving in order to point out what students should use in their problem-solving process, or know for future mathematical studies. For example: So here we have 5 leaves and here we have 2 caterpillars…?
Pointing out something to recap	Teacher wants to summarize important point(s) or steps taken to reach solution. For example: Okay. So. First step. Isolate the variable.
Talk move used across all three discourse actions	
*Teacher revoicing	Teacher repeats student response to affirm or question what student said. For example: It isn't constant? Okay…

Notes: Adapted from Drageset, 2015
* Indicates new code added.
^ Indicates talk moves that typically facilitate deeper student math talk.

Progressing actions were used to move problem-solving progress forward, while *redirecting actions* were used to change student approaches to problem-solving by asking a correcting question. Ms. Roosevelt carried out progressing actions in many ways, including *demonstrating a solution, simplifying the task, requesting closed process details,* or *initiating an open process.* For example:

Ms. Roosevelt: *So, how fast is she going when she takes 2.5 hours?* (closed
process details)
Student: 4.8
Ms. Roosevelt: 4.8. Well, I need to know how fast she was going when she
took 3 hours. *So, what do I do next?* (initiating open process)

Ms. Roosevelt used *focusing actions* to stop progress in order to look into the details or reasons behind an answer or approach. Focusing was generally done in one of two ways, either by pointing out key information or requesting students to do something. When pointing out information, Ms. Roosevelt told the students to take note of something or provided a brief recap of important steps taken to reach a solution. When requesting students to do something, the teacher either asked students to *enlighten details, provide justification, apply themselves to a similar task,* or *make an assessment.*

The final category for teacher talk was labeled *teacher revoicing,* which occurred when the teacher repeated what a student said. This category was found across and within the three different actions as it could have been used by the teacher to affirm a students' response (progressing action) or to question what a student said or did to solve a problem (redirecting/focusing action). Although revoicing has not been found to promote academically productive talk or dialogic teaching since teacher tone can speak volumes (Michaels & O'Connor, 2015), Ms. Roosevelt's use of revoicing appeared to affirm her students' thinking or prompt them to question their thinking.

The coding for student talk followed the same process for that of teacher talk (Table 14.2).[2] We added the categories *unintelligible* and *no answer* to fit with the data we compiled from Ms. Roosevelt's class. Three of our eight codes were grouped together as explanations—*explanation reason* (justification), *explanation action* (what was done; how something was done), and

TABLE 14.2 Student Discourse	
Student Talk	
Code	**Definition and Example**
No answer	Students offered no answer; teacher answered her own question and did not give students the opportunity to answer (e.g., silence).

(continued)

TABLE 14.2 Student Discourse (continued)	
Student Talk	
Code	**Definition and Example**
Explanation-reason (justification)	The response focuses on the "why"; typically requested by the teacher and focus is on giving explicit details on reason(s) why the action was taken. T: Why do we need to do the opposite? S: So you can get "b" by itself.
Explanation-action (what was done; how something was done)	The response focuses on the "what" or "how" behind students' responses; typically requested by the teacher and focus is on giving explicit detail(s) behind "what" was done or "how" the action was completed. T: Where did the 6 come from? S: Because 2 times 6 equals 12.
Explanation-concept (understanding of domain)	The response focuses on the student's understanding of the domain; typically requested by the teacher and focus is on giving explicit detail(s) about conceptual understanding behind algorithms or procedures. T: How did you get 6 here? S: We have to divide 12 into half because it says "each day."
Teacher-led responses	Answers facilitated by the teacher, usually by reducing complexity or by leading the students towards the answer; Typically, responses to "overly basic tasks" (i.e., CPD; student-initiated interventions; simplification). T: What is happening to the "b" and the 2.25? What operation is happening? S: Subtracting.
Initiatives	Asking what (or how) to do (something); making suggestions; pointing out important details without teacher requesting. S: How do you get the 12?
Unexplained answers	Responses that were correct or incorrect answers without any obvious reason or information as to how the student arrived at the answer; could include hidden steps to the solution that were not made visible by the answer; student thinking is not visible, so this may be followed by the teacher requesting an explanation. T: And what do we do next? S: Subtract 2.25 from the 1.
Unintelligible	Instances when we were not able to discern what students were saying. *Note:* It is possible that some responses were coded with two codes when part of the explanation was clear and the other part unintelligible.

Note: Adapted from Drageset (2015).

explanation concept (understanding of domain). Other codes included *teacher-led responses, initiatives, unexplained answers, no answer,* and *unintelligible.*

Quality of Mathematics Discussions

In addition to the discourse analysis, we also examined the quality of the focal classroom's math-talk learning community using a 4-point scale (*0–3*) rubric focused on four dimensions: *questioning, explaining mathematical thinking, source of mathematical ideas,* and *responsibility for learning* (Hufferd-Ackles, Fuson, & Sherin, 2004; Table 14.3). Gauging the quality of classroom dialogic teaching is important as it can provide accountability while teachers are attempting to take up a dialogic stance.

BEFORE AND AFTER LANGUAGE IN MATH

Looking across the 3 time points, comparing discourse patterns before and after the LiM professional development, we noticed a distinctive shift in both teacher talk and student talk (Tables 14.4 and 14.5, respectively; note that percentages were rounded to the nearest whole number; therefore, columns do not sum to 100%). During Time Point 1, Ms. Roosevelt's use of *requesting closed process details* and *pointing out something for student(s) to notice* dominates her discourse, while *teacher-led responses* and *unexplained answers* dominates student discourse. This aligns with the recitation-style discourse Ms. Roosevelt used prior to experiencing the LiM professional

TABLE 14.3 Rubric to Assess Quality of Math Talk			
0	**1**	**2**	**3**
The math-talk learning community is a traditional, teacher-directed classroom with brief responses from students.	The teacher is beginning to seek student understanding of mathematical thinking, but still plays a fundamental role in the math-talk community.	The teacher utilizes modeling to help students build new roles. The teacher also begins to incorporate some co-teaching and co-learning as student-to-student talk increases and the teacher begins to physically move to the side or back of the classroom.	The teacher serves a dual role as both a co-teacher and co-learner, more on the sideline, monitoring the students as they progress through the different stages of problem solving.

Note: Based on Hufferd-Ackles, Fuson, & Sherin (2004).

TABLE 14.4 Shifts in Ms. Roosevelt's Discourse Over Three Time Points in Focal Classroom

	Time Point 1	Time Point 2	Time Point 3
Requesting closed process details	38%	24%	11%
Simplification	4%	2%	2%
Initiating open process	1%	2%	12%
Teacher revoicing	15%	22%	26%
Pointing out: Notice	27%	26%	24%
Correcting question	4%	2%	3%
Pointing out: Recap	8%	7%	4%
Requesting student(s) to justify	1%	1%	0%
Requesting student(s) to enlighten detail	0%	6%	13%
Teacher demonstration	0%	3%	0%
Requesting student(s) to apply to similar task	0%	3%	0%
Requesting student(s) to make an assessment	0%	3%	3%

TABLE 14.5 Shifts in Ms. Roosevelt's Students' Discourse Over Three Time Points

	Time Point 1	Time Point 2	Time Point 3
Unexplained answers	25%	35%	17%
Teacher-led responses	52%	48%	19%
Unintelligible	11%	2%	30%
Explanation-concept	0%	7%	3%
Explanation-reason	2%	1%	0%
Explanation-action	3%	1%	9%
Initiatives	0%	5%	19%
No answer	7%	1%	3%

development. During Time Point 2, we begin to see more variation in the talk moves used by Ms. Roosevelt to include *request to enlighten detail, teacher demonstration, apply to similar task,* and *requesting assessment,* while student discourse also demonstrates more variation with some *initiative* and *explain concept* talk moves. Finally, Time Point 3 indicates substantial changes in the variation of teacher discourse, with a reduction of *closed process details,* and a great increase in use of *open process* and *enlighten detail* codes, which function as means to explore students' understandings of the topic and focus on reasons behind problem-solving actions, respectively; student discourse had less *teacher-led responses* and *unexplained answers,* and more *explain action* and *initiative* coded.

STUDY IMPLICATIONS FOR MATHEMATICS DISCUSSIONS

In the first lesson, the majority of the teacher talk was identified as requesting *closed process details* (38%) and *pointing out* something for students to notice (27%). The corresponding student talk consisted largely of *teacher-led responses* (52%) and *unexplained answers* (25%). This type of classroom discourse was limiting and provided students with few opportunities to participate in math talk. In the example from Time Point 1 below, the teacher requested *closed process details* while the students provided *teacher-led responses* to each of her questions.

> **Ms. Roosevelt:** And how do we do that? [create an equivalent fraction]
>   **Student:** By multiplying...
> **Ms. Roosevelt:** What's the number on the top?
>   **Student:** The numerator.
> **Ms. Roosevelt:** And the bottom number?
>   **Student:** The denominator.

This type of discourse is seen throughout the first time point, and because the interaction patterns largely resembled a traditional approach to teaching mathematics, we scored the focal classroom's quality of math-talk learning at 0 for each of the four dimensions (Hufferd-Ackles et al., 2004). Focusing on the questioning dimension, the teacher was the only questioner. She asked short, frequent questions to keep students listening and paying attention which resulted in short responses from the students with no student-to-student math talk. For the explaining mathematical thinking dimension, the teacher did not elicit student thinking or explanations. Instead, she expected known-answer responses only with no explanation of concepts, reasoning, or actions. Upon examining the discourse for source of mathematical ideas, we found that the students did not offer any of their own math ideas. Rather, the teacher remained physically at the board, telling and showing students how to do math without engaging them to participate beyond the known-answers for the questions she used. The fourth dimension, responsibility for learning, showed that students played the role of passive listeners throughout the lesson. The teacher repeated students' answers for the class to hear and responded to their answers by verifying the correct answer or showing the correct method rather than digging deeper into students' understandings.

The second time point was noticeably different from the first in that the teacher incorporated new talk moves. While she still frequently requested *closed process details* (24%) and *pointed out* something for students to notice (27%), she also utilized *revoicing* (22%) to affirm students' responses in order to move the discourse forward. In addition, she also started to request students to *enlighten detail, apply to similar task,* and *make an assessment.* The analysis revealed minor changes in student talk, as well. Although student talk was still largely limited to *unexplained answers* (35%) and *teacher-led responses* (48%), there was a small shift in discourse as students provided *explanations* (concept; 7%), and took *initiative* (5%).

Ms. Roosevelt: What side is the 1 on?
    Student: *Right.*
Ms. Roosevelt: *Right.* So, are we going to subtract the 1?
    Student: No.
Ms. Roosevelt: Which one do you think we would need to look at?
    Student: *The 2.25.*
Ms. Roosevelt: *The 2.25.* What is happening to the "b" and the 2.25? What operation is happening?
    Student: Subtracting

Overall, the discourse from Time Point 2 did not alter the score of 0 for the dimensions of questioning and responsibility for learning on the math-talk learning community rubric (Hufferd-Ackles et al., 2004). However, the dimensions of explaining mathematical thinking and source of mathematical ideas increased from 0 to 1. While the teacher did not elicit student thinking or explanations during the first time point, she did make more of an effort to probe student thinking in this second lesson, as demonstrated below. Additionally, rather than remaining physically at and writing on the whiteboard showing students how to do math, the teacher followed up on students' responses, asking them to build on their ideas and thinking.

Ms. Roosevelt: So, let's go back to one of our examples that we did. This would be your time and this would be your distance (gesturing to numbers written on the board). What is our rate?
    Student: In between
Ms. Roosevelt: The things in between. Can you elaborate on that? Can you be more specific? In between what?
    Student: The numbers in between.
Ms. Roosevelt: The numbers in between here (gesturing to board)? Tell me what numbers because you're telling me numbers and I have a whole bunch of numbers.
    Student: Between the x and the y.

The third and final time point showed the most significant differences in both teacher talk and student talk. While the teacher still requested *closed process details* (11%), *pointed out* something for students to notice (24%), and used *revoicing* (26%), she also initiated *open process* (12%) and asked students to *enlighten detail* (13%). By adding these new dimensions to her discourse, the teacher elicited more involvement from the students, challenging them to take responsibility for their learning by explaining their mathematical thinking. This resulted in an increase in student *explanations* (action; 9%) and a decrease in overall instances for both *unexplained answers* (17%) and *teacher-led responses* (19%). The most notable change in student talk was an increase in student *initiatives* which increased 14% from Time Point 2 (5%) to Time Point 3 (19%). The excerpt of dialogue below focuses on a discussion between the teacher and students as they attempted to find the best way to solve the assigned word problem:

A 7th grade class needs five leaves each day to feed its two caterpillars.

How many leaves would they need each day for 12 caterpillars?

Ms. Roosevelt: You're multiplying by 2. Is that what I'm hearing? So I have two . . . two what?
Student: Caterpillars
Ms. Roosevelt: 2 caterpillars and what do I do next?
Student: . . . 12 that's 2 times 6
Student: I did it different.
Ms. Roosevelt: Okay, can you show us how you did it?
Student: [Student walks to the board] 2 times 6 equals 12, then I got 5 times the same number.

The discourse from Time Point 3 resulted in higher scores in the areas of questioning, explaining mathematical thinking, and responsibility for learning, according to the math-talk learning community rubric (Hufferd-Ackles et al., 2004; Table 14.6). In the area of questioning, the teacher's focus began to shift from students' answers to students' thinking. This was evident in the teacher's increased requests for students to enlighten detail. The dimension of explaining mathematical thinking was scored at a 2 as the teacher probed more deeply for students to explain their thinking and the students began to stake a position in their learning. The source of mathematical thinking

TABLE 14.6 Change in the Quality of Ms. Roosevelt's Facilitation of Math Talk

Talk Moves	Time Point 1	Time Point 2	Time Point 3
Questioning	0	0	1
Explaining mathematical thinking	0	1	2
Source of mathematical ideas	0	1	1
Responsibility for learning	0	0	1

Note: Based on Hufferd-Ackles et al. (2004).

remained at a score of 1 from Time Point 2 as the teacher continued to follow up on student's explanations. The final dimension, responsibility for learning, was scored at a 1, as students became more engaged in the learning process with initiatives and showing how they solved problems.

Looking across the three time points, the teacher's discourse shifted to open up more opportunities for student participation (Figure 14.1). The teacher's request for *closed process details* decreased steadily from Time Point 1 to Time Point 3 while her *initiation of open process* and request for students to *enlighten details* increased. By incorporating a variety of talk moves to include those that function to progress and focus on problem-solving processes (e.g., Teacher: "Is there any other way that you can solve this other than tables and graphs?"), the teacher enabled students to participate more in math discussions. As students began to take a more active role in the mathematics learning, their use of *initiatives* increased (e.g., "How do you do that?"), however, their use of *explanations* was still limited and could have been a next step in Ms. Roosevelt's developing repertoire of talk moves. Overall, it is evident that Ms. Roosevelt was moving towards adapting a dialogic stance for instruction. Her discourse changed, indicating that her beliefs about teaching and learning (and abilities) evolved from being a supplier of knowledge to actively involving and engaging students in the learning process. As seen from the data collected over 2 years, this is not an easy nor instant transition; time and support are essential for most teachers to make these changes.

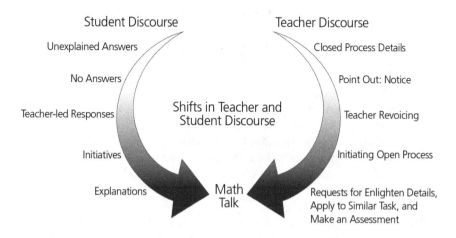

Figure 14.1   Trajectory of talk moves to shift teacher and student discourse.

SUGGESTIONS FOR IMPLEMENTING MATH TALK

Changing teacher discourse and classroom interaction patterns requires a concentrated effort on the part of the teacher and the students. Older students who have been socialized to a more traditional teaching style, as demonstrated in Ms. Roosevelt's first time point, may resist and need to understand the purpose of adopting a more dialogical stance for instruction (Avalos & Secada, 2019). To overcome the challenges associated with implementing and sustaining equitable mathematics discussions, it is important to work with a network of teachers and/or teacher leaders who can support or coach to provide critical feedback on practices that lead to a more democratic classroom environment. Additionally, knowing how to respond to students can help with implementing and sustaining equitable mathematics discussions. Accountable Talk® moves (Michaels, O'Connor, Williams Hall, & Resnick, 2010) were used for the LiM project and helped teachers with varying their responses:

- Say more (i.e., encourage individual students to share, expand, and clarify their thinking):
  - Can you say more about that?
  - What do you mean by that?
- Verify/clarify by revoicing:
  - Are you saying . . . ?
- Provide wait time:
  - Go ahead, take your time, we'll wait.
- Encourage students to listen carefully to one another:
  - Who can repeat what Gemma just said or put that in their own words?
  - Who can explain what Tomás means when he says that?
- Press for deeper reasoning (i.e., asking for evidence):
  - Why do you think that?
  - Where is your evidence?
- Challenging or asking for a counterexample:
  - Does it always work that way?
  - How does your thinking fit with what Jennifer just said?
- Press students to apply their reasoning to that of others:
  - Who can add onto the idea Tamar is building?
  - Do you agree/disagree?

LiM teachers focused on adding one to two talk moves to their repertoire each week, and then asked their students to start using them to apprentice them into politely disagreeing or challenging a peer's solution or process during problem-solving discussions. The students' focal talk moves were posted on the board each week so students could refer to them, if needed, during discussions. While the talk moves were awkward at first, they proved to be helpful in implementing and promoting classroom norms during discussions (Avalos & Secada, 2019). Mohr and Mohr (2007) provide a response protocol to assist teachers with knowing how to expand ELs' contributions during class discussions. If an EL provides a confusing response, the teacher may respond with "Help me understand what you mean. Tell me again" or "I want to know what you are thinking. Can you tell me more?" (Mohr & Mohr, 2007, p. 446). Thus, in sustaining and orchestrating equitable discussions so that ELs have opportunities to participate, and implementing appropriate classroom norms, a deliberate focus on how to respond can move all students to participate more fully.

CONCLUSION

Shifting teacher discourse and teacher–student interaction patterns in mathematics classrooms holds promise for fostering ELs' participation in mathematics discussions, albeit this shift is generally not a quick or easy transition. Time and multiple supports are needed for teachers to be aware of how their use of language engages (or disengages) students with the content and learning objectives. Our results indicate that when the focal teacher varied use of talk moves for different purposes, primarily focusing and progressing actions, the floor was open to exploring the mathematics content to build on and develop students' understandings.

Although how language is used in diverse classrooms is recognized by the field as important for teaching and learning, more research is needed to implement and assess teacher and student classroom discourse and interaction to better understand what drives equitable opportunities to learn and participate. Because most teachers do not use a dialogic approach to teaching (Liberali, 2017), there are still many questions about how the use of language impacts learning outcomes, specifically how the use of discussion as a learning tool over multiple years and across grade levels could change the way diverse students are positioned to learn and, as a result, their reasoning and communication skills. Additionally, further exploring varying professional development components (e.g., learning community, model lessons, coaching) to determine teachers' perspectives about what is most helpful for adapting more of a dialogic stance and shifting discourse is also needed. Finally, more research is needed that links dialogic teaching with ELs' learning outcomes to ascertain the cognitive benefits of this approach.

We therefore conclude with several action research suggestions and inquiry questions for the field. Teachers may conduct action research projects to systematically examine their discourse and classroom interaction patterns. Following the LiM project example, there are multiple possibilities for action research depending upon the goals in implementing or sustaining mathematics discussions. Similarly, we encourage education researchers to further examine dialogic teaching, especially in classrooms with ELs.

Action Research

1. Adopt one or two different talk moves with students each week, starting with moves that are based on your students' needs to promote deeper math talk (generally this reflects the need to have students dig deeper to explain their thinking, or understand how to politely disagree with a peer and request more of an explanation behind the proposed solution). Keep anecdotal notes of what is working well or needs improvement to assist in the transition and help with moving discourse to more progressing or focusing actions. Be cognizant of which students are called on to provide equitable opportunities for ELs and struggling students to participate. Note how student participation and engagement shifts, or if not, try adjusting or using different talk moves to determine why students aren't responding to the invitations to participate. Be mindful of pulling the information from the students to promote their explanations, rather than presuming to understand their thinking around problem solving or solutions. Ask students to begin using certain talk moves to help them acquire appropriate ways to respond or challenge their peers' contributions.
2. Interview ELs and other students to find out their perspectives about participating in mathematics discussions and how, or if, the use of specific talk moves help them to do so. It is important to remember that appropriate classroom norms must be in place in order for all students to feel comfortable and safe to participate in discussions of problem-solving processes or the result may be more disputational than productive talk (Avalos & Secada, 2019; Langer-Osuna & Avalos, 2015).

Inquiry Questions

1. What question types or talk moves are used more in classrooms enrolling ELs or diverse populations in comparison with classrooms enrolling more native English speakers, and what is the effect on learning?
2. Overall, are teachers positioned to acquire a dialogic stance in teacher education programs or inservice professional development programs?

3. How does a transition to dialogic teaching in mathematics effect ELs' language development, reasoning, and/or learning outcomes?

ACKNOWLEDGMENTS

This work was made possible by a grant from The Institute of Educational Sciences, Award Number R305A100862. This chapter does not necessarily reflect the views or policies of IES or the U.S. Department of Education nor does mention of trade names, commercial products, or organizations imply endorsement by the U.S. Government. We acknowledge the teachers, students, district administrators, and project team members who contributed to this project.

NOTES

1. All names are pseudonyms.
2. Our adapted framework resulted in eight codes for student talk as opposed to eleven since we elected to use initiative as one category, rather than separating it into three as Drageset (2015) did.

REFERENCES

Achinstein, B., & Ogawa, R. T. (2006). (In)Fidelity: What the resistance of new teachers reveals about professional principles and prescriptive educational policies. *Harvard Educational Review, 76*(1), 30–63.

Au, W. (2011). Teaching under the new Taylorism: High stakes testing and the standardization of the 21st century curriculum. *Journal of Curriculum Studies, 43*(1), 25–45.

Avalos, M. A., Medina, E., & Secada, W. G. (2015). Planning for instruction: Increasing multilingual learners' access to algebraic word problems and visual graphics. In A. Bright, H. Hansen-Thomas, & L. C. de Oliveira, (Eds.), *The Common Core State Standards in mathematics for English language learners: High school* (pp. 5–28). Alexandria, VA: TESOL.

Avalos, M. A., & Secada, W. G. (2019). Linguistically responsive mathematics teaching to foster ELL engagement, reasoning, and discourse. In L. C. de Oliveira, K. Obenchain, R. Kenney, & A. Oliveira (Eds.), *Approaches to teaching the content areas to English language learners in secondary schools* (pp. 165–179). Cham, Switzerland: Springer.

Avalos, M. A., Zisselsberger, M., Langer-Osuna, J., & Secada, W. G. (2015). Building teacher knowledge of academic literacy and language acquisition: A framework for cross-disciplinary professional development. In D. Molle, T. Boals, E. Sato, & C. A. Hedgspeth (Eds.), *Sociocultural context of academic literacy development for adolescent english language learners* (pp. 255–276). New York, NY: Routledge.

Bailey, A. L. (2015). How have the language expectations for students and teaches at school changed with the adoption of the Common Core State Standards? In G. Valdés, K. Menken, & M. Castro (Eds.), *Common Core bilingual and English language learners: A resource for educators* (pp. 50–52). Philadelphia, PA: Caslon.

Boyd, M. P., & Markarian, W. C. (2015). Dialogic teaching and dialogic stance: Moving beyond interactional form. *Research in the Teaching of English, 49*(3), 272–296.

Cengiz, N., Kline, K., & Grant, T. J. (2011). Extending students' mathematical thinking during whole-group discussions. *Journal of Mathematics Teacher Education, 14*(5), 355–374.

Díaz-Rico, L. T. (2004). *Teaching English learners: Strategies and methods.* Boston, MA: Allyn & Bacon.

Drageset, O. G. (2015). Student and teacher interventions: A framework for analysing mathematical discourse in the classroom. *Journal of Mathematics Teacher Education, 18*(3), 253–272.

Edwards, D., & Mercer, N. (1987). *Common knowledge: The development of understanding in the classroom.* London, England: Routledge.

Foorman, B., Koon, S., Petscher, Y., Mitchell, A., & Truckenmiller, A. (2015). Examining general and specific factors in the dimensionality of oral language and reading in 4th–10th grades. *Journal of Educational Psychology, 107*(3), 884–899.

Forman, E. A., Ramirez-DelToro, V., Brown, L., & Passmore, C. (2017). Strategies that foster an epistemic community for argument in a biology classroom. *Learning and Instruction, 48,* 32–39.

Huang, J., Normandia, B., & Greer, S. (2005). Communicating mathematically: Comparison of knowledge structures in teacher and student discourse in a secondary math classroom. *Communication Education, 54*(1), 34–51.

Hufferd-Ackles, K., Fuson, K. C., & Sherin, M. G. (2004). Describing levels and components of a math-talk learning community. *Journal for Research in Mathematics Education, 35*(2), 81–116.

Kumpulainen, K., & Rajala, A. (2017). Dialogic teaching and students' discursive identity negotiation in the learning of science. *Learning and Instruction, 48,* 23–31.

Langer-Osuna, J., & Avalos, M. A. (2015). "I'm trying to figure this out. Why don't you come up here?": Heterogeneous talk and dialogic space in a mathematics discussion. *ZDM (Zentralblatt für Didaktik der Mathematik), 47*(7), 1313–1322.

Liberali, F. (2017). Commentary: Analyzing classroom dialogue to create changes in school. *Learning and Instruction, 48,* 66–69.

McConney, M., & Perry, M. (2011). A change in questioning tactics: Prompting student autonomy. *Investigations in Mathematics Learning, 3*(3), 26–45.

Mehan, H. (1979). *Learning lessons.* Cambridge, MA: Harvard University Press.

Merriam, S. B. (2001). *Qualitative research and case study applications in education.* San Francisco, CA: Jossey-Bass.

Michaels, S., & O'Connor, C. (2012). *Talk science primer.* Cambridge, MA: Technical Education Research Center.

Michaels, S., & O'Connor, C. (2015). Conceptualizing talk moves as tools: Professional development approaches for academically productive discussions. In L. B. Resnick, C. Asterhan, & S. N. Clarke (Eds.), *Socializing intelligence through talk and dialogue* (pp. 347–361). Washington, DC: American Educational Research Association.

Michaels, S., O'Connor, M. C., Williams Hall, M., & Resnick, L. B. (2010). *Accountable Talk® sourcebook for classroom conversation that works, Version 3.1.* Pittsburgh, PA: University of Pittsburgh, Institute for Learning.

Miles, M. B., Huberman, A. M., & Saldaña, J. (2014). *Qualitative data analysis: A methods sourcebook.* Thousand Oaks, CA: SAGE.

Mohr, K. A. J., & Mohr, E. S. (2007). Extending English-language learners' classroom interactions using the Response Protocol. *The Reading Teacher, 60*(5), 440–450.

Moschkovich, J. (2007). Examining mathematical discourse practices. *For the learning of Mathematics, 27*(1), 24–30.

National Council of Teachers of Mathematics. (1989). *Curriculum and evaluation standards for school mathematics.* Reston, VA: Author.

National Council of Teachers of Mathematics. (1991). *Professional standards for teaching mathematics.* Reston, VA: Author.

National Council of Teachers of Mathematics. (2001). *Principles and standards for school mathematics.* Reston, VA: Author.

National Governors Association Center for Best Practices, Council of Chief State School Officers. (2010). *Standards for mathematical practice.* Washington, DC: Author. Retrieved from http://www.corestandards.org/Math/Practice

Nystrand, M., & Gamoran, A. (1991). Instructional discourse, student engagement, and literature achievement. *Research in the Teaching of English, 25*(3), 261–290.

O'Connor, C., Michaels, S., Chapin, S., & Harbaugh, A. G. (2017). The silent and the vocal: Participation and learning in whole-class discussion. *Learning and Instruction, 48,* 5–13.

Rittenhouse, P. S. (1998). The teacher's role in mathematical conversation: Stepping in and stepping out. In M. Lampert & M. L. Blunk (Eds.), *Talking mathematics in school: Studies of teaching and learning,* (pp. 163–189). New York, NY: Cambridge University Press.

Secada, W. G., & Avalos, M. A. (2010–2013). *Language in math.* Washington, DC: U.S. Department of Education. Retrieved from http://ies.ed.gov/ncer/projects/grant.asp?ProgID=59&grantid=1034

Sherry, M. B. (2014). Indirect challenges and provocative phrases: Using cultural conflict-talk practices to promote students' dialogic participation in whole-class discussions. *Research in the Teaching of English, 49*(2), 141–167.

Strauss, A., & Corbin, J. M. (1998). *Basics of qualitative research: Techniques and procedures for developing grounded theory.* Thousand Oaks, CA: SAGE.

Van der Veen, C., de Mey, L., Van Kruistum, C., & Van Oers, B. (2017). The effect of productive classroom talk and metacommunication on young children's oral communicative competence and subject matter knowledge: An intervention study in early childhood education. *Learning and Instruction, 48,* 14–22.

Van der Veen, C., van Kruistum, C., & Michaels, S. (2015). Productive classroom dialogue as an activity of shared thinking and communicating: A commentary on Marsal. *Mind, Culture, and Activity, 22*(4), 320–325.

van der Wilt, F., van Kruistum, C., van der Veen, C., & van Oers, B. (2016). Gender differences in the relationship between oral communicative competence and peer rejection: An explorative study in early childhood education. *European Early Childhood Education Research Journal, 24*(6), 807–817.

Weber, R., & Longhi-Chirlin, T. (2001). Beginning in English: The growth of linguistic and literate abilities in Spanish-speaking first graders. *Reading Research & Instruction, 41*, 19–49.

Wegerif, R. (2007). *Dialogic, education and technology: Expanding the space of learning.* New York, NY: Springer.

CHAPTER 15

INTEGRATING CODING AND COMPOSITION

Linking English Language Arts, Computer Programming, and Mathematics to Develop English Learners' Strengths Across the Content Areas

Suzie Dollesin
California State University, Sacramento

Harry Cheng
University of California at Davis

Porfirio Loeza
California State University, Sacramento

ABSTRACT

This is a reflective essay in which the authors introduce an experience that provides insight into leveling the learning field through integrated computing, science, technology, engineering, and mathematics (C-STEM) for under-

Culturally and Linguistically Diverse Learners and STEAM, pages 313–331

represented students in a low-income secondary public-school setting. Drawing primarily from the experiences of the only language arts teacher selected to participate, the authors describe, evaluate, and analyze C-STEM enrichment to enhance equal access to grade level curriculum for second language learners and at-risk students involved in a research project sponsored by the National Science Foundation. The purpose of this essay is to explore the importance of developing metacognitive skills in students and suggests that teachers include integrated computing as a means to enhance student engagement and academic success through both technical and academic language.

21st CENTURY LEARNING

In 2010, the University of California, Davis Center for Integrated Computing and STEM Education (C-STEM) was founded by Dr. Harry Cheng. Over 5 years prior to the inauguration of the C-STEM Center, Dr. Cheng experimented with the use of computing and robotics as a teaching tool to close the achievement gap for underrepresented K–12 students by providing them with computer science education. Findings revealed that students who were already struggling with science and math did not have access to computer programming instruction, or to coding. Dr. Cheng approached this problem from an engineering perspective and developed a comprehensive curriculum that uses robots and programming to teach math and science for *every* student, in addition to computing curriculum for use as electives. This chapter discusses how one teacher integrated this curriculum into English language arts, finding and teaching important connections between coding, literacy, math, and science, and as such truly making it accessible to *every* student.

THE LITERACY CONNECTION

In 2012, the National Science Foundation awarded the University of California, Davis C-STEM Center with a grant for a 2-year project aimed to transform math education by integrating computer programming, robotics, and handheld computing into middle and high school classrooms. The focus was on the use of robotics to enhance collaborative student learning of algebra through real-world problem-solving with engaging and fun activities; algebra was the chosen subject because it is the gatekeeper to accessing STEM (Cheng, 2011). Under the National Science Foundation grant, Dr. Cheng reached out to public school districts across California and selected secondary teachers to integrate computer programming in the instruction of math.

As a teacher known to be proactive in the use of technology in the classroom, Suzie Dollesin was selected by her district to participate in the summer C-STEM project. Dollesin brought the project to a different level because she was not a math or science teacher. She was the only language arts teacher in the pilot program, under the guidance of Dr. Cheng. Accepting the challenge, Dollesin immediately recognized that Dr. Cheng's approach to teaching math and science for *every* student would first require them to learn the *language* of code used in computer programming, and she hypothesized that this was comparable to the learning of a *new* language because language, in itself, begins with coding and decoding.

Students learn to recognize sound based on symbols, or codes, represented by the alphabet, and the scaffolding of phonemic awareness, or sight to sound recognition, is the essence of coding and decoding in learning English. All teachers should become familiar with the coding and decoding of North American English, because it can move students towards building word recognition, which, in turn, can impact the students' ability to gain fluency in all domains of English language fluency—listening, speaking, reading, and writing (see, e.g., August & Shanahan, 2006).

Cox (2005) points out that "[students] with relatively low aptitude, but high cognitive ability, often use metacognitive skills to compensate for low ability so that their performance is equivalent to high aptitude [students]" (p. 110). In fact, not having the strength in mathematics that other teachers in the pilot program already possessed, Dollesin relied on her prior knowledge of connecting sounds and symbols through which she applied metacognitive skills to facilitate her learning of the language of code. Somewhat similar to recall, metacognitive processing allowed Dollesin to instinctively access what she already knew and identify commonalities between computer programming, or code, and academic composition (see Figure 15.1).

By introducing this contrastive analysis as a form of metacognitive processing to her students, Dollesin (2012) expected that those who were proficient in the language of academic writing would utilize the composition

Both:
- are basic literacies
- are present everywhere
- require a specified audience
- are activities that train our minds to think in ways that give order to the world
- are ways to interface with tools

Both:
- involve a process

programming	composition
-Header File	-Title
-Declaration of Variables	-Thesis Statement
	-Introduction
-Initialization	-Body Paragraphs
-Processing	-Conclusion
-Termination	
-quotation marks to print a statement	-quotation marks to make a statement
-semi-colon completes a command statement	-period completes a sentence

- adhere to rules of format and syntax

Figure 15.1 Commonalities between computer programming and academic composition.

comparison to facilitate their abilities in the writing of code. On the other hand, those proficient in the language of code would reverse the comparison in its application to address any weaknesses in their understanding of the foundational components of writing an academic essay. Learning takes place across the curriculum and opportunities to integrate language instruction, in its various forms, promote language learning because these opportunities expose students to the semantics necessary to progress successfully in *all* content areas, also strengthening cognitive ability.

A simple definition of writing is that it is thinking in a particular kind of way and putting those thoughts in print by using a school-learned type of symbol or code system. The symbols of the Latin alphabetic structure provide a system that is recursive and reflective of the discrete sounds that make up the English language. Beginning writers use an ephemeral but real concept of the alphabetic or code principal to draft their first compositions. As they mature, writers expand their repertoire into sophisticated webs of discursive elements that have the intent of conveying a central message. Like computer programming, academic composition involves the progression of writing from a mechanical process of focusing on representing discrete symbols to generating larger ideas that are interconnected through the concepts that a writer intends to convey. Whether writing code or academic composition, the importance of authorial intentionality impacts how a writer will articulate meaning to an anticipated audience.

Academic composition involves the manipulation of language to demonstrate an understanding of learned concepts, and computer programming can further develop critical thinking skills through logical reasoning in the writing of code. Across the curriculum various organizational structures in composition, or writing for academic purposes, involve linear and sequential processes also identifiable in the writing of code. Composition includes informative text that can be more technical in the areas of science and mathematics yet more descriptive in the social sciences. In language arts, language becomes the *art* in the use of rhetorical devices meant to persuade, explain, or simply tell a story, through which teachers can employ practical applications of computer programming because it can be integrated creatively in the development of academic composition.

Similarly, there is a complex manipulation of language with specific meanings that is embedded in computer programming. It is a genre in itself that has an ideology and historical vestiges that a competent user of this *discourse* must master (Gee, 2012). This literate genre means that it is learned in school and that it is foregrounded by mathematical literacy. This latter literacy, also known as numeracy, is a mode of linguistic thinking that integrates language, actions, interactions, objects, tools, technologies, beliefs, and values in specific ways.

With this in mind, Dollesin (2012) further converted the research-based reasoning—"If A is directly connected to B and B is directly connected to C, then A is indirectly connected to C via a path over B"—to her own C-STEM project correlation as, "If language arts is directly connected to computer programming and computer programming is directly connected to math, then language arts is indirectly connected to math via a path over computer programming." The applicability of this reasoning was demonstrated by students whom she involved in a research task that required multiple steps (Figure 15.2).

Essentially, students began with a research task in language arts, then utilized integrated computer programming—in this case *Ch* scripted language, a computer coding language described in the next section—with mathematical computations to generate the graph shown in Figure 15.3.

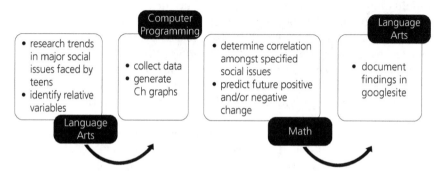

Figure 15.2 · Learning targets for student research task.

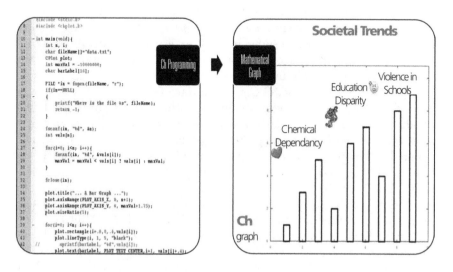

Figure 15.3 Ch programming generated graph.

Once the graph was completed, the students were able to better conduct an analysis of their data through mathematical concepts such as determining correlations or positive and/or negative trends. Finally, students could articulate their findings through expository writing in language arts, which is the indirect connection between language arts and math via a path over computer programming, or integrated computing. The graph became a visual that students utilized to move forward, with confidence, in the development of coherent academic composition, or an essay about their research.

THE Ch SCRIPTING LANGUAGE

While Cummings (2006) agrees that teachers of academic composition should integrate computer programming into the curriculum, he also compares the difficulties of learning the language of code to those encountered in learning a second language. The obstacle, as he states, is "if composition teachers were to select a programming language for inclusion into the pedagogy of teaching writing, it would need to be a stable and robust language that is freely accessible to all and that also minimizes risk of obsolescence while maximizing the applicability of the programming knowledge in other classes" (p. 441).

The authors believe that the scripted language Ch, originally created by Dr. Cheng,[1] fits all of the criteria posed by Cummings (2006). Ch is a superset of C, an important and widely used coding language, and incorporates salient extensions from other common coding languages. Ch is especially effective for teaching and learning computing, mathematics, and robotics as well as interfacing with hardware. The relationship between Ch and other major computer programing languages and software packages is illustrated in Figure 15.4, which shows how it is realistically all inclusive. In other words, students who learn to program in Ch will have a reasonable grasp of the concepts present in many other common programming languages.

As noted, Ch is a superset of C, which is one of the foundations for modern information technology and computer science. C is an international standardized programming language and is the base for almost all popular programming languages (Cheng, 2011). For this reason, C is one of the most commonly used programming languages in colleges, universities, and industry; according to a ranked comparison by the Institute of Electrical and Electronics Engineers (2016), C tops the list, C++ ranks second, and Java is the third (see Figure 15.5). Students who master C through Ch are more readily prepared learn other computer languages without much difficulty.

With a better understanding of the advantages of Ch as the scripted language of choice, teachers can move forward, confident that they are integrating a programming language that is the most beneficial for their students. While core content area teachers do not have to become experts

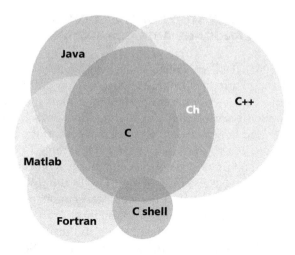

Figure 15.4 The relationship between Ch and other major programming languages.

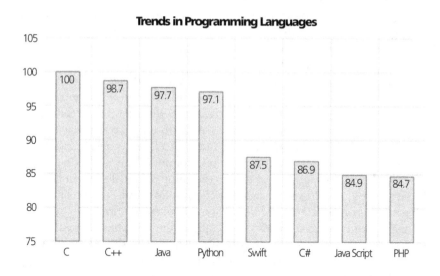

Figure 15.5 The top programming languages (adapted from the Institute of Electrical and Electronics Engineers, 2016).

in the language of code nor that of academic composition, they too can utilize the metacognitive processes introduced in Figure 15.1 to enhance their understanding of both. As a pertinent part of the learning process, a teacher's ability to creatively integrate computer programming and academic composition into content instruction also meets the expectations of integrating literacy in the technical subjects presented in the Common Core State Standards.

A CASE STUDY OF THE CODING—
LANGUAGE ARTS CONNECTION

In the Spring of 2013, Dollesin collaborated with a colleague who was teaching robotics through another program. The objective of this project-based learning experience was to determine whether students who already possessed some familiarity with computer programming, but were struggling in language arts, might benefit from the academic composition comparison. Through a request for volunteers, five students accepted an opportunity to participate in a coding and robotics competition sponsored by the University of California, Davis C-STEM Center. Two of the five, however, were unable to maintain a commitment to meet after school and become more familiar with the Ch coding language and robotics.

Of the three who remained, Vihaan[2] came to the United States in the seventh grade and was fully fluent in Hindi and Punjabi. Noah was a native speaker of American English, and Li came to the United States in the fifth grade. Li was only partially fluent in Mandarin because he had lost both reading and writing skills in his native language during his focus on learning English. All were in the eleventh grade, credit deficient, and neither Vihaan nor Li were reclassified as fully English proficient.

As it turned out, none of the three were participants in the school's site-adopted robotics program, but they were familiar with video games, which provided basic awareness of concepts in robotics. The students were weak in the area of academic composition; therefore, based on their already established interest in technology, they were first introduced to the structures of computer programming outlined in Figure 15.1. Within two weeks they were able to program the robots to follow simple commands through Ch scripted language. They were later introduced to the comparative alignment between computer programming and academic composition and became enthusiastic because, as one student expressed, "it made perfect sense."

This introduction to the comparative alignment was what Swain and Lapkin (1995) would refer to as external feedback because it shifted the students' attention from a refusal to write to an awareness of linguistic characteristics that had not been made obvious to them previously. By noticing the comparative alignment between computer programming and academic composition, the students were able to convert the external feedback into internal feedback, or metacognitive processing, from which they made appropriate adjustments to their completion of writing tasks across the curriculum (Dollesin, 2013).

Over the course of 10 weeks, the three students were required to decipher complicated instructions and a schematic diagram to create a mock challenge board on which they tried out various maneuvers with the robots. They had a newfound interest in the reading of more complex text related to computer programming and technology, and their grades improved because they were completing writing tasks that they once either refused to do or completed based on formulaic guidelines that included sentence frames—in the eleventh grade. On the day of the event, they found the robotics competition at the University of California, Davis to be intimidating, but they beat the odds and won second place. They also decided that they *would* go to college. Vihaan expressed an interest in becoming a computer engineer, Noah a mathematician, and Li a biomedical engineer.

PROJECT-BASED LEARNING

Project-based learning empowers students because they take ownership of the quality and the quantity of information to be learned, and the teacher becomes the facilitator of knowledge as opposed to the omnipotent master of knowledge. In addition, project-based learning requires collaborative efforts, which promotes language acquisition and communicative competence, because it encourages students to negotiate meaning through discourse. Edmunds, Arshavsky, Glennie, Charles, and Rice (2016) posit that project-based learning further enhances students' abilities to solve problems and promotes intrinsic motivation because students will selectively access more advanced reading materials, particularly through investigative tasks.

Prior to the success of the project-based robotics enrichment project, Dollesin had already developed a language arts project-based learning curriculum around the following quarterly research projects. Each required students to master both the structures of computer programming and that of academic composition simultaneously:

1. *Quarter 1:* Identify the trends in the erosion of national pride/identity over a 5-year span.
2. *Quarter 2:* Compare and contrast the trends in single parent households and obesity over a 5-year span.
3. *Quarter 3:* Evaluate the trends in materialism, growing up too fast, and a shifting economy over a 5-year span.
4. *Quarter 4:* Correlate the trends in education disparity, violence in schools, drug/alcohol abuse, and poverty over a 5-year span.

Research across a 5-year span provided students with a significant amount of annual data to plot on a Ch programming-generated graph. The topics were also relevant to current real-world living conditions that the majority of the students dealt with on a daily basis. Dollesin piggybacked on the C-STEM Center objectives as follows:

1. Close the achievement gap by broadening participation of students typically underrepresented in computing and STEM.
2. Develop students' 21st century problem-solving skills to tackle real-world problems.

Students were expected to work through the metacognitive processes in the ongoing contrastive analysis of computer programming and academic composition outlined in Figure 15.1. Their cognitive abilities were further enhanced through collaborative efforts to troubleshoot errors in scripted language, or coding, and/or logical reasoning in the context of their academic writing. As Edmunds et al. (2016) suggest, an enhanced interest in reading more complex texts, prompted by investigative tasks, would also lead to noticeable improvement in the structures and coherence of student writing because students would be accessing models of complex writing.

PEDAGOGICAL IMPLICATIONS

Moving students, especially English learners (ELs), up to the next level of linguistic and academic achievement calls for scaffolded instruction. To facilitate the scaffolding process, Bransford, Brown, and Cocking (2000) explain that instruction must promote metacognitive practices through which a focus on sense-making, self-assessment, and reflection on what worked and what needs improvement leads to the development of automaticity for the learner. Objectives must be specific and made clear to the learner, and teachers must scaffold new knowledge from that which the learner has already attained.

Integrated computing is successful with second language learners because it puts all students on the same level of learning a new concept—in essence, a new language. Because all language learning begins with code—symbols that represent sound and meaning—ELs are better able to grasp the concepts of computer coding based on their own prior knowledge of language learning. In other words, they can use their language learning experiences as a tool to learn code as new language. Pedagogical practices can also enhance the learning experience for *all* students by scaffolding computer coding into the instruction of academic writing through the contrastive analysis shown in Figure 15.1.

Learning involves the transfer of knowledge across both academic and social experiences, and relevant curriculum enhances student motivation. Saunders and Goldenberg (2010) further explain that both interactive and interrelated activities are beneficial particularly when collaborative learning is well organized, as with project-based learning. In addition, when students are introduced to the creation of graphs through computer coding, they are more interested to learn if the topic is relevant and age-appropriate. For example, in Dollesin's classroom, high school students were assigned to graph trends in eating disorders after conducting a project-based learning research project that was introduced through the reading of an article entitled "Too Thin is not in—just ask around." This brief article, published in a local newspaper, was written by a high school student who criticized the overemphasis on being thin and encouraged teens to just be themselves (Robeson, 2002).

An outline of the project-based learning project on society's emphasis on thinness (see Figure 15.6), integrated the elements of language fluency—reading, writing, listening, and speaking—as it brought students through Bloom's taxonomy of cognitive abilities to ensure the inclusion of rigor, or higher order thinking, in both content and language instruction, and encouraged students to connect to real world perspectives on debatable issues (Pappas, Pierrakos, & Nagel, 2013).

Furthermore, the curriculum strategically transferred knowledge because it included math concepts in the analysis of trends over time to enhance student learning across the curriculum. Bransford et al. (2000) refer to this as process scaffolding from the concrete to the representational to the abstract. Likewise, Saunders and Goldenberg (2010) emphasize that explicit instruction requires both deductive and inductive approaches. Through educational experiences, *all students* benefit from opportunities to notice concepts that overlap across the curriculum.

Project-Based Learning: society's emphasis on thinness

Activity Process

ELA Standard 2.6	Step 1: Knowledge / Remembering, Understanding	Step 2: Application, Analyze, Evaluate	Step 3: Synthesize / Create	Step 4: Data Analysis
Critique the power, validity, and truthfulness of arguments set forth in public documents; their appeal to both friendly and hostile audiences; and the extent to which the arguments anticipate and address reader concerns and counterclaims (e.g., appeal to reason, to authority, to pathos and emotion).	Read the article, "Too thin is not in - just ask around", by Lauren Robeson and make inferences. Robeson, L. (2002, September). Too thin is not in - just ask around. *Sacramento Bee*	Analyze the use power, validity, and truthfulness of the arguments set forth in the article, and to the extent to which the arguments anticipate and address reader concerns and counterclaims.	Access each online tool in the listed in the Activity Guidelines to, *first*, post an analytical comment, *second*, create an group online Glogster, and, *third*, develop a group Powerpoint that best illustrates your combined overall analysis.	Research trends of anorexia in one of the following: 1. teens over a five year span 2. teens amongst 5 different ethnicities • Access the barGraph program in the ChIDE. • Change values and name each category in the data text file. • Predict future trends • Upload findings into student wiki.

Figure 15.6 Sample project-based learning instructional components.

Figure 15.7, provides activity objectives and guidelines pertaining to each of the technology-based tools ("Web 2.0 Tools") that students applied as described in Step 3 of the project-based learning project (see Synthesize/Create in Figure 15.6).

One of these tools, Haiku, now known as PowerSchool, is one of many online platforms made available for teachers to encourage continued discourse

Activity Guidelines
Teacher's Note - Selection of Web 2.0 Tools is based on prior instruction.

Web 2.0 Tools	URL	Activity Objective	Activity Guideline
haiku	http://www.haikulearning.com/	Discussion Post: Initiate personal commentary that encourages further discussion in response to the following: "Is our society's emphasis on thinness helpful or harmful?"	• Post at least one analytical comment in reference to the discussion objective. • Respond to the primary comments of a minimum of two different class members. • Use standard academic language and be respectful of all readers. • Be considerate and polite when responding. • Response should be specific to the post you are writing on. • Use the internet, as needed, to conduct further research to enhance the content of your discussion. • Share any outside resources you review in support of your opinions. • The **deadline** to complete submit your primary comment and respond to two members of the class is one week from today. ○ <u>The discussion board will close next Wednesday, 3/7 at 11:00PM.</u> • The discussion board is graded as Pass / No Pass as outlined in the Glogster Rubric.
Email skype Glogster EDU	www.skype.com http://edu.glogster.com/	Skype: Hold a group conference via Skype or another video chat interface Glogster: Create an online group glogster that best illustrates the strengths and weaknesses of the arguments based on whether our society's emphasis on thinness *helpful or harmful.*	• Set up a Skype appointment time with your identified group members via email. • During the Skype session, develop an online glogster that reflects the glogster objective. • Use standard academic language and be respectful of all group members. • Be considerate and polite when responding. • Use the internet, as needed, to conduct further research to enhance the content of your discussion. • Share any outside resources you review in support of your opinions. • The **deadline** to complete submit your online group poster is Wednesday, 3/13 at 11:00PM. • The Glogster is graded as scale of 1-3 as outlined in the Grading Rubric.
Google docs	http://www.google.com/google-d-s/documents/	Powerpoint: Develop a shared powerpoint that persuades an audience to agree with the stance of your group - *"helpful or harmful"*	• Set up a shared Ppt with your group members via Googledocs. • Develop a group Ppt that reflects the Powerpoint objective. • Use standard academic language and be respectful of all group members. • Be considerate and polite when responding. • Use the internet, as needed, to conduct further research to enhance the content of your discussion. • Share any outside resources you review in support of your opinions. • The **deadline** to complete submit your online group poster is: • The Ppt is graded as scale of 1-3 as outlined in the Powerpoint Rubric.

Figure 15.7 Sample project-based learning activity objectives and guidelines.

Student-Sample Discussion Post in Online Learning Network

Freda K.

Society's emphasis on thinness is harmful because being "stick-thin" can cause many problems. Aside from low self-esteem, girls won't eat well which causes bad headaches that lead to difficulties in concentrating - especially in school. Is it okay to stop eating just to be "stick-thin" for guys? What can happen if a girl stops taking care of herself just to be "stick-thin? The body will lose shape because it will lack the nutrients needed to stay healthy. There are other ways to stay healthy without becoming too skinny. Girls are better off if they maintain an exercise routine and eat a well-balanced diet - so why don't we teach them more of this, instead of allowing bad influences, like Britney Spears, to lead the way?

Student-Sample Discussion Response in Haiku in Online Learning Network

Freda K.

Hello Diego,

I agree that a 'plump' woman is definitely more attractive for a man, but even 'plumpness', to a certain degree can pose health concerns. I disagree with the idea that every generation has role models that are just 'in the passing'. Public figures have too much influence over teenage behavior - perhaps even younger. This makes it more difficult for even parents to step in.

We can't go on pretending that this is not a growing concern - even an economic concern due to health expenses that can come about for taking care of girls who become both emotionally and physically ill but cannot afford medical services - don't you think?

Thanks for sharing,

Freda

Figure 15.8   Sample project-based learning discussion student outcomes in the web-based tool haiku.

outside of the classroom. In the case of Dollesin's project-based learning activity, students posted comments and/or partook in analytical discussions on the topic of society's emphasis on thinness. The online platform provided a nonthreatening environment for open discussion because all posts were monitored by the teacher. An example of a communication exchange is shown in Figure 15.8. (Some of the questions posed and the reference to Britney Spears are from the article by Robeson, 2002).

A simple discussion rubric was provided to students to help them assess and enhance their use of language in the online discussions through critical thinking, analytical discussion, and the use of complete sentences (see Figure 15.9). The discussion rubric was not meant to discourage participation; therefore, the descriptions remained simple and straightforward. Students were encouraged to engage with others, although it was not required. In other words, it was more significant for a student to post within

Discussion Rubric

	Pass	No Pass
Analysis	Consistently posts ideas that show a clear analysis of the content from materials provided, additional research, and/or content of other members' discussions. Offers ideas that help to continue the discussion.	Does not show a clear analysis of the content from materials provided, additional research, and/or content of other members' discussions. Does not offer ideas that help to continued the discussion.
Responses	Minimum number of responses are made, and they are of high quality.	Does not meet minimum posting requirements. Does not participate in on-going discussions, minimum responses are not made, or they are of low quality.
	Note: It is highly encouraged that all posts and replies demonstrate the use of complete sentences with attention to voice, tone, and audience—free of grammatical, spelling, and punctuation errors.	

Figure 15.9   Sample project-based learning online discussion rubric.

the realms of the topic as opposed to posting random comments and/or purposely instigating an unjustifiable debate.

Students were given several options to meet as a group—in class or on-line—and Skype, while not widely used by today's youth, was what most students utilized to hold virtual face-to-face group meetings. These encounters allowed students simultaneous internet access to further research or translate information during discussions. In fact, online translation devices facilitated the participation of ELs during the preparation of a group Glogster, or online poster. Glogster is an online tool that allowed students to collaborate in the virtual design of a poster, under the direct supervision of the teacher. Glogsters were later presented in class (see Figure 15.10).

The Glogster rubric, shown in Figure 15.11, was also created utilizing an online tool for teachers called RubiStar. Although teachers have access to student work throughout the student creation process in Glogster, the rubric allowed students to set their own parameters around the quality and quantity of information to include based on their self-assessment of what they needed to meet exemplary expectations.

Student groups were also required to complete a Google PowerPoint meant to provide them with a vehicle to expand on one side of the argument (see Figure 15.12; not all slides included). In this case, the student group chose to argue against the idea of thinness and focused on five health concerns related to being too thin.

Similar to the Glogster rubric, the PowerPoint rubric shown in Figure 15.13 was designed using the RubiStart online tool for teachers. Both rubrics employ the same language, and each includes a check box for quick reference for teachers to note whether the group had applied the tool. The

-Sample Group "Glogster"

Figure 15.10 Sample project-based learning glogster student outcome.

Glogster Rubric

Y/N	Tool Applied	Exemplary (3)	Fluent (2)	Developing (1)
☐	Glogster EDU	The analytical illustration demonstrates an effective use of time, content and creativity. The activity incorporates full analysis of the text and evaluation of pertinent details to include.	The analytical illustration demonstrates a consistent use of time, content and creativity. The activity incorporates some analysis of the text and evaluation of pertinent details to include.	The analytical illustration does not demonstrate an effective use of time, content and creativity. The activity incorporates very little analysis of the text and evaluation of pertinent details to include.

Rubric Made Using: **RubiStar** (http://rubistar.4teachers.org)

Figure 15.11 Sample project-based learning glogster rubric.

various components are related to an evaluation of the language the group utilizes to articulate their points and justify their argument(s).

The final step in the project-based learning project was to create a bar graph using Ch to analyze trends across a 5-year period that included teens

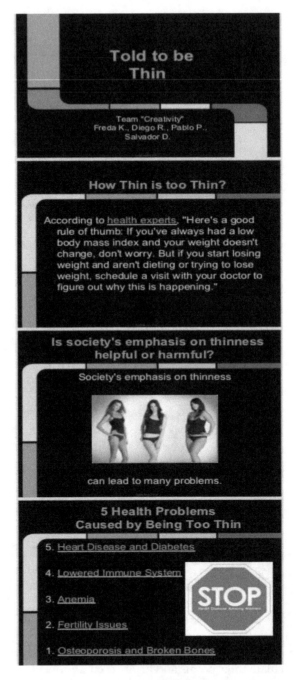

Figure 15.12 Sample project-based learning Powerpoint (four of 13 student slides shown).

Powerpoint Rubric

Y/N	Tool Applied	Exemplary (3)	Fluent (2)	Developing (1)
☐	Google docs	The analytical illustration demonstrates an effective use of time, content and creativity. The activity incorporates full analysis of the text and evaluation of pertinent details to include.	The analytical illustration demonstrates a consistent use of time, content and creativity. The activity incorporates some analysis of the text and evaluation of pertinent details to include.	The analytical illustration does not demonstrate an effective use of time, content and creativity. The activity incorporates very little analysis of the text and evaluation of pertinent details to include.

Rubric Made Using: **RubiStar** (http://rubistar.4teachers.org)

Figure 15.13 Sample project-based learning student Powerpoint presentation rubric.

from different ethnicities. With all of the information gathered and shared through project-based learning, students were able to use their information and bar graphs to work individually on formulating their own personal opinions in a persuasive essay.

CONCLUSION

English language instruction is the responsibility of *all* teachers, and the use of contrastive rhetoric between scripted/technical and academic language can enhance student success as they learn both computer programming and academic composition. The purpose of this reflective essay was to show how one teacher was able to integrate these seemingly separate modalities, linking English language arts to computer programming, ultimately to mathematics.

The authors want to emphasize the importance of developing metacognitive skills in students and suggest that teachers include integrated computing as a means to enhance student engagement and academic success through both technical and academic language. With this in mind, the authors pose the following questions to both researchers and practitioners:

Inquiry Questions

1. What resources do teachers need to have access to in order to successfully implement integrated computing?
2. Does the instruction of contrastive rhetoric between scripted and academic language impact student performance in the production of academic composition?
3. How can the impact of quality or quantity in metacognitive processing be measured?

Action Research Questions

1. How might a teacher scaffold vocabulary and academic language to provide greater access to C-STEM discourse consistent with the English language development (ELD) standards for integrated ELD?
2. How might a teacher incorporate the comparison between computer programming and academic composition to enhance metacognitive skills for students?
3. How can coding and robotics activities help students in reading and writing in English?
4. Should administrators be trained in coding in order to better support the pedagogical expectations of implementation?

NOTES

1. Ch means C with high-level extension, and it contains the initials of the last and first name of the Ch chief architect, Harry Cheng, PhD.
2. All student names are pseudonyms.

REFERENCES

August, D., & Shanahan, T. (2006). *Developing literacy in second-language learners: Report of the national literacy panel on language minority children and youth.* Mahwah, NJ: Erlbaum.

Bransford, J. D., Brown, A. L., & Cocking, R. R. (2000). *How people learn: Brain, mind, experience, and school.* Washington, DC: National Academy of Sciences.

Cheng, H., (2011). Ten reasons to teach and learn computer programming in C. Retrieved from http://iel.ucdavis.edu/publication/WhyC.html

Cox, M. T. (2005). Metacognition in computation: A selected research review. *Artificial Intelligence, 69*(2), 104–141.

Cummings, R. E. (2006). Coding with power: Toward a rhetoric of computer coding and composition. *Science Direct: Computers and Composition, 23*(2006), 430–443.

Diakopoulos, N., & Cass, S. (2016, July 26). *Interactive: The top programming languages 2016.* Retrieved from https://spectrum.ieee.org/static/interactive-the-top-programming-languages-2016

Dollesin, S. (2012, August). *Integrating programming and robotics into English language arts curriculum.* PowerPoint presented at the UC Davis C-STEM Center's Transformative Computing and STEM Education with Common Core Standards workshop, Davis, CA.

Dollesin, S. (2013, May). *Enhancing academic literacy and collaborative conversations through dual programming using C/C++ interpreter Ch and modular robots.* PowerPoint presented at the 3rd Annual Conference on Integrated Computing and STEM Education, Davis, CA.

Edmunds, J., Arshavsky, N., Glennie, E., Charles, K., & Rice, O. (2017). The relationship between project-based learning and rigor in STEM-focused high schools. *Interdisciplinary Journal of Problem-Based Learning, 11*(1), 1–23. https://doi.org/10.7771/1541-5015.1618

Gee, J. P. (2012). *Social linguistics and literacies: Ideology in discourses.* London, England: Routledge.

Pappas, E., Pierrakos, O., & Nagel, R. (2013). Using Bloom's Taxonomy to teach sustainability in multiple contexts. *Journal of Cleaner Production, 48,* 54–64. http://dx.doi.org/10.1016/j.jclepro.2012.09.039

Robeson, L. (2002). Too thin is not in—just ask around. *Sacramento Bee.*

Saunders, W., & Goldenberg, C. (2010). Research to guide English language development instruction. In California Department of Education (Ed.), *Improving education for English learners: Research-based approaches* (pp. 21–83). Sacramento, CA: California Department of Education.

Swain, M., & Lapkin, S. (1995). Problems in output and the cognitive processes they generate: A step towards second language learning. *Applied Linguistics, 16,* 371–391.

CHAPTER 16

EXPLORING SCAFFOLDS AND FEEDBACK FOR IMPROVING COMMUNICATION IN A WATER RESOURCES ENGINEERING LABORATORY COURSE

Cristina Poindexter
California State University

Barbara J. Merino
University of California

Lab reports have been found to be among the most frequent kind of writing assigned to engineering students (Braine, 1989; Conrad, 2017; Wiebe et al., 2001), and reporting on experiment results is fundamental to all engineering disciplines (Wolfe, 2009). Indeed, a recent web search yielded over a million results on the topic of lab reports, addressing all engineering disciplines and a wide variety of topics and questions. Effective written

Culturally and Linguistically Diverse Learners and STEAM, pages 333–355
Copyright © 2019 by Information Age Publishing

communication is valued by many professional engineers. Nonetheless, student writing in lab reports is often deficient in the areas of accurate word choice and rhetorical moves, such as description of data and explanation of engineering analysis or evaluation (Conrad, 2017).

In this chapter, we explore how engineering laboratory experiences, including scaffolded lab report preparation and focused feedback, influence effective communication and conceptual understanding of writing lab reports in civil engineering hydraulics lab classes at the university level. We first present three cycles of lab lessons targeting three key concepts and their lab reports. The three key concepts in hydraulics early, midway, and late in the course were constriction meters, pumps, and hydraulic jumps, respectively. We then outline a modified lab lesson on a hydraulic jump presented to high school students and offer suggestions for guiding principles to use in adapting college level lab experiments and scaffolds for younger students.

SCAFFOLDING OF ENGINEERING LAB REPORT WRITING

Formats for lab reports vary widely. Among professional engineers the distinction is sometimes made between internal versus external reports, with internal reports responding to very specific questions and presenting less detailed protocols, particularly if focusing on a common problem or question. A report written by an engineer to another engineer can be as brief as an outline of the problem and its solution with a short comment on the approach to the solution. External reports on the other hand may be quite extensive depending on the needs of the client or agency and the size of the budget allocated (Kowalski, 2012a). Reports for institutional clients, addressing a complex problem can be the length of a monograph. Recognizing the importance of lab reports in the profession, engineering faculty strive to support students' expertise in this genre of writing in various ways.

In a recent search of university engineering departments in the United States and Canada, however, we found that scaffolding for lab report preparation varied greatly. Some departments provided extensive explanations of the lab report genre, giving examples of different types of reports and providing rubrics. Others provided focused protocols with the goal of providing simulations of what students might expect in professional practice. Here, we briefly discuss a sampler of approaches used to scaffold students' development of lab report writing.

At Colorado State University, the writing center provides writing guides for multiple disciplines. For engineering, these include sample technical reports, proposals and lab reports. In the discussion of lab report types for electrical engineering (Kowalski, 2012b), possible approaches are presented including detailed outlines for specific sections such as the procedures and the findings, or in the case of a presentation of a project, a full report. At the City College of New York, detailed lab manuals or protocols are provided for students outlining the theoretical background and the protocols for conducting the lab experiment, for example, an experiment on hydraulic jumps in civil engineering (City College of New York Department of Civil Engineering, 2014). At the University of Toronto, the engineering communication program provides an overview of the types of documents engineering students are expected to explore or emulate with detailed outlines for each (University of Toronto Engineering Communication Program, 2017). For example, for lab reports, the typical components presented included specific examples for each section: title page abstract, methods and materials, experimental procedure, and so on. Strategies designed to scaffold how to develop specific sections are also provided. For example, for discussion of results, multiple options for analysis are presented, such as comparing expected results with those obtained, analysis of experimental error, providing explanations for results in terms of theoretical issues and instruction on how to develop effective conclusions.

In the literature, we found that more intensive approaches to scaffolding of engineering lab report writing have been applied such as: developing an engineering communication course incorporating genre analysis and linked to an engineering laboratory course at Embry-Riddle Aeronautical University (Beck, 2004), establishing an engineering writing center at the University of Southern Carolina where writing professionals and engineers co-construct scaffolds for students (Walker, 1999), and devising an interactive website for lab report generation at North Carolina State University (Wiebe et al., 2001).

The scaffolding documented in this chapter falls between the two extremes of online resources that students can optionally access on the one hand and a semester-long linked writing course on the other hand. Students are provided detailed protocols similar to those provided by the City University of New York, rubrics, focused feedback informed by Hattie and Timperley (2007) and model lab reports, as well as in-class instruction on engineering communication limited to one full class period.

Scaffolding is particularly important for linguistically diverse students. In the United States, in states with high proportions of English learners, there is a growing consensus that all teachers and most especially secondary teachers must do more to respond to the needs of English learners in core college prep classes such as physics, chemistry and biology (Moje, 2007; Spires, Kerkhoff, & Graham, 2016). Sometimes referenced as "disciplinary literacy teaching" this approach has been more widely known and used among teachers, with bilingual and English as a second language education certification, as "scaffolding language and scaffolding learning" (Gibbons, 2002). Among linguists, this approach is informed by a long tradition of scholarship on the language of "schooling" from a functional linguistics perspective (Schleppegrell, 2004). In this perspective, the context of language use becomes paramount and the focus shifts to unpack two kinds of context: the context of "culture," how members of a cultural group make assumptions about how things are done—participating in a lab class, for example; and the context of a "situation" or its unique features, that is, (a) what is being talked (or written) about, (b) the relationship between the speaker and listener (or writer and reader), and (c) the channel of communication—written or oral.

"Scaffolding" was first used as a term to illustrate parent-child talk in early childhood by Wood, Bruner, and Ross (1976) as "the steps taken to reduce the degrees of freedom in carrying out some tasks so that the child can concentrate on the difficult skill she is in the process of acquiring" (p. 19). It has been widely used by linguists and educators to characterize temporary assistance that is eventually faded (Gibbons, 2002).

In the literature on pedagogy and research on academic writing for older students, among the best-known researcher practitioners are John Swales and Christine Feak (2001, 2004). Their work has been seminal in the reform effort to better prepare students in all disciplines to write clearly and effectively. Channels of communication in engineering vary widely and can be challenging to master for all students. Swales and Feak in their work discuss a variety of text types including summaries, critiques, data commentary, and research papers. In their unit on data commentary they target several key features of data commentary: the strength of the claim, structure of the data commentary, and summaries. They also provide guidance on approaches to use in data presentation and ways of moderating or qualifying claims as well as dealing with graphs and tables. We have found, as others have, that students, particularly undergraduates with limited exposure to academic writing, benefit from explicit attention, mentoring, and feedback on this aspect of academic writing and discourse (Belland, Walker, & Ju Kim, 2017). In the next section, we describe how we provide these types of support for students to write academic lab reports.

THE ENGINEERING COURSE

This chapter focuses on a 15-week lab course titled Hydraulics Laboratory (Lab) offered through the Department of Civil Engineering at California State University, Sacramento (Sacramento State). Within the Department of Civil Engineering, the male to female ratios have remained fairly constant for the period Fall of 2011 to Spring of 2017. Female enrollment ranged from 21% in Fall of 2011 to 25% in Fall of 2017, generally a steady increase of 1–2% every year. Enrollment by ethnicity for Whites dropped from the low 30's in Fall 2011 to the high 20's in 2016. Asian American students have maintained a steady pattern, representing about a quarter of the civil engineering majors. African American students have typically represented about 3% of the majors throughout this period. Latino students represented 28% to 34% of enrolled students (Sacramento State Office of Institutional Research, Effectiveness, & Planning, 2017a). At the College of Engineering at Sacramento State, a typical pattern for the vast majority of students is to complete the major in 6 years.

Sacramento State's diversity is reflective of California's public schools, which serve the largest number of bilingual English learner students in the United States in both K–12 public schools and in its public university system. In school year 2016/2017, there were 1.33 million English learners (EL) and 2.66 million English language proficient (former EL) in the state's K–12 public schools (California Department of Education, 2017). The majority of ELs, 72%, were enrolled in elementary grades (K–6) and speak Spanish (83.1%). A smaller percentage, 8.5%, speak the Asian languages of Vietnamese, Mandarin, Filipino, Cantonese, Korean, Hmong, or Punjabi. A total of 6.56 million, the combined total of ELs and former ELs, represents 42.6% of the total K–12 public school enrollment in California.

Public university enrollments in California as a whole present a more complex picture of bilingual, former EL, and ethnic minority student representation in engineering, with lower proportions of some ethnic minority students. In Fall 2016, there were 11,660 Hispanic students enrolled in California State University (CSU) undergraduate engineering programs, representing 34.6% of total CSU engineering program enrollment. That same semester, there were 4,285 Hispanic students enrolled in University of California (UC) engineering programs, representing 21.3% of the total UC engineering program enrollment (National Center for Education Statistics [NCES], 2018). Asian students numbered 7,662 at CSU engineering programs, 22.7% of the total, and 8,553 at UC engineering programs, 42.5% of the total (NCES, 2018). The lower representation of Hispanics in UC engineering programs may signal an equity issue for the state that needs to be addressed. Even in CSU where Hispanic and other underrepresented minority enrollment is higher, a graduation gap still persists. For example, Sacramento State's underrepresented minority student enrollment was 37% while underrepresented minority student degrees numbered only 31% in the 2015–2016 academic year (Sacramento State Office of Institutional Research, Effectiveness, & Planning, 2017b). Among the cases analyzed here are former ELs and ethnic minority students.

The weekly sessions of Hydraulics Lab alternated between a lab experiment and a lecture designed to introduce students to the lab and revisit core concepts through experimentation. Our data are drawn from three recent lab class cohorts—Spring 2017: $N = 15$; Fall 2017: $N = 14$; and Spring

2018: $N = 9$. The instructor was the first author, Cristina Poindexter. Cristina had had one to two years of experience teaching the Hydraulics Lab course when she taught the sections from which these cases were drawn. She also worked as a professional engineer for a consulting firm in water resources engineering prior to enrolling and completing a PhD in civil engineering, where she also worked as a research assistant and teaching assistant. Cohorts were highly diverse ethnically and linguistically with a high ratio of former ELs. Students in this class are civil engineering majors typically in the last 2 years of their program. The scaffolds typically used in the lab classes were: detailed laboratory procedures, documents, template Microsoft Excel workbooks with pre-prepared figures, sample exemplary lab reports from previous cohorts and one from the professional literature—a memo written by a professional engineer for a municipal client, a review of the rubric with some illustration of typical misperceptions in dealing with each component of the lab report, and feedback from the instructor using the rubric (see the Appendix). The first half of the course also included direct instruction on specific rhetorical moves to make in data commentary.

The Lab Experiments and Reports

The Hydraulics Lab course consists of six lab experiments; however, here only lab reports from three experiments, an early experiment, an experiment midway through the course, and a late experiment are analyzed. The three experiments target flow measurement in pipes with constriction meters, the operation of pumps to move water through pipe systems, and hydraulics jumps. Further details on the experiments can be found in Table 16.1 and the paragraphs below.

Flow Measurement in Pipes With Constriction Meters

Flow measurement in pipes is an important aspect of water resources engineering because of the scarcity and value of water. Constriction meters are simple devices composed of a constriction or narrowing in a pipe and a pressure meter. They are used to measure the volumetric flow rate of a liquid in a pipe. Within the constriction, the velocity of the liquid increases. From Bernoulli's principle, a fundamental principle of fluid mechanics, the increase in velocity results in a decrease in the pressure (Munson, Rothmayer, Okiishi, & Huebsch, 2013). The theoretical flow rate can be computed if the decrease in pressure is measured. Different types of constrictions have different properties. The classic Venturi constriction meter involves a gradual decrease in the pipe cross sectional area followed by an even more gradual expansion. The constriction in a nozzle is more abrupt. Finally, an orifice consists of a simple metal plate with a hole in it placed inside

			Session Experiment Performed
TABLE 16.1 Three Lab Experiments Targeted			
Experiment	**Experiment Name**	**Experiment Description**	
Early	Flow Measurement in Pipes With Constriction Meters	Students measure the pressure drop at a constriction in a pipe (Venturi, nozzle, or orifice) and use it to calculate flow rate, then compare the calculated flow to a direct measurement of flow rate.	3rd
Mid	Pump Curves and System Curves	Students measure pressure upstream and downstream of a pump and at the beginning of end of a pipe system to construct a pump curve and system curve and identify the operating point.	7th
Late	The Hydraulic Jump	Students measure depths upstream and downstream of multiple hydraulic jumps and compare the ratio of these depths to the ratio calculated using theory (the momentum equation).	12th

the pipe and is most abrupt. In this lab experiment, students direct flow through a Venturi, nozzle, and orifice placed inside three different pipes and measure the decrease in pressure in the constrictions. Simultaneously, they measure the time required for 700 pounds of water flowing through the constriction to accumulate in a tank resting on a scale, enabling the direct (or gravimetric) measurement of the volumetric flow rate through the constriction. They then calculate the discharge coefficient (or K value), which relates the theoretical flow through a constriction meter to the directly measured flow rate. They compare these discharge coefficients with discharge coefficients from the literature and fit the data to two equations, one that constrains the exponent in the equation and another where the exponent is unconstrained.

Pump Curves and System Curves

Pumps are essential to move water from place to place, for example drinking water to a storage tank or drainage water out of low-lying areas. For an individual pump, the energy imparted to the water by the pump is inversely related to the volumetric flow rate of the water. This relationship is captured by a plot known as a pump curve. To move water through a pipe system, the pump must be able to impart sufficient energy to (a) lift the water to the highest point in the system and (b) overcome the friction in the pipes. The energy required by a system for both lifting water and overcoming friction is termed the system curve. System curves can be predicted given information about the length of the pipe in the system and the composition of the pipe. The intersection of the pump and system curves represents the operating point of the system. Other topics covered by this lab experiment include pump efficiency and the operation of multiple pumps in combination (in series or in parallel). For this experiment, students measured water pressures on each side of an operating pump and at the beginning and end of a system to create pump and system curves. In the pre-lab, they predicted the system curve after measuring the length of pipe in the system.

The Hydraulic Jump

While the previous two lab experiments deal with flow of water in pipes, the late lab deals with the flow of water in an open channel, where the water surface is exposed to atmospheric pressure. The hydraulic jump is a rapid change in the depth and velocity of an open channel flow. Upstream of a hydraulic jump, the water moves swiftly and is shallow in depth. The water flow depth is termed y_1 or D_1. Downstream of the hydraulic jump, the water moves slowly and is substantially deeper. This depth is termed y_2. Hydraulic jumps generate waves, turbulence, and white water and are very effective in dissipating energy. Hydraulic jumps can be used to dissipate energy at the bottom of dam's spillway (Peterka, 1978). The ratio of the upstream depth to the downstream depth can be calculated theoretically as a function of a non-dimensional number known as the Froude number: F_1 or Fr_1 (Munson et al., 2013). Students create different hydraulic jumps with a range of upstream Froude numbers by moving a gate up and down in the laboratory open channel (or flume), measure the upstream and downstream depths, calculate the theoretical ratio of depths, and calculate the energy dissipation in the hydraulic jumps.

The Study: Scaffolding for Writing Engineering Lab Reports

The role of three scaffolds in particular (Table 16.2) will be addressed here: exemplary reports from previous cohorts, a workshop lecture with a sampler of exercises drawn from Swales and Feak (2001) described in greater detail in the following section, and feedback using a lab report 4-point rubric adapted from a rubric developed by engineering faculty at Sacramento State and informed by standards from ABET (Accreditation Board for Engineering and Technology; see Appendix).

Instruction On Data Commentary

After the class where the mid lab experiment was performed in Session 7, Cristina gave a presentation on data commentary adapted from Swales and Feak (2001). The presentation covered a definition of what data

TABLE 16.2 Scaffolding Used in Sections of Hydraulics Lab		
Scaffolding Type	Scaffolding Description	To Benefit Preparation of Which Lab Report
Modeling	Two to three model lab reports from students in previous cohorts are provided to students before they write their first lab report for the class. *Discussion Focus:* Common and unique features of strengths/challenges.	Early
Modeling	A memo written by a professional engineer on tests to determine the pump curves and system curve for a water pump and pipe system in King County, WA is presented to students. Location, highlighting, and discussion statements are identified in the professional memo.	Mid
Instruction	A presentation on the different moves of data commentary, and the use of claims of appropriate strength is given in class. Students participate in an activity where they are asked to select the stronger of two verbs in a claim about data and in another activity where they work in groups to craft a location, highlighting, or discussion statement related to the data collected the previous week.	Mid
Feedback	Scores on five criteria related to general communication are provided to students for each lab report via the course learning management system. Detailed qualitative feedback is provided where scores are less than 100% for all labs except for the late lab.	Mid, Late

commentary is, a description of the three main moves of data commentary: location, highlighting, discussion statements, differences between location and location + summary statements, highlighting statements do's and don'ts, the importance of making claims of appropriate strength, tools for modulating claim strength, and dealing with so called data problems (inconsistencies, surprises or anomalies in the data). During the presentation, students participated in two exercises based on Unit 4 of Swales and Feak (2001). In the first, they ranked six claims in order of strength. In the second, they identified the stronger of two verbs in nine claims about data. The claims in both exercises were modified from Swales and Feak to address issues that had arisen in the mid lab. For example, Swales and Feak's sample claim "The results given in Figure 4 validate/support the second hypothesis" (p. 88) was modified to "The results in Figure 1 validate/support standard pump theory on pumps operating in combination."

Then, a memo written by a professional engineer regarding tests performed on the North Beach Pump Station in King County, WA (M. Kaplan, personal communication to the North Beach Combined Sewer Overflow Control Team, November 3, 2009) was presented to students. Location, highlighting, and discussion statements in the memo were pointed out to students. For example, the following series of location, highlighting, and discussion statements guide the reader to the conclusion reached by the author that the pipes connected to the pump station are blocked or extremely degraded.

> *Location Statement:* "Figure 1 shows the system curves for both pumps, what the system curve would be for a new 14" steel pipe force main, the manufacturer's full speed pump curve and the actual pump curve calculated using affinity laws."

> *Highlighting Statement:* "The actual system curves rise quickly (and have a very steep slope) compared to the system curve for a new steel pipe as the flow rate increases beyond 1 mgd [millions of gallons per day]."

> *Discussion Statements:* "The steep slope and quick rise of the actual system curves compared to the system curve for a new pipe indicates that significant friction losses or pressure gains are occurring in the pipe as the flow rate increases. That is, the pipe is probably either extremely degraded, has large obstructions, or both."

Following the presentation, students worked together in groups of 2–4 to generate location, highlighting, and discussion statements about the data they had collected the previous week. Examples of student generated statements based on the data they had collected and plotted for two different sections are provided below:

Spring 2018 Cohort:

Location Statement: "The operating point chart [Figure A] reveals a relationship between the pump curve, efficiency curve and the system curve."

Highlighting Statement: "Figure A depicts that pump efficiency begins to decrease after the operating point."

Spring 2017 Cohort:

Location/Discussion Statement: "According to theory, a system curve at zero should equate to the static head. The experimental curve seen in Figure 1 illustrates a negative head at zero, which does not agree with theory."

Discussion Statement: "It is possible at lower flow rates, the pressure gages used in the experiment became less accurate and a different calibration factor may need to be used in calculations."

These student-generated statements suggest students saw distinctions between the different moves of data commentary and grasped that a high-lighting statement should point out trends in the data and that (at least in the Spring 2017 Cohort) claims should be crafted so that they are of appropriate strength. Specifically, in the discussion statement generated by the Spring 2017 cohort, the phrase—"It is possible"—is used to moderate the claim that pressure gages were less accurate for certain flow rates. The statements generated in class were posted in the learning management system for students to see and even use as they wrote their mid lab reports.

Journey Into the Cases

The lab reports of 11 students from three recent offerings of the Hydraulics Lab course offered at California State University Sacramento were reviewed by both authors to identify illustrative examples of exemplary performance based on the rubric and a holistic analysis of the reports early, mid, and late in the course by key elements (organization, explanations, figures/tables presentation and commentary, language use, mechanics) and informed by the rubric. Students were selected using the following criteria: (a) consistent attendance, (b) active lab participation, and (c) strong report writing based on established rubric criteria. Of these 11 students, five were selected as cases for this study because of notable improvement over the semester or evident usage of scaffolding provided. Selecting five diverse cases with different responses is recommended by Stake (2006).

The five students: Gabe, Kate, Valeria, Charles, and Danielle had a median GPA of 3.5. GPA's ranged from 2.5 to 3.9. All students received at least an A– in the course. Three of five were transfer students from other universities or community colleges, and two had started their college education at Sacramento State (native; see Table 16.3).

TABLE 16.3 Cases Selected

Student Name	Section	Transfer or Native
Gabe	Fall 2017	Native
Kate	Spring 2017	Transfer
Valeria	Spring 2017	Native
Charles	Spring 2018	Transfer
Danielle	Spring 2018	Transfer

Note: All student names are pseudonyms.

RESULTS FROM THE CASES

Cases that clearly reflect the influence of the main scaffolding techniques provided in the class are discussed first below. Three students, Danielle, Charles, and Valeria, each relied on a different, specific scaffold provided by the instructor to write their lab reports. Two additional cases of students, Kate and Gabe, show improvement overall with less direct links to any specific scaffold, though we suspect that feedback was important.

In some cases, examples of feedback from the instructor (Cristina) are presented. Feedback protocols were informed by Hattie and Timperley's (2007) work on the power of feedback, which defines feedback as reducing "discrepancies between current understanding of performance and a desired goal." Per Hattie and Timperley, effective feedback answers three questions: "Where am I going? (What are the goals?)"; "How am I going? (What progress is being made?)"; and "Where to next? (What activities need to be undertaken to make better progress?)." Feedback that answer these three questions is referred to as "feed up," "feed back," and "feed forward," respectively. Feedback was primarily provided via a quantitative score on a scale of 1 to 4 using the rubric provided in the Appendix. Feed forward was primarily provided via narrative comments with specific suggestions for how to improve.

Usage of Different Scaffolds (Different Paths to Success)

Modeling—Danielle

Before the assignment of the first lab report, students in the class were provided with lab reports from previous sections as models. One of the three model reports provided to the Spring 2018 section was a report from the previous semester that used bold type for each figure reference. For example:

> *Model report:* "It is seen in **Figure 4** that the K (experimental) is relatively close to the K (literature) values for each constriction meter. For the Orifice, most of the values for K(exp) and K(lit) are close (10.1% difference) meaning that our theory of the apparatus' calibration coefficient K is what it should be when compared to what our theoretical literature K is. The other K values for the Venturi and the Nozzle show a larger variance from the theoretical literature K values. These values are larger with respect to the experimental value of K (20.1%–20.8% bigger) when compared to the theoretical literature K value."

This student's work was chosen as a model for his effective figure references and thoughtful discussion. Danielle's use of the model in the writing of her own lab report is suggested by her similar use of boldface type to refer to tables and figures. In addition, she follows the example of the previous student in her calculation of percent error to quantitatively compare values for the discharge coefficient (*K* value) obtained in the experiment and values for the discharge coefficient from literature.

> *Danielle's report:* "In **Table 1** the lowest *K* literature value was the Orifice... In the constrained case the error between the experimental and literature value were relatively small, the highest percent error was with the Orifice meter with 10.02%. In the unconstrained case the experimental *K* values have over 100% error except for the nozzle which has 19.70% error."

Role of Instruction—Charles

Prior to the mid lab report, students were instructed on the genre of data commentary using material derived from Swales and Feak (2001). Specifically, this instruction discussed three moves in the subgenre: location statements, highlighting statements, and discussion statements. It also discussed the importance of crafting claims of appropriate strength.

Charles' first lab report received a lower score for the criterion—"Effectively uses visual materials"—because only a subset of the figures and tables in his report were directly referenced within the narrative of the lab report. On the mid lab report, Charles used this feedback as well as the instruction on word choices for the moves of lab reports from Swales and Feak (2004) to craft a location statement using a variety of verbs:

> *Charles's report:* "Figure 1 reveals the relationship between head and flow."
>
> "Figure 3 displays the pump curves and relationships of a single pump, pumps in series, and pumps in parallel."
>
> "Figure 4 represents the efficiency with respect to flow of the pumps."

Role of Feedback—Valeria

Detailed feedback was provided, particularly for low scores on any of the criteria used in grading. Feedback related to technical content of each lab experiment only was intended to allow students to correct misconceptions and be better prepared for the final exam. Feedback on the performance on any of the five "General Communication" criteria could be and was used by students to improve subsequent lab reports. One example is Valeria, a former EL. Her first lab report included strong location statements, for example:

> *Valeria's report:* "In Figure 3: *K* vs *Re* in the Appendix, it is evident that venturi and nozzle *K* values are closest together, while the orifice *K* values appear lower on the graph."

While she received a 3.5 out of 4 on Criterion 2, the following feedback was provided:

> *Feedback from the Instructor to Valeria:* "It can help your argument to be specific about lines and markers you refer to in plots (e.g., "In Figure 3, it is evident that Venturi and nozzle K values (diamonds and squares) are closest together").

Valeria appears to have reviewed and made use of this feedback. In the late lab report, she wrote:

> *Valeria's report:* "Figure 1 displays a graph of y_2/y_1 vs Fr_1 for laboratory data (points) and theoretical values (curve) based on the theoretical equation for y_2/y_1 outlined in attached hand calculations."

This sentence would be preferable for many readers with the parenthetical notations Valeria has included, which clearly distinguish theoretical and experimental results.

Improvement Across Early, Mid, and Late Lab Reports

Richer Explanations—Kate

Kate is a case of a student who progressed over the course in terms of her explanations (criterion "Provides adequate explanations, justifications, or supporting evidence") from 2 to 3 to 4 (out of 4). In the early report, she wrote about how the discharge coefficients (K values) determined in the lab class differed from the K values in the literature:

> *Kate's report:* "Comparing the experimental and literature K values, there is a slight difference that was produced among the numbers. This is likely due to the fact that the elevation changes were ignored, even though there was a small amount of elevation change that was present."

In this early report, her commentary lacks a location statement making it challenging to interpret. She also uses imprecise words ("small" and "slight") without further elaboration to describe differences between data points. The feedback she received included the following:

> *Feedback from the Instructor to Kate:* "Effective formatting of Figures 1 to 4—they look great. However, you never mention them in the discussion. If a figure is included, it must be referred to at least once. Referring to a figure can also help you support an argument."

In her mid-lab report she includes a concrete reference to a figure, but one of her explanations is brief and not specific.

> *Kate's report:* "Pump curves were created from each set of experimental data and shown on one plot in Figure 3. This shows a visual comparison of a single pump vs. pumps in parallel, and a single pump vs. pumps in series. It is noted that the trend line for pumps in parallel strongly resembles the trend line for a singular pump."

The feedback provided indicates the need for more extensive discussion.

> *Feedback from the Instructor to Kate:* "A bit more discussion of the pumps in combination, e.g., in what way the pumps in parallel curve resembles the single pump curve, would have been helpful."

By the late lab report, her descriptions and explanations are much richer.

> *Kate's report:* "When comparing the experimental and theoretical ratios of y_1 and y_2, the results are not an exact match; however they do appear to follow the trend line of the theoretical values, as shown in Figure 1. However when looking at the individual results for each trial, there is a maximum percent difference between the experimental and theoretical values of 27.8%, which shows there are some discrepancies between the two methods used for analysis. This could likely be due to different students reading the point gage for the trials, which would result in less accuracy overall. Additionally, it was difficult to get a stable flow rate reading, and an average value was assumed. This could have resulted in an incorrect velocity, and Froude number, being calculated."

Kate's explanation for the possible sources of error in the late lab report draws on her personal experience conducting the experiment. She also uses a quantitative measure for the differences between theoretical and experimental values and continues to reference figures directly.

Stronger Support for Claims—Gabe

Gabe is a student who improved in his use of specific evidence to support claims as well as his appropriate referencing of figures and tables. In Gabe's first report, he does not include a figure reference or specific data to back up one of his claims, though he does explain his general rationale.

> *Gabe's second report:* "For this experiment, seems like the unconstrained equation best fits the data. This is done by comparing the coefficient of determination (R^2) for the three meters between the constrained and unconstrained graphs."

In Gabe's second report he referenced a table to back up his claim that the predicted system curve head values don't match measured system curve head values, making specific reference to the factor by which the measured system curve head values differed from the predicted system head values.

> *Gabe's mid-report:* "When comparing the measured system curve vs. the predicted system curve, the values don't match up. They have the same shape but the measured system curve has higher head values, almost double or more. This can be seen in Table 2 which compared the 3 predicted system curve values to the measured system curve values."

In his mid-report, he goes beyond expectations by creating a table that was not required but provided support for his conclusions about two types of data he compared (predicted and measured system curve head).

Cross Case Insights

Students in these lab courses varied in several key ways: in their writing skills, in their history of learning English, and in their degree of engagement with different lab report scaffolds provided. Still, when we analyzed the lab reports, we noticed several similarities. It was very common for students to omit direct references to figures and tables in the early lab report. Most students, illustrated in the cases presented above, included such references by the late lab report. It was also very common for students to provide insufficient explanations, justifications, or evidence for claims at the beginning. Explanations are critical in engineering. A recommendation in a report may be the basis for the large and expensive overhaul of infrastructure (as may be the case with the memo regarding the North Beach Pump Station used as a model in the course). In such cases, the engineer must provide supporting evidence so that stakeholders and funding agencies can be confident that the costs and impacts are justified. Several students did begin to provide more detailed justification for claims over the semester. Gabe's preparation of and reference to a table that directly compares two system curves, one predicted and one measured, provides more than enough support for his claim that the two curves did not match. Kate's calculation of a percent difference between values supported her claim that there were some discrepancies between theory and experimentally observed values.

Focused feedback appears to have been effective in most of the cases. Both Kate and Valeria appear to have taken advantage of the feedback provided to adjust their lab report writing. Valeria became more specific in her figure references. Kate provided more elaborate and adequate explanations.

A logistical challenge of focused feedback is the instructor time required. Some Hydraulics Lab instructors at Sacramento State teach four sections per semester, a total of 60 students and 360 lab reports over the course of 15 weeks. A possible solution to this challenge may be providing focused feedback on a subset of lab reports only. Instructors would then periodically stage self-review of lab reports via checklists that outline required moves of lab reports and data commentary and thus promote self-regulation. As Hattie and Timperley (2007) outline, self-regulation is an essential component of internalizing feedback.

Another challenge lies in the students using feedback. While these cases are drawn from students who wrote exemplary lab reports who often used feedback to improve their performance, sometimes other students did not appear to read or use feedback. Including positive feedback has been suggested as an approach for increasing student engagement with instructor feedback (Taylor, 2007). This may be a solution in Hydraulics Lab if more focused attention is given to providing specific praise on key elements of lab report writing. Promoting self-review and self-regulation may also increase engagement with instructor feedback.

One reason students may not engage with scaffolds for lab report writing is a lack of appreciation for the importance of writing in engineering disciplines. The memo written by a professional engineer used as a model in the course was in part intended to demonstrate to students how writing is used in the profession. Some students may expect that their technical skills alone will be important in their future careers and for that reason do not strive to improve in their writing. On the other hand, many students appear to have engaged with and used the scaffolding on the subgenre of data commentary. This suggests that when instruction and guidance on technical writing are available, students make use of them productively.

The scaffolding provided to students in the Hydraulics Lab course at Sacramento State differed from scaffolding provided for similar courses at other universities. Colorado State and the University of Toronto focused more on lab report section by section content. Embry-Riddle Aeronautical University and the University of South Carolina involved writing faculty or staff working collaboratively with engineering faculty, to provide students either a linked engineering communication course or scaffolds through a writing center. Nevertheless, it appears that the scaffolding used in the Hydraulics Lab course and documented here was effective for many students in a variety of ways. Charles' use of varied language in his location statements, Danielle's and Gabe's use of quantitative measures to compare data, Valeria's use of specific description to help readers understand a figure, and Kate's rich description of sources of error all demonstrate improvement and progression towards mastery of the subgenre for these exemplary cases. In addition, these results suggest that even high performers can improve given feedback, instruction, modeling, and other scaffolding.

To increase student performance, additional scaffolds could be integrated into future offerings of the Hydraulics Lab course. Lab report section by section content guidance could be easily integrated more systematically by connecting students to the online resources like those hosted by the University of Toronto and Colorado State University. Providing writing instruction through a linked course or engineering writing center would require more institutional resources and may run the risk of promoting the notion that writing is an ancillary rather than integral aspect of engineering professional practice.

CONNECTIONS TO SECONDARY SCHOOLING

A modified version of the hydraulic jump experiment (the late experiment) was presented to high school students visiting Sacramento State for a program known as Women's Shadow Day. This is a visit day sponsored by the Society of Women Engineers' student chapter at Sacramento State and intended to increase the number of women majoring in engineering fields. High school girls from a number of local high schools attended sessions at multiple laboratories within the College of Engineering, including the hydraulics laboratory. Because of time limitations (30 minutes per session) and the visiting students' familiarity with the necessary math but not the necessary fluid mechanics, a modified version of the hydraulic jump experiment was conducted by the visiting students. In the modified version of the experiment, students measured the speed of flow upstream of the hydraulic jump using a float (a rubber ducky) and a timer. They measured the depth upstream of the hydraulic jump using a tape measure. With these two measurements they were able to calculate the Froude number for the flow upstream of the hydraulic jump (Fr_1). Rather than comparing observations of the depth ratio across the jump to theory, the students classified the jump using Fr_1 and a system developed by the United States Bureau of Reclamation (Peterka, 1978; Figure 16.1).

This laboratory experience allowed the visiting high school students to learn about the hydraulic jump, collect data regarding the jump, and compare their experimental results to literature. Terminology including "hydraulic jump" and "spillway" were introduced to discuss how hydraulic jumps are effective at dissipating energy at the base of spillways. An even simpler version of this lab might be possible for high school students unable to visit lab facilities by placing a flat surface, like a cookie sheet, under a faucet. Depending on the flow rate from the faucet, such a set up will produce a circular hydraulic jump that behaves similarly but not identically to the linear hydraulic jump created in the hydraulics laboratory flume. Secondary teachers might scaffold lab report writing about a circular hydraulic jump using the scaffolds applied in the university level Hydraulics Lab course—modified and supplemented.

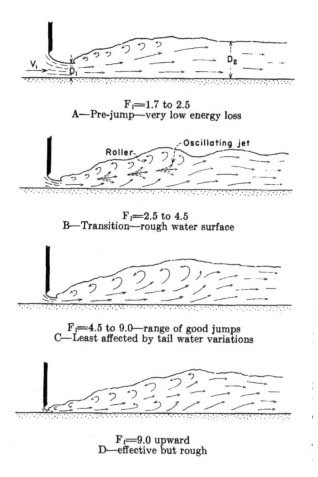

F_1=1.7 to 2.5
A—Pre-jump—very low energy loss

F_1=2.5 to 4.5
B—Transition—rough water surface

F_1=4.5 to 9.0—range of good jumps
C—Least affected by tail water variations

F_1=9.0 upward
D—effective but rough

Figure 16.1   Classification system for hydraulic jumps. *Note:* Source is Peterka (1978). Here D_1 and D_2 (not y_1 and y_2) denote the depths upstream and downstream of the hydraulic jump and F_1 (not Fr_1) denotes the upstream Froude number.

Research on scaffolds offers a wide variety of approaches especially designed for younger students that could support secondary students' writing of lab reports about a hydraulic jump or any other topic. Based on an integrated scaffolding model adapted from Van de Pol, Volman, and Beishuizen (2010), Merino, Fortes, Dubcovsky, and Galli-Banducci (2014) suggest that both so-called cognitive and affective activities could help younger students. Cognitive activities can involve feedback, questioning and reducing degrees of freedom, and slicing down tasks, for example. In the case of lab reports, slicing down the task may involve focusing instruction on location and highlighting statements over one lesson and discussion statements and appropriate strength of claims in an entirely separate lesson. Questioning, could occur in class before writing of data commentary to spur student thinking about data commentary. In the following list, we provide a sampler of questions that could be used to spur thinking about a hydraulic jump by secondary students.

- How is the water flow upstream (before) the hydraulic jump different from the water flow downstream (after) the hydraulic jump?
- How does the hydraulic jump change as the faucet is opened to increase the flow rate?
- How is the hydraulic jump similar to or different from the hydraulic jumps shown in the "Classification System for Hydraulic Jumps" from Peterka (1978)?

Affective activities are also important to consider in scaffolding learning of complex concepts by younger students. Two key affective activities are recruitment and frustration control. Recruitment might involve beginning a lab experiment with material that is exciting and accessible such as videos of large-scale hydraulics jumps in channels (Albuquerque Metropolitan Arroyo Flood Control, 2014; Chanson, 2017; Hoffman, 2016).

Frustration control activities could include assigning team-based lab report writing, similar to the practice adopted in the Hydraulics Lab course of team-based crafting of data commentary statements. Exposing secondary students to an engineering lesson integrating scaffolds such as those we describe may encourage more students (including women, underrepresented minorities, and ELs) to consider engineering as a major at the university level and continue through the major to graduation.

INQUIRY QUESTIONS AND ACTION RESEARCH IDEAS

Inquiry Questions

- How does explicit instruction on essential "moves" in data commentary influence students' performance on lab reports?
- What strategies are effective for fading support and scaffolds in engineering labs?
- What strategies are effective in providing support to former English learners in the writing of data commentary?

Action Research Ideas

- How do positive comments affect students' engagement with feedback and performance in future lab reports?
- How do specific suggestions for improvement impact quality in future lab reports?

APPENDIX
Rubric for Lab Reports

Category	Rubric
Organizes material in a logical manner	1. Report lacks an overall organization. Reader has to make considerable effort to understand the underlying logic and flow of ideas 2. Report is unorganized, but the reader can understand the general idea and logic used. 3. Report is organized and clearly written for the most part. In some areas the logic or flow of ideas is difficult to follow. 4. Report is well organized and clearly written. The underlying logic is clearly articulated and easy to follow.
Provides adequate explanations, justifications, or supporting evidence	1. Claims not well explained, justified or supported with evidence. Major elements of supporting information are missing. 2. Some important explanation, justification, or evidence needed to support claims is missing. Supporting information is incomplete. 3. Explanations, justifications, and/or evidence are mostly included to support claims, with some exceptions. Supporting information is mostly included. 4. Explanations, justifications, and/or evidence are complete. All applicable aspects are addressed in the narrative.
Effectively uses visual material (e.g., figures and tables) to support narrative	1. Visual materials are unclear in content and use incorrect format; not referenced in narrative. 2. Visual materials are mostly clear in content; some format errors; materials inconsistently referenced in narrative or referenced in an awkward manner. 3. Visual materials are mostly clear in content and format with a few exceptions; materials mostly, if not always smoothly, referenced in narrative. 4. Visual materials are clear in content and visual presentation; correctly formatted; materials integrated seamlessly into narrative.
Applies appropriate language, sentence structure, and terminology	1. Language is ambiguous, incorrect terminology. Sentences are overly simple or repetitive. 2. Language is often ambiguous, mostly correct terminology, clear. Sentences lack variety. 3. Language is mostly unambiguous, correct terminology. Sentences reasonably variable. 4. Language is unambiguous, correct for subject matter. Sentence structure is varied and promotes flow.
Constructs grammatically correct text	1. Grammatical errors confuse meaning 2. Meaning is clear to readers who can ignore errors 3. Occasional errors that don't affect meaning 4. No grammar, spelling or punctuation errors

REFERENCES

Albuquerque Metropolitan Arroyo Flood Control Authority. (2014). Hydraulic jump in the north diversion channel 7-19-13 Part 2 [Video file]. Retrieved from https://www.youtube.com/watch?v=sQaWB7nMZ_I

Beck, A. (2004). Collaborative teaching, genre analysis, and cognitive apprenticeship: Engineering a linked writing course. *Teaching English in the Two-Year College, 31*, 388–398.

Belland, B., Walker, A., & Ju Kim, N. (2017). A Bayesian network meta-analysis to synthesize the influence of contexts of scaffolding use on cognitive outcomes in STEM education. *Review of Educational Research, 87*(6), 1042–1081.

Braine, G. (1989, March). *Writing in the natural sciences and engineering: Implications for ESL composition courses.* Paper presented at the Annual Meeting of the Teachers of English to Speakers of Other Languages, San Antonio, TX.

California Department of Education. (2017*). Facts about English learners in California—CalEdFacts.* Retrieved from https://www.cde.ca.gov/ds/sd/cb/cefelfacts.asp

Chanson, H. (2017). Air entrainment in a hydraulic jump [Video file]. Retrieved from http://media.efluids.com/galleries/geophysical?medium=569

City College of New York Department of Civil Engineering. (2014). *Hydraulic engineering laboratory experiments for CE 365, hydraulics and hydrology.* Retrieved from http://daisy.ccny.cuny.edu/~michael/Courses/CE_36500/CCNY_Lab-Manual.pdf

Conrad, S. (2017). Comparison of practitioner and student writing in civil engineering. *Journal of Engineering Education, 106*(2), 191–217.

Gibbons, P. (2002). *Scaffolding language, scaffolding learning: Teaching second language learners in the mainstream classroom.* Portsmouth, NH: Heineman.

Hattie, J., & Timperley, H. (2007). The power of feedback. *Review of Educational Research, 77*(1), 81–112.

Hoffman, B. (2016). Big hydraulic jump [Video file]. Retrieved from https://www.youtube.com/watch?v=OC4sPlXEqt0

Kowalski, D. (2012a). *Communicating as an engineer.* Writing@CSU. Colorado State University. Retrieved from https://writing.colostate.edu/guides/guide.cfm?guideid=84

Kowalski, D. (2012b). *Electrical engineering lab reports.* Writing@CSU. Colorado State University. Retrieved from https://writing.colostate.edu/guides/guide.cfm?guideid=87

Merino, B., Fortes, M., Dubcovsky, L., & Galli-Banducci, J. (2014). Scaffolding academic literacy in a science inquiry project. In P. Spycher (Ed.), *Common Core State Standards in English language arts for English language learners* (pp. 17–34). Alexandria, VA: TESOL Press.

Moje, E. B. (2015). Doing and teaching disciplinary literacy with adolescent learners: A social cultural enterprise. *Harvard Educational Review, 85*(2), 254–278.

Munson, B. R., Rothmayer, A. P., Okiishi, T. H., & Huebsch, W. W. (2013). *Fundamentals of fluid mechanics* (7th ed.). Hoboken, NJ: John Wiley.

National Center for Education Statistics. (2018). *Compare Institutions.* Retrieved from https://nces.ed.gov/ipeds/use-the-data

Peterka, A. J. (1978). *Hydraulic design of stilling basins and energy dissipators* (USBR Engineering Monograph No. 25). Retrieved from https://www.usbr.gov/tsc/techreferences/hydraulics_lab/pubs/EM/EM25.pdf

Sacramento State Office of Institutional Research, Effectiveness, & Planning. (2017a). *Fact book: Civil engineering.* Retrieved from http://www.csus.edu/oir/datacenter/departmentfactbooks/civil17.pdf

Sacramento State Office of Institutional Research, Effectiveness, & Planning. (2017b). *University fact book.* Retrieved from http://www.csus.edu/oir/datacenter/universityfactbook/

Schleppegrell, M. J. (2004). *The language of schooling.* Mahwah, NJ: Erlbaum.

Spires, H. A., Kerkhoff, S. N., & Graham, A. C. (2016). Disciplinary literacy and inquiry: Teaching for deeper content learning. *Journal of Adolescent & Adult Literacy, 60*(2), 151–161.

Stake, R. E. (2006). *Multiple case study analysis.* New York, NY: The Guildford Press.

Swales, J. M., & Feak, C. B. (2001). *Academic writing for graduate students: A course for nonnative speakers of English.* Ann Arbor: University of Michigan Press.

Swales, J. M., & Feak, C. (2004). *Academic writing for graduate students: Essential tasks and skills* (2nd ed.). Ann Arbor: University of Michigan Press.

Taylor, S. S. (2007). Comments on lab reports by mechanical engineering teaching assistants: Typical practices and effects of using a grading rubric. *Journal of business and technical communication, 21*(4), 402–424.

University of Toronto Engineering Communication Program. (2018). *Lab reports.* Retrieved from http://ecp.engineering.utoronto.ca/resources/online-handbook/types-of-documents/lab-reports/

Van de Pol, J., Volman, M., & Beishuizen, J. (2010). Scaffolding in teacher–student interaction: A decade of research. *Educational psychology review, 22*(3), 271–296.

Walker, K. (1999). Using genre theory to teach students engineering lab report writing: A collaborative approach. *IEEE Transactions on Professional Communication, 42*(1), 12–19.

Wiebe, E. N., Hare, H. M., Carter, M., Fahmy, Y., Russell, R., & Ferzli, M. (2001, July). Supporting lab report writing in an introductory materials engineering lab. Paper presented at the meeting of the American Society for Engineering Education, Albuquerque, NM.

Wolfe, J. (2009). How technical communication textbooks fail engineers. *Technical Communication Quarterly, 18*(4), 351–375.

Wood, D., Bruner, J. S., & Ross, G. (1976). The role of tutoring in problem solving. *Journal of Child Psychology and Psychiatry, 17*(2), 89–100.

CHAPTER 17

WHAT'S LANGUAGE GOT TO DO WITH IT?

Theory and Evidence Linking Multilingualism and Mathematics Skills

Rachel Garrett
American Institutes for Research

Erin F. Haynes
Engage Language

Over the last 3 decades, a number of studies have demonstrated a correlation between multilingualism and mathematics skills (Clarkson & Galbraith, 1992; Garrett, 2010; Golash-Boza, 2005; Mouw & Xie, 1999). Despite the potentially groundbreaking nature of these findings, they have not been widely exploited by researchers and educators, possibly because the relationship between language and math is not well understood. However, an exploration of research related to cognition provides some potential clues, namely heightened cognitive processes among multilingual individuals (e.g., Bialystok, 1999; Bialystok, Craik, & Luk, 2008) and the relationship between cognitive processes such as executive function and

Culturally and Linguistically Diverse Learners and STEAM, pages 357–375
Copyright © 2019 by Information Age Publishing
All rights of reproduction in any form reserved.

early mathematics skills (e.g., Blair & Razza, 2007; Welsh, Nix, Blair, Bierman, & Nelson, 2010). Moreover, research from the field of linguistics has shown potential connections among multilingualism, cognitive skills, and mathematics achievement (Clarkson, 2007; MacGregor & Price, 1999).

In this chapter, we offer a theoretical framework to integrate this body of empirical evidence, suggesting explanations for enhanced mathematical abilities of multilingual children. The framework advances our understanding of the relationship between multilingualism and mathematics skills, arguing that multilingualism is a salient factor related to the underlying cognitive processes that contribute to mathematics achievement. Our framework also serves to advance recognition in the field of education that English learners (ELs) who are developing their English proficiency may bring unrecognized abilities to the process of mathematics learning. We conclude with suggestions for further research and practical applications.

THEORETICAL FRAMEWORK

Our framework identifies metalinguistic skills and executive function as underlying cognitive processes that either mediate or moderate the influence of multilingualism on the development of mathematical skills. Metalinguistic skill, or the ability to think about and talk about language itself, helps us understand the abstract structures that are the foundation of all languages (Tunmer, Herriman, & Nesdale, 1988). Human brains are organized to automatically perceive and use language, but people with enhanced metalinguistic skills also perceive how language *works*. Executive function is the set of cognitive processes that we use for cognitive control and to direct behavior. For example, we use executive function as we process information to determine what is relevant or irrelevant. We may present a child with two stacks of blocks and ask which stack uses more blocks. If one stack has more small blocks and is shorter while the other stack has fewer but larger blocks and is taller, a child would use their executive function skill to focus on the number of blocks, rather than the height, to provide the correct answer. Executive function is also used to direct our behavior, for example by allowing us to think about the steps we need to take instead of merely acting. We use executive function skills for planning, problem-solving, and activities related to achieving goals (Miyake, Friedman, Emerson, Witzi, & Howerter, 2000).

Both theory and empirical research have demonstrated links among multilingualism, metalinguistic skill, executive function, and mathematics skills, but we offer the first unifying framework to connect the prior research. For example, multilingualism has been linked separately to enhanced metalinguistic skills, executive function, and mathematics skills across various research studies. Further, both metalinguistic skills and executive function have been shown, in turn, to bear direct associations with

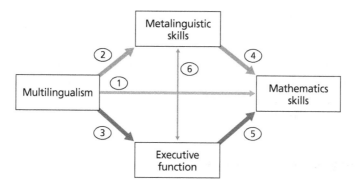

Figure 17.1   Theoretical model of the relationship between multilingualism and mathematics.

mathematics skills, and also with each other. We offer a theoretical model that brings together these previously distinct research streams to explain the relationship between multilingualism and mathematics skills, presented in Figure 17.1. The proposed pathways, numbered sequentially in Figure 17.1, and the research that supports them, are described below.

Pathway 1: Multilingualism and Mathematical Skills

Multiple studies using national longitudinal data sets have shown positive correlations between multilingualism and mathematics skills for students in the United States (Garrett, 2010; Golash-Boza, 2005; Mouw & Xie, 1999). For example, Garrett (2010) found that students with home exposure to non-English languages had higher growth in mathematics scores from kindergarten to Grade 5 compared to monolingual English children, with the largest gains observed among students with the greatest amount of exposure to a non-English language. Internationally, Clarkson and Galbraith (1992) drew on data from Papua New Guinea and found that bilingual students in Grade 6 who were proficient in both their first and second languages had higher scores on mathematics assessments than monolingual children, despite attending schools with significantly fewer resources.

Pathway 2: Multilingualism and Metalinguistic Skills

Metalinguistic awareness may be present in all students, but it has long been acknowledged that it develops more quickly in multilingual students, even those who are preliterate (Aronsson, 1981; Galambos & Goldin-Meadow, 1990).[1] What is still unknown is the degree of multilingualism required to enhance metalinguistic skills. Some prior research has shown that people gain subtle abilities in a second language after even minimal exposure to it, such as more native-like pronunciation (e.g., Chang, Yao, Haynes, & Rhodes, 2011; Haynes, 2010; also see Montrul's [2010] discussion of heritage language acquisition). If metalinguistic skills are acquired similarly to other linguistic skills, these findings suggest that students may be able to benefit from learning another language even if they are not fully bilingual.

Pathway 3: Multilingualism and Executive Function

Executive functions, such as cognitive control and attention, are strengthened as the area of the brain most associated with linguistic function learns to process multiple language systems, properly making use of and separating all languages appropriately (Bialystok, 1999, 2001). Multilingual individuals have been shown to develop these forms of executive control at an earlier age as compared with monolingual individuals, to sustain an advantage at early adulthood, and to decline at slower rates at the end of the life span (Bialystok, 1999; Bialystok et al., 2008). Multilingual individuals demonstrate linguistic flexibility and selective attention, which can translate into improved performance on nonverbal tasks that require high levels of control and attention (Bialystok, 1999). This linguistic flexibility stems from being more practiced in explicit representation and ignoring irrelevant dimensions in language processing. For example, multilingualism appears to make the brain more flexible and sensitized to handling ambiguity, characterized by a heightened ability to recognize dual-embedded images (Bialystok & Shapero, 2005). Research by both Bialystok (1988) and Bialystok and Majumder (1998) indicate that the level of exposure and degree of proficiency in a second language might be associated with higher cognitive control, but with benefits still observed even at low levels of bilingual ability.

Pathway 4: Metalinguistic Skills and Mathematics Skills

Metalinguistic skills were linked to mathematics skills in a study by MacGregor and Price (1999), who examined the relationship between the awareness of specific metalinguistic concepts related to symbols, syntax, ambiguity of form, and algebra notation. Their findings suggested a positive correlation between metalinguistic awareness and algebraic achievement. Additional support for this pathway comes from research on the semiotics of mathematics (e.g., de Oliveira & Cheng, 2011; Ernest, 2008), which explores the signs, rules, and meanings of mathematical language. In identifying the challenges of mathematics, this research also highlights the importance of the analysis of linguistic knowledge (the ability to distinguish form from meaning) and the control of processing (regulation of multiple linguistic demands) in successfully navigating mathematics problems. Taken together, these studies suggest that mathematics and language have underlying structures with similar features, such that a person with control in one area could have enhanced skills in the other.

Pathway 5: Executive Function and Mathematics Skills

Executive function or cognitive executive processes are demonstrated through working memory, flexibility, attention, and control. These functions are key for higher order thinking and fluency with mathematical content. Early attention-related skills are especially important for subsequent school achievement, including mathematics (Breslau et al., 2010; Breslau et al., 2009; Claessens, Duncan, & Engel, 2009; Duncan et al., 2007; Entwisle, Alexander, & Olson, 2005; Howse, Lange, Farran, & Boyles, 2003; McClelland, Morrison, & Holmes, 2000; Rabiner, Coie, & Conduct Problems Prevention Research Group, 2000; Raver, Smith-Donald, Hayes, & Jones, 2005; Yen, Konold, & McDermott, 2004). Early executive function also has been linked to the reasoning process (Richland & Burchinal, 2012), which is important for mathematics skill development. Previous research has linked executive function to mathematics skill acquisition at school entry (Blair & Razza, 2007; Welsh et al., 2010) and the association of behavioral–attentional measures in first grade with mathematics performance at the end of fifth grade (Bodovski & Youn, 2011).

Pathway 6: Metalinguistic Skills and Executive Function

The pathway between metalinguistic skills and executive function has been explored implicitly in other research. For example, multiple studies in prior decades found that bilingual children exhibit an advantage in metalinguistic skills that require control of processing (Bialystok, 1986, 1988; Cromdal, 1999), such as being able to recognize and correct only the grammatical errors in semantically odd sentences like, *The dog fly very high.* Bilingual children are better able to correct such sentences grammatically (the dog *flies* very high) without being distracted by or attempting to alter the unusual meaning—that is, changing *dog* to an animal that usually flies, like *bird.*

CONNECTIONS BETWEEN FUNDAMENTAL CONCEPTS IN LANGUAGE AND MATHEMATICS

The domains of language and mathematics both reflect underlying structures that reflect how humans organize knowledge (see Lakoff & Nuñez, 2000). Our theoretical framework recognizes this fundamental link between these two domains and posits that as a person enhances her ability to draw on knowledge and understanding in one domain, this increases her ability to draw on the other. Expanding on the theoretical model, we present in this section a set of definitions for structures fundamental in both language and math, access to which we hypothesize is greater (although perhaps subconsciously) for bilingual students, or students with multilingual exposure. We present these structures from the perspective of the hierarchy of language, moving from the lexical/orthographical level, to morphology (both of which deal with word knowledge), and then to syntax. At each level, we describe underlying linguistic structures and provide examples from mathematics.

Lexical/Orthographical Structures

In their description of the link between metalinguistic awareness and mathematics, MacGregor and Price (1999) note that "numerals, letters, and other mathematical signs can be treated as symbols detached from real-world referents" (p. 452). For example, there is no intrinsic relationship between the English word *cat* and the animal it refers to; we can just as easily call it *gato*. Similarly, numeric symbols have fixed meanings, but can be substituted or rearranged in systematic ways to refer to the same fundamental thing (e.g., 8, 5 + 3, 9 − 1). We draw from this concept to describe two lexical/orthographical structures: symbol/word representation and polysemy.

Symbol/word representation refers to the fact that symbols and strings of symbols index *fixed* (albeit abstract) meanings. An example in mathematics is place value; a given place value (e.g., 10s, 100s) always has the same fundamental meaning, no matter how it is transformed (through, for example, addition or subtraction). Similarly, in literacy, a given word is always indexed by the same string of letters—we do not sometimes spell the word for a feline critter "cat" and in other instances spell it "dog." Symbol/word representation is foundational to both literacy and numeracy because it provides a standardized and consistent reference point for meaning.

Polysemy, on the other hand, is the coexistence of many possible meanings for a word or phrase. It refers to the fact that symbols and strings of symbols can index *multiple,* context-specific meanings. In literacy, the noun "table" refers to a piece of furniture, but when used as a verb, it means to postpone a discussion. In mathematics, algebraic variables are an obvious

TABLE 17.1   Lexical/Orthographical Structure Definitions, With Language Structure Examples and Links to Related Mathematical Structure Examples

Structure	Definition	Language Structure Example	Related Mathematical Structure Examples
Symbol/word representation	Letters and strings of letters index fixed meanings in a given language system.	"c-a-t" as a string of letters that indexes a fixed meaning	• Numbers and strings of numbers index fixed meanings • Place value
Polysemy	Letters and strings of letters can index multiple meanings.	plus (mathematical operation to add) vs. plus (furthermore)	• Numbers represent a concept of quantity that can be applied to most nouns (four hats, four fingers, four minutes) • Use of algebraic variables, which have context-dependent values

mathematical concept linked to polysemy, since in the expression "$x + 10$," x can represent an infinite number of values (however, set the equation equal to another value, like "15," and the meaning of x becomes fixed). As another example, the fundamental concept that *quantity* is transferable across objects and concepts reflects polysemy; four hats might look very different than four fingers, and both are very different from the abstract concept of 4 minutes, but all represent the same commonly understood *quantity*.

Table 17.1 presents the two types of lexical/orthographical structures with language examples and related mathematical concepts.

Morphology

Morphology refers to the structure of words, including the prefixes and suffixes we use to transform them. We perform morphological transformations on words to mark how they are used within a sentence (e.g., they *go*, but he *goes*). We can also derive new but related meanings with morphological transformations; for example, happy describes how someone feels, which is different but related to the more abstract emotional state of happi-*ness*. In mathematics, we similarly use established procedures to transform numbers. For example, when multiplying a number by five the new number retains an element of the original number (as a factor), but now refers to a larger quantity. As shown in Table 17.2, morphological transformations can be linked to many mathematical procedures, including counting patterns, multiplication, and fractions, but, as in our multiplication example, all produce new numbers that still retain properties of the original number.

TABLE 17.2 Morphology Definition, With Language Structure Example and Links to Related Mathematical Structure Examples

Structure	Definition	Language Structure Example	Related Mathematical Structure Examples
Morphology	Derivational affixes form new words.	happy → happiness	• Counting patterns, such as counting by fives • Multiplication • Fraction transformations

Syntax Structures

Syntax refers to the arrangement of words and phrases to create well-formed sentences in a language. Multiple syntactical structures are related to mathematics. The four presented in Table 17.3 include: surface structure, governance, association, and distribution. These language structures are linked to important mathematical properties that are critical to mastering algebra and higher levels of mathematics.

Surface structure recognizes that two sentences or phrases that look the same or similar on the surface may not have the same meaning. A popular example of this concept is *man bites dog*, which looks very similar to *dog bites man*, with obviously different connotations. However, *man is bitten by dog*, which has the same word order as the former example but different structure, has the same meaning as the latter example. Surface structure, perhaps easier to perceive in the context of languages with more descriptive morphology, is similar to the commutative property in math, in which $a + b = b + a$, but $a - b \neq b - a$: order matters in some structures and not in others.

Governance refers to how elements of a sentence or phrase can *govern*, or impart meaning, on other elements. In the Table 17.3 example, *she caught him running quickly*, "running quickly" could be governed by either *she* or *him*—either she was running quickly when she caught him, or (the more likely interpretation) he was running quickly when she caught him. Or we could assume *quickly* is governed by *caught*; the sentence might imply that she quickly caught him (while he was running). Governance also occurs in mathematics, for example as processes are determined by order of operations, essential for arriving at the correct meaning of a mathematical phrase. Governance is also related to set theory, a branch of mathematical logic that for lower grades is practiced by recognizing like sets of objects; a given object or number (e.g., 2, 4, 6) is governed by the set of which it is an element (e.g., even numbers).

Association is in contrast to governance in that it applies to independent phrases, which, precisely because there are no governance relationships, have free order. We see this frequently with independent phrases like *he*

TABLE 17.3 Syntax Structure Definitions, With Language Structure Examples and Links to Related Mathematical Structure Examples

Structure	Definition	Language Structure Example	Related Mathematical Structure Examples
Surface structure	Different surface structures can have the same meaning, with restrictions.	The cat eats the fish. = The fish is eaten by the cat. ≠ The fish eats the cat.	Commutative property of numbers: $a + b = b + a$ $a - b \neq b - a$
Governance	Syntactic structures govern other structures, imparting meaning.	She caught him running quickly. Possible interpretations: • She caught him while he was running quickly. • She was running quickly when she caught him. • She quickly caught him running. [rare]	• Grouping like sets (e.g., squares, rectangles, and trapezoids are all quadrilaterals). • Order of operation: $a + b \times c \neq (a + b) \times c$
Association	Independent phrases have free order.	I thought he said the cat who eats fish is happy. = He said the cat who eats fish is happy, I thought. = The cat who eats fish is happy, I thought he said.	Associative property of numbers: $(a + b) + c = a + (b + c)$ $(c + a) \times b = b \times (c + a)$
Distribution	Multiple words within phrases can share the same syntactic operation.	The cat and the fish are happy. = The cat is happy and the fish is happy.	• Manipulating arrays of objects. • Distributive property of numbers: $a \times (b + c) = (a \times b) + (a \times c)$

thought or *she said*, which can occur before or after the thing he or she thought or said without consequence to the meaning—we can say either *he thought it was special* or *it was special, he thought*. Mathematically, this structure is related to the associative property of numbers; for some operations, order is irrelevant, as in $(a + b) + c = a + (b + c)$.

Finally, distribution recognizes that multiple words or phrases can share the same syntactic operation. This is a common phenomenon when two nouns share the same verb—for example, *Fred and Mary live in England* is the same as *Fred lives in England and Mary lives in England*. Similarly, possessive markers can apply to multiple nouns—for example, *This is Fred and Mary's house*. Distribution is related to the distributive property of numbers, in which a single operation applies to multiple elements (e.g., $x * (2 + 4) = x * 2 + x * 4$), and is relevant for manipulating arrays, common in linear algebra and also relevant for applied skills such as computer programming.

Practical Importance

The linguistic structures discussed in the prior section are complex and often subtle. As discussed earlier, one does not need to be able to understand these concepts explicitly to understand language. Nonetheless, students regularly encounter these language structures throughout their education, and the extent to which they are able to successfully recognize and draw from the connections between language and mathematics will support development of their conceptual understanding across both domains.

To illustrate this, Figure 17.2 shows an example of a typical reading question a teacher might ask a kindergarten student. Note that in this example of a simple interaction, the child looks at a letter on the page in addition to listening to oral instructions; the letter also is part of the interaction's linguistic content. Recognizing the letter, which indexes a fixed meaning (symbol representation), is essential for a correct response. Students must also understand the terms "name" and "letter," both polysemous words, to respond correctly. Similarly, the math question in Figure 17.2 requires students to understand the symbols, 3 and 2 (as well as "+"). The stars below the numbers are meant to help students arrive at the correct response, but also index a type of quantity polysemy. Finally, to arrive at the answer, students must be able to grasp that the symbols "3 + 2" are effectively the same as the symbol "5."

The Algebra II problem in Figure 17.3 provides an analysis of a high school mathematics question.

Here, polysemy, morphology, governance, and association are related to the mathematical structures in a problem about logarithms. A student with a solid grasp of these features in language could presumably apply

Reading Question	[Teacher points to letter A] *What is the name of this letter?*				
	[Letter A]	What is the	name	of this	letter
Language Structure	symbol representation	n/a	polysemy	n/a	polysemy

Math Question	
Related Mathematics Structure	symbol representation — 3, +, 2
	polysemy — the expression '3 + 2' is the same as '5'

Figure 17.2 Example kindergarten reading and math questions analyzed for metalinguistic structures.

Math Question	If $n = 2^8$ and $x = \log_2(n)$, find the value of x.	
Related Language Structure	polysemy	the variable n is dependent on the equation for meaning, and the variable x is dependent on n; any symbol could be substituted for these two variables
	morphology	2^8 is a transformation of 2 $\log_2(n)$ is also a transformation of 2
	governance	the answer to $n = 2^8$ governs the result of the $\log_2(n)$ operation; students must perform the task in the correct order to arrive at the result
	association	The question could be posed equivalently in the following ways: If $x = \log_2(n)$ and $n = 2^8$, find the value of x. Find the value of x if $n = 2^8$ and $x = \log_2(n)$. Find the value of x if $x = \log_2(n)$ and $n = 2^8$.

Figure 17.3 Example of an Algebra II question analyzed for related metalinguistic awareness. *Note:* Question adapted from the New York State Department of Education's Grade 11 Algebra II curriculum (Module 3, Topic B, Lesson 8; https://www.engageny.org/resource/algebra-ii-module-3-topic-b-lesson-8)

them to the mathematics problem, understanding the context-dependency of the variables, the way log transforms numbers, and the interdependent relationship between the two equations. Conversely, a student who quickly grasps these features in mathematics but struggles in literacy could apply their understanding to the relationships among words. In both cases, most students would need explicit guidance to make these important connections. But as we argue in the next section, such connections would be self-reinforcing, with potentially powerful implications for student achievement across subject areas for all students, and especially for multilingual students.

The Mediating Roles of Metalinguistic Skill and Executive Function

Based on the connections between linguistic and mathematical concepts, our theoretical framework hypothesizes that students who can find and exploit these common features, even subconsciously, are more likely to perform well academically. Therefore, and as an explanation of the empirical evidence relating multilingualism and improved mathematics outcomes, our framework predicts that multilingualism benefits the development of math skills through enhancements to metalinguistic skills and improved executive function.

Specifically, children working across multiple languages can more readily access these linguistic structures and concepts. This ability to access concepts across languages in turn develops the cognitive process that allows recognition of similar patterns in mathematics, and may support facility in gaining conceptual understanding more broadly. The evidence behind the theoretical framework here closely dovetails with the literature that demonstrates how metacognition supports student academic performance (e.g., Azevedo & Hadwin, 2005; Flavell, 1979). We provide a deeper focus on metalinguistics as an aspect of metacognition, but the theoretical model can be easily broadened to the larger metacognition umbrella.

As multilingualism improves understanding of mathematics concepts through metalinguistic skills, it also enhances mathematics learning through executive function. In order to capitalize on the benefits of improved conceptual understanding, children need the ability to organize, sustain attention, process, and appropriately draw from relevant constructs while ignoring irrelevant ones. And while the research has focused on the benefits of multilingualism for cognitive executive function, this holds implications this holds implications for behavioral aspects of executive function executive function, given their positive correlation (Blair & Razza, 2007). Previous interventions, particularly in early education, have tried to focus on incorporating executive function into curricula with mixed success in enhancing academic outcomes

(Barnett et al., 2008; Blair & Raver, 2014; Diamond, Barnett, Thomas, & Munro, 2007; Farran, Wilson, Meador, Norvell, & Nesbitt, 2015). These efforts may need a closer tie to the underlying cognitive processes—including the potential to capitalize on benefits of multilingualism to enhance metalinguistic skills alongside executive function—to robustly produce meaningful improvements in student learning, including mathematics.

IMPLICATIONS FOR THE FIELD

This theoretical framework holds significant implications for both practice and policy. In particular, this framing has important implications for an improved understanding of how to effectively develop mathematics skills for students. With technology moving the world toward an increasingly global and STEM-based economy (Davidson, 2012; Friedman, 2007), the importance of improving the mathematics performance of students in the United States has increased. States across the country have adapted rigorous college and career readiness standards to promote improved conceptual understanding of mathematics and student performance (Ujifusa, 2016), but educators are struggling with how to teach in a way that engenders deep conceptual understanding (Kober, McIntosh, & Rentner, 2013). Improved knowledge of the cognitive processes that underlie conceptual understanding for students is critical for determining the success of this approach. This framework therefore has important implications for instruction and support.

The implications for instruction are important to educating both multilingual and non-multilingual students for several reasons. For multilingual students, educators may capitalize on the students' predisposition for heightened metalinguistic and executive function skills to support mathematics learning. Perhaps more importantly, bringing an awareness of this multilingual advantage may bring about further benefits. Among students who are English learners and often facing a deficit-based perspective, educators, students, and families alike may benefit from an explicit recognition of the assets English learner students bring through their exposure to multiple languages. Moreover, educators can explicitly support the development and use of metalinguistic skills and executive function to enhance mathematics learning for all students, including non-multilingual students, since multilingualism is not the only way to enhance these supportive skills.

At the policy level, this framework contributes to a robust rationale for allocating resources to bilingual programs and world language instruction, not to mention teacher professional learning. Too often, policymakers and educators are informed by a deficit-based perspective of multilingualism, taking a negative view of the skills of children from non-English households and categorizing school-based language programs in an elective (i.e., not essential) category of instruction. This perspective can have negative consequences for many aspects of students' development, including their self-esteem, valuation of home culture, and the development of identity and social skills in a non-English context (Gándara & Contreras, 2009). Instead, this asset-based perspective, rooted in empirical evidence of cognitive development, would support academic growth in mathematics and across the disciplines concurrent with providing validation of multicultural diversity.

CONCLUSION AND FUTURE RESEARCH DIRECTIONS

This chapter has introduced a model linking multilingualism and mathematics across multiple cognitive pathways. It is critically important that we continue to explore these links empirically. This line of inquiry holds potential to better understand student learning, and in an educational context it may help to avoid overlooking student assets, present just below the surface and ripe for development. We have outlined several practical implications of our theoretical framework, but further research evidence and empirical information is necessary to inform a comprehensive, whole-child educational approach.

We propose the inquiry and action research questions that follow, with the desire that we as a field move continuously towards a more comprehensive understanding of what multilingualism means for students, not just related to their ability to make meaning and communicate in mathematics, but to their ability to achieve across content areas.

Inquiry Questions

1. What types of relationships can we observe between access to multilingual education or input (e.g., language classes, spending time with speakers of another language) and improved executive function or metalinguistic skills? To what extent must a student be multilingual or multiliterate to see enhancements in these areas?
2. In what ways do metalinguistic skills and executive function mediate the relationship of multilingual input with mathematics skill development?
3. Do these relationships vary by language (e.g., students who are bilingual in English and Spanish versus students who are bilingual in English and Mandarin)?

Multiple approaches could be used to answer these questions. For example, these questions could be examined by assessing executive function, metalinguistic skills, and mathematics skills among students entering a dual language program and comparing them to students with similar demographics entering a monolingual English program, with comparisons repeated over time as students progress in their respective programs. Researchers could look at variation in student outcomes across groups of students with similar language input, for example those experiencing Mandarin and English language instruction separately from those experiencing Spanish and English language instruction. A follow-up study could then explore outcomes from other types of language learning programs, such as after-school or weekend heritage language lessons (e.g., Mandarin school).

Action Research Questions

Beyond these knowledge-building inquiries, our theoretical framework suggests a set of action-oriented questions.

1. *Teacher educators and professional development providers:* Provide mathematics teachers with professional learning to help them understand the links between language and mathematics, and build their understanding of metalinguistics and executive function. Illustrate instruction-based applications of these links that can be implemented through their curricula and classroom interactions. In what ways does this professional learning for teachers support teacher learning? In what ways does it support improved student mathematics outcomes, particularly for multilingual learners and English learners?

2. *Teachers:* Form a team of English language arts, English language development, and mathematics teachers and select a handful of students who are experiencing challenges in one of the two subjects. Identify the topics and concepts where each student experiences difficulty, and then identify the parallels of those concepts in the subject in which they are experiencing more success. Provide students instruction that explicitly addresses the links identified in this chapter and addresses those between their successes and challenges across courses. Does offering these explicit links between the two subjects help students improve?

NOTE

1. Literacy may further enhance metalinguistic skills (e.g., Bialystok, 1991; Ehri, 1975; Lundberg, Olofsson, & Wall, 1980; Van Kleeck, 1982).

REFERENCES

Aronsson, K. (1981). The bilingual preschooler as grammarian: Children's paraphrases of ungrammatical sentences. *Psychological Research Bulletin, 11*, 1–26.

Azevedo, R., & Hadwin, A. F. (2005). Scaffolding self-regulated learning and metacognition—implications for the design of computer-based scaffolds. *Instructional Science, 33*(5–6), 367–379.

Barnett, W. S., Jung, K., Yarosz, D. J., Thomas, J., Hornbeck, A., Stechuk, R., & Burns, S. (2008). Educational effects of the Tools of the Mind curriculum: A randomized trial. *Earl Childhood Research Quarterly, 23*(3), 299–313.

Bialystok, E. (1986). Factors in the growth of linguistic awareness. *Child Development, 57*(2), 498–510.

Bialystok, E. (1988). Levels of bilingualism and levels of linguistic awareness. *Developmental Psychology, 24*(4), 560–567.

Bialystok, E. (1991). *Language processing in bilingual children.* Cambridge, England: Cambridge University Press.

Bialystok, E. (1999). Cognitive complexity and attentional control in the bilingual mind. *Child Development, 70*(3), 636–644.

Bialystok, E. (2001). *Bilingualism in development: Language, literacy and cognition.* New York, NY: Cambridge University Press.

Bialystok, E., Craik, F., & Luk, G. (2008). Cognitive control and lexical access in younger and older bilinguals. *Journal of Experimental Psychology: Learning, Memory and Cognition, 34*(4), 859–873.

Bialystok, E., & Majumder, S. (1998). The relationship between bilingualism and the development of cognitive processes in problem-solving. *Applied Psycholinguistics, 19*(1), 69–85.

Bialystok, E., & Shapero, D. (2005). Ambiguous benefits: The effect of bilingualism on reversing ambiguous figures. *Developmental Science, 8*(6), 595–604.

Blair, C., & Raver, C. C. (2014). Closing the achievement gap through modification of neurocognitive and neuroendocrine function: Results from a cluster randomized controlled trial of an innovative approach to the education of children in kindergarten. *PLoS ONE, 9*(11): e112393. https://dx.doi.org/10.1371/journal.pone.0112393

Blair, C., & Razza, R. P. (2007). Relating effortful control, executive function, and false belief understanding to emerging math and literacy ability in kindergarten. *Child Development, 78*(2), 647–663.

Bodovski, K., & Youn, M. (2011). The long term effects of early acquired skills and behaviors on young children's achievement in literacy and mathematics. *Journal of Early Childhood Research, 9*(1), 4–19.

Breslau, N., Breslau, J., Peterson, E., Miller, E., Lucia, V., Bohnert, K., & Nigg, J. (2010). Change in teachers' ratings of attention problems and subsequent change in academic achievement: A prospective analysis. *Psychological Medicine, 40*(1), 159–166.

Breslau, J., Miller, E., Breslau, N., Bohnert, K., Lucia, V., & Schweitzer, J. (2009). The impact of early behavior disturbances on academic achievement in high school. *Pediatrics, 123*(6), 1472–1476.

Chang, C. B., Yao, Y., Haynes, E. F., & Rhodes, R. (2011). Production of phonetic and phonological contrast by heritage speakers of Mandarin. *The Journal of the Acoustical Society of America, 129*(6), 3964–3980.

Claessens, A., Duncan, G., & Engel, M. (2009). Kindergarten skills and fifth-grade achievement: Evidence from the ECLS-K. *Economics of Education Review, 28,* 415–427.

Clarkson, P. C. (2007). Australian Vietnamese students learning mathematics: High ability bilinguals and their use of their languages. *Educational Studies in Mathematics, 64*(2), 191–215.

Clarkson, P., & Galbraith, P. (1992). Bilingualism and mathematics learning: Another perspective. *Journal for Research in Mathematics Education, 23*(1), 34–44.

Cromdal, J. (1999). Childhood bilingualism and metalinguistic skills: Analysis and control in young Swedish–English bilinguals. *Applied Psycholinguistics, 20*(1990), 1–20.

Davidson, A. (2012, January/February). Making it in America. *The Atlantic Monthly.* Retrieved from http://www.theatlantic.com/magazine/archive/2012/01/making-it-in-america/308844/

de Oliveira, L. C., & Cheng, D. (2011). Language and the multisemiotic nature of mathematics. *The Reading Matrix, 11*(3), 255–268.

Diamond, A., Barnett, W. S., Thomas, J., & Munro, S. (2007). Preschool program improves cognitive control. *Science, 318,* 1387–1388.

Duncan, G., Dowsett, C., Claessens, A., Magnuson, K., Huston, A., Klebanov, P., . . . Duckwork, K. (2007). School readiness and later achievement. *Developmental Psychology, 43*(6), 1428–1446.

Ehri, L. (1975). Word consciousness in readers and prereaders. *Journal of Educational Psychology, 67,* 204–212.

Entwisle, D., Alexander, K., & Olson, L. (2005). First grade and educational attainment by age 22: A new story. *American Journal of Sociology, 110,* 1458–1502.

Ernest, P. (2008). Towards a semiotics of mathematical text (Part 2). *For the Learning of Mathematics, 28*(3), 39–47.

Farran, D. C., Wilson, S. J., Meador, D., Norvell, J., & Nesbitt, K. (2015). *Experimental evaluation of the Tools of the Mind pre-K curriculum: Technical report* (Working Paper). Nashville, TN: Vanderbilt University, Peabody Research Institute.

Flavell, J. H. (1979). Metacognition and cognitive monitoring: A new area of cognitive–developmental inquiry. *American Psychologist, 34*(10), 906–911.

Friedman, T. (2007). *The world is flat: A brief history of the twenty-first century.* New York, NY: Farrar, Straus and Giroux.

Galambos, S. J., & Goldin-Meadow, S. (1990). The effects of learning two languages on levels of metalinguistic awareness. *Cognition, 34,* 1–56.

Gándara, P. C., & Contreras, F. (2009). *The Latino education crises: The consequences of failed social policies.* Cambridge, MA: Harvard University Press.

Garrett, R. (2010). *Multilingualism, mathematics achievement, and instructional language policy* (Doctoral dissertation). Available from ProQuest Dissertations and Theses database. (Accession Order No. 3419635)

Golash-Boza, T. (2005). Assessing the advantages of bilingualism for children of immigrants. *International Migration Review, 39*(3), 721–753.

Haynes, E. F. (2010). *Phonetic and phonological acquisition in endangered languages learned by adults—A case study of Numu (Oregon Northern Paiute)* (Doctoral dissertation). Available from ProQuest Dissertations and Theses database. (Accession Order No. 3413386)

Howse, R. B., Lange, G., Farran, D. C., & Boyles, C. D. (2003). Motivation and self-regulation as predictors of achievement in economically disadvantaged young children. *The Journal of Experimental Education, 71,* 151–174.

Kober, N., McIntosh, S., & Rentner, D. S. (2013). *Year 3 of implementing the Common Core State Standards: Professional development for teachers and principals.* Washington, DC: Center on Education Policy.

Lakoff, G., & Nuñez, R. E. (2000). *Where mathematics come from: How the embodied mind brings mathematics into being.* New York, NY: Basic Books.

Lundberg, I., Olofsson, A., & Wall, S. (1980). Reading and spelling skills in the first school years predicted from phonemic awareness skills in kindergarten. *Scandinavian Journal of Psychology, 21,* 159–173.

MacGregor, M., & Price, E. (1999). An exploration of aspects of language proficiency and algebra learning. *Journal for Research in Mathematics Education, 30*(4), 449–467.

McClelland, M., Morrison, F. J., & Holmes, D. L. (2000). Children at risk for early academic problems: The role of learning-related social skills. *Early Childhood Research Quarterly, 15*(3), 307–329.

Miyake, A., Friedman, N. P., Emerson, M. J., Witzki, A. H., & Howerter, A. (2000). The unity and diversity of executive functions and their contributions to complex "frontal lobe" tasks: A latent variable analysis. *Cognitive Psychology, 41*(1), 49–100.

Montrul, S. (2010). Current issues in heritage language acquisition. *Annual Review of Applied Linguistics, 30,* 3–23.

Mouw, T., & Xie, Y. (1999). Bilingualism and the academic achievement of first-and second-generation Asian Americans: Accommodation with or without assimilation? *American Sociological Review, 64*(2), 232–252.

Rabiner, D., Coie, J. D., & Conduct Problems Prevention Research Group. (2000). Early attention problems and children's reading achievement: A longitudinal investigation. *Journal of the American Academy of Child and Adolescent Psychiatry, 39,* 859–867.

Raver, C. C., Smith-Donald, R., Hayes, T., & Jones, S. M. (2005, April). *Self-regulation across differing risk and sociocultural contexts: Preliminary findings from the Chicago School Readiness Project.* Paper presented at the biennial meeting of the Society for Research in Child Development, Atlanta, GA.

Richland, L., & Burchinal, M. (2012). Early executive function predicts reasoning development. *Psychological Science, 24*(1), 87–92.

Tunmer, W., Herriman, M., & Nesdale, A. (1988). Metalinguistic abilities and beginning reading. *Reading Research Quarterly, 23,* 134–158.

Ujifusa, A. (2016, October 27). Map: Tracking the Common Core State Standards. *Education Week.* Retrieved from http://www.edweek.org/ew/section/multimedia/map-states-academic-standards-common-core-or.html?cmp=eml-enl-eu-news1

Van Kleeck, A. (1982). The emergence of linguistic awareness: A cognitive framework. *Merrill-Palmer Quarterly, 28,* 237–265.

Welsh, J. A., Nix, R. L., Blair, C., Bierman, K. L., & Nelson, K. E. (2010). The development of cognitive skills and gains in academic school readiness for children from low income families. *Journal of Educational Psychology, 102*(1), 43–53.

Yen, C., Konold, T. R., & McDermott, P. A. (2004). Does learning behavior augment cognitive ability as an indicator of academic achievement? *Journal of School Psychology, 42*(2), 157–169.

CHAPTER 18

APPENDIX

Developing Successful Projects Within a Research–Practice Partnership by Using Stakeholder Advisory Groups

Julie Kochanek
American Institutes for Research

Carrie Scholz
American Institutes for Research

The chapters in this volume expand our field's repertoire of tools to meet the needs of culturally and linguistically diverse students in STEAM subjects. However, further research is needed to help these students develop their talents and excel in an increasingly technology-driven world. The authors featured here describe and encourage applied research and research–practice partnerships, with the goal of ensuring that research is relevant to practice, and that practice is based in research.

However, we recognize that research–practice partnerships can feel complicated and difficult to implement, especially given the divergent needs of people working primarily in research and people operating primarily in

Culturally and Linguistically Diverse Learners and STEAM, pages 377–387
Copyright © 2019 by Information Age Publishing

school environments. Drawing from our own extensive experience working in and advising research–practice partnerships, we discuss how stakeholder advisory groups can facilitate processes and outcomes that are beneficial to all members of a research–practice partnership.

HOW DO STAKEHOLDER ADVISORY GROUPS BENEFIT RESEARCHERS AND PRACTITIONERS?

A stakeholder advisory group is a subgroup of individuals from the research–practice partnership or designees from their organizations. Stakeholder advisory group members meet regularly with the research–practice partnership's researchers. Stakeholder advisory groups are charged with ensuring that products and services from a project are relevant and useful for the intended stakeholders. Stakeholder advisory groups yield three primary benefits for research–practice partnerships. They (a) build practitioner and researcher trust and capacity, (b) lead to greater ownership of the work, and (c) drive knowledge utilization.

Build Practitioner and Researcher Trust and Capacity

Stakeholder advisory groups offer practitioners and researchers an opportunity to engage in authentic collaborative work with one another. Researchers turn to stakeholder advisory group members for their constructive feedback, knowledge about the data as well as the context in which the research is being conducted, and deep understanding about how best to communicate findings to targeted audiences. By actively listening and revising projects to incorporate stakeholder advisory group member feedback, researchers demonstrate that they trust the practitioners' expertise. Practitioners' trust of researchers often is developed when researchers invite stakeholder advisory group members to critique decisions made throughout a project. Although the trust is being built throughout these collaborative exchanges, researchers develop a great capacity to understand how to design research that will be relevant and useful for practitioners. In turn, practitioners deepen their appreciation of the research process.

Ensure Greater Ownership of the Work

By serving as thought partners at every stage of the research process, stakeholder advisory groups ensure that practitioners have an authentic role to fulfill. In addition to serving as researchers' thought partners, stakeholder advisory group members also play a key role in describing a study's progress and related strategic decisions to the larger research–practice partnership. By presenting the work to their colleagues, stakeholder advisory group members begin to sharpen their messaging about the study. This helps to prepare them to champion the work in front of broader audiences later in the project's life cycle.

Drive Knowledge Utilization

When stakeholder advisory group members have had a stake in the research from its earliest stages, we posit that practitioners are much more likely to use it to inform their decisions and actions. The following quote from a stakeholder advisory group member summarizes how engaging with researchers on a study improved her capacity, led to greater ownership of the work, and positioned her to drive knowledge utilization:

> I am now more aware and appreciative of the research process, less perplexed by the complexities of how research is conducted, and even more committed to taking what we learned from the research and applying it to improve student achievement...
>
> —Stakeholder Advisory Group Member,
> REL Midwest Virtual Education Research Alliance[1]

WHO SHOULD BE ON A STAKEHOLDER ADVISORY GROUP?

Ideally, two to three individuals serve on a stakeholder advisory group. Stakeholder advisory group members should be recruited to play one or more of the following roles:

- Informant
- Learner
- Boundary Spanner
- Champion

Informants

Informants have a deep understanding of the topic being studied and/or the data that will be analyzed for the project. For example, an informant may be a teacher or curriculum director who is implementing the policy or program being studied. These informants are positioned to provide insights to the project team about issues related to implementation or challenges they may face when measuring intended outcomes. This information is critical for the research team to consider when designing the study. Alternatively, an informant might be an individual from a district's research office who has a deep understanding of the extant data that will be analyzed for the study. This individual may be able to help advise the research team on data limitations they should be aware of while planning the study design and analysis.

Learners

Learners are in a position to replicate a similar study in another setting. As mentioned earlier, stakeholder advisory group roles are not exclusive, as an advisor on the data quality also may serve as a learner on the stakeholder advisory group. That person may be interested in learning more about particular study designs and analyses that could be adapted to answer other questions using the district's data. By serving on the stakeholder advisory group, the learner has the opportunity to access the code used to clean and analyze the data. A learner also may be from another organization and take lessons back to his or her context to attempt to replicate the same study.

Boundary Spanners

Boundary spanners have strong working relationships with other research–practice partnership members or are well connected with multiple organizations outside the partnership. Through their relationships, these individuals are keenly aware of how to communicate with targeted audiences: They know the audience's contexts, how the work might compliment current efforts, and which communication channels may be leveraged to share the study findings across pre-existing networks.

Champions

Finally, each project's stakeholder advisory group could benefit from someone serving as a champion. These members typically are decision makers in their organizations and have the power to commit organizational resources needed to act on the results of a particular study. For example, they would be in the position to critically think about whether to modify or cancel a program or policy if the research–practice partnership's study found that it did not lead to its intended outcomes. In many cases, the champions' other work demands may prevent them from serving on projects' stakeholder advisory groups. In these instances, champions often designate staff to work with the project teams to inform the work and maintain its usefulness. A champion may be a district superintendent who has requested the work but must appoint an assistant superintendent to participate on the stakeholder advisory group. A champion might also be a curriculum director who also serves as an advisor on the project.

In general, the stakeholder advisory group members meet every 4–6 weeks during the life of a given project to discuss decisions by the project team that shape the project. The topics will vary depending on the stage and type of the project. For example, the discussions with the stakeholder advisory group may focus on confirming the research questions, framing the problem, determining the sampling strategy, identifying the data sources, and reviewing protocols and methods. Stakeholder advisory group members will have varying levels of expertise to discuss and weigh in on these topics. However, it is often during conversations about the reasons for specific decisions that each side learns about and better understands the contexts of research and practice. When a project team attempts to find solutions to stakeholder concerns while maintaining the integrity of the project, stakeholders are more likely to find the project relevant and useful.

To clarify the responsibilities of the stakeholder advisory group members and the project team members, we share Table A.1 with potential stakeholder advisory group members and revisit it as needed throughout the course of a project.

TABLE A.1 Roles and Responsibilities for Stakeholder Advisory Group (SAG) Members and Project Teams

SAG Member Roles and Responsibilities	Project Team Roles and Responsibilities
• Attend one-hour meetings every 4–6 weeks. • Review materials prior to meetings. • Actively participate in group discussions to represent alliance, organizational, and stakeholder interests. • Discuss project progress with others in organization and/or alliance members. • Provide feedback on planning, implementation, product design, and dissemination. • [Add any project specific responsibilities such as providing data for the project or granting access to teachers.]	• Schedule, plan, and convene SAG meetings. • Provide agenda and meeting materials for SAG members at least one week in advance of meeting. • Explain rationale for project team decisions and pros and cons of alternatives. • Listen to and summarize SAG member perspectives. • Provide potential solutions to remedy concerns and negotiate resolutions. • Gather additional information and resources related to the discussion. • Follow up on unresolved items after the meeting.

WHAT TOPICS SHOULD BE COVERED IN STAKEHOLDER ADVISORY GROUP MEETINGS?

We have found that the topics covered with the stakeholder advisory group vary through the life cycle of the project work. Typically, we find the following important topics: (a) relevant questions, (b) methods, (c) data quality, and (d) end product.

First, researchers work with stakeholders to develop projects based on the established research agenda. As projects are designed to address research questions, stakeholders are asked to revisit the questions in light of the project design. We specifically ask whether our projects address the *questions as members intended.* At times, these conversations bring misunderstandings to the surface signaling quickly that the project design, although appropriate for the research questions, does not meet the core need of the stakeholders.

In other cases, these conversations have revealed practitioner beliefs about certain research methods that make practitioners less likely to trust the findings of a study. In all cases, we have attempted to ground projects solidly in stakeholder needs to better position our work to result in relevant and useful products.

Once the research question is finalized, the topics of the next critical conversations address the *project's methods.* Specifically, researchers and stakeholder advisory group members discuss the sampling plan, the variables to be measured, and the instruments to be used to gather the data.

A third critical juncture for the stakeholder advisory group input is a discussion about *data quality.* Although important when primary data are collected, this discussion is particularly important when extant data is being analyzed for the project. As mentioned earlier, at least one stakeholder advisory group member should have familiarity with any extant data being used for the project. Insights about the data will inform the research team about limitations to consider prior to conducting the analysis. Similarly, a stakeholder advisory group member's familiarity with the data will help the researchers interpret any surprising findings that may arise due to extraneous variables.

The final topic to be addressed by stakeholder advisory group members is the research project's *end product.* It is important for researchers and stakeholder advisory group members to discuss the project's end product from the beginning. Being clear about the audience(s) helps to inform the questions asked, the sampling strategy, and the data to be analyzed. Once the stakeholder advisory group and researchers identify the ideal audience(s), they begin to outline the outlets that the intended audience(s) (e.g., parents, teachers, principals, superintendents, legislators) typically access to get information about the latest education research. How information is packaged and communicated within those outlets helps to inform the format of the final product (e.g., a town hall meeting, blog, memo, briefing) as well as its content (e.g., quotes from key stakeholders that exemplify the project's findings, data visualizations, actionable next steps). By thinking through these details ahead of time, stakeholder advisory group members also are able to find out whether there are upcoming meetings at which the project's results could be shared.

This preplanning also positions the partnership to select who from the stakeholder advisory group or larger research–practice partnership will lead the communication efforts. Scheduling the communication about a project well in advance is arguably as important as coordinating the participant recruitment and data collection. When researchers and their partners strategically communicate about research findings and their implications, the opportunity for knowledge utilization increases.

HOW ARE STAKEHOLDER ADVISORY GROUPS USED FOR PROJECTS OTHER THAN RESEARCH STUDIES?

In addition to supporting a research–practice partnership's research, stakeholder advisory groups have an important role to play in informing the partnership's trainings or events, technical assistance, or infographics or other communication tools. Although the goal of working with advisors to ensure a project is relevant and useful remains the same, additional stakeholder advisory group members may be needed to advise on non-research projects.

As research–practice partnerships build out portfolios of research studies, they often design events as a communication strategy about the results of their work. For example, although a team conducting a study of culturally responsive leadership strategies may plan to brief district leadership on study findings, they may also realize that the findings need to be shared with school leaders across the district if they are to be incorporated into practice. Discussions with district leadership reveal that the district-sponsored professional development plans already are solidified for the school year. However, given the importance of the findings to the district, leadership wants to partner on a series of workings that will help schools teams in each region better understand the study findings and plan for how best to incorporate them into their work this year. Recruitment of a stakeholder advisory group to inform both the design of workshop contents and logistics can ensure a more successful series of trainings. Stakeholder advisory group membership for trainings should include a champion who is able to help bring participants to the event. By participating in the stakeholder advisory group, the champion will have confidence in the event quality and intended outcomes and contribute her own political capital to spread enthusiasm across regional leaders to recruit school teams for participation. In addition to the champion, the stakeholder advisory group should include two or three informants from the group intended as the main audience for the event—in this case, school leaders. The champion can help identify school leaders who will be eager participants and at least one who will be a critical voice. These informants can help check event planning assumptions about timing of sessions, design of exercises, and the balance of lecture and discussion. Although the eager informants can add positive feedback to the planning, the critical informant will help surface potential problems, which can be addressed prior to the event for a more successful training.

Research–practice partnerships also can engage in technical assistance projects that do not fit a typical study framework. For example, a research team may support a district in the design and testing of a school climate survey protocol. Although survey development requires both methodological and content expertise, feedback from a stakeholder advisory group will determine whether the survey is addressing constructs of interest to the district with measures that have face validity for those in practice. Stakeholder advisory group membership is similar to that of a research study, with a champion who will ultimately administer the survey, informants who come from the role of those who will complete the survey, and learners from the district research and data team. The stakeholder advisory group meeting topics can be derived from the work at hand. For survey development, topics follow the steps a team takes to develop a survey: construct selection and definition, reviews of measure and item banks, item development where necessary, sampling, promotion of the survey, administration logistics, and data cleaning.

Many research–practice partnerships create products that go beyond a typical research report to communicate study findings such as infographics or short videos. When moving to this stage of a project, it is important to highlight feedback from informants on the stakeholder advisory group while maintaining the priorities of the champion. As with the design of a workshop, infographics and videos benefit from the input of the intended audience in the design stage. Draft scripts can be shared prior to investing in graphic design or filming to help stakeholder advisory group members envision the direction of the work. For example, a team developing a 3-minute video on a literature review regarding the Black–White achievement gap shared a script with their stakeholder advisory group that detailed the goals, audience, timeline, and resources to be used. In a two-column table, the script then detailed the planned points of the voiceover or other audio and the visual to accompany it. Stakeholder advisory group members shared their concerns that the planned language and framing of the video focused on a deficit model of achievement gap. They suggested changes that would highlight supporting Black student success rather than closing achievement gaps. They also suggested the inclusion of student voices to humanize the findings. The stakeholder advisory group feedback provided a subtle but meaningful shift in the planning of the filming and storytelling.

HOW DOES THE STAKEHOLDER ADVISORY GROUP RELATE TO THE RESEARCH–PRACTICE PARTNERSHIP?

Stakeholder Advisory Group Structure

Stakeholder advisory groups take many forms. The group's structure and roles within a particular project often depend upon the size of the research–practice partnership. The stakeholder advisory group's roles also depend upon the extent to which the research–practice partnership's researchers and practitioners collaboratively conceptualize, conduct, and develop public-facing materials about the partnership's research studies.

When a research–practice partnership is small (i.e., fewer than five practitioner partners), the formation of a stakeholder advisory group may not be necessary because the partnership members are able to communicate frequently among themselves to make decisions about a given study's direction. Smaller research–practice partnerships also may have fewer projects under way at a given time. Therefore, everyone may be able to attend to the same project at the same time. In other cases, those involved in small research–practice partnerships may form a stakeholder advisory group and request feedback on the research question, suggest who the intended audience(s) might be, and vet drafts of the final products and communication plans.

When a research–practice partnership consists of five or more practitioners within or across organizations, the practitioners will likely have multiple perspectives; in these cases, stakeholder advisory group feedback throughout the research, publication, and communication stages are critical to each project's success. The ideal membership and the topics to address with a stakeholder advisory group are described later in this section.

Logistics

As noted previously, stakeholder advisory groups are important mechanisms for feedback in larger research–practice partnerships where multiple projects are underway simultaneously. Therefore, one research–practice partnership may have many stakeholder advisory groups working at once with project teams. When this is the case, communication strategies between stakeholder advisory group members and other members of the research–practice partnership become important. The research–practice partnership may need to be more intentional in closing communication loops. One strategy is to hold monthly convenings across projects with the research–practice partnership leadership team. Each project team designates a representative to attend this convening and discuss the progress of the work. The goal of this cross-project meeting is to share information so that project goals and decisions are aligned with each other and remain aligned with research–practice partnership goals. A second strategy is to require short, written updates from each project that can be combined into a monthly email update for all to read. Although this strategy provides a more comprehensive report for all research–practice partnership members, it does not provide the back-and-forth discussion between projects that can be productive. Third, the research–practice partnership may devote regular meeting time to project updates. Research–practice partnership meetings are not intended to be one-way communications with one speaker after another reporting on projects. Therefore, it can be important to limit the time devoted to updates or limit the number of projects highlighted when using this strategy. With either method, the intentional communication strategy should be tailored to the size of the research–practice partnership and the needs of the members.

As more formal communication strategies are developed, project teams should consider the role of stakeholder advisory group members in reporting on project activities. Stakeholder advisory group members can represent the project in a cross-project meeting or in a report to the research–practice partnership. Playing a representative role can support the growth of a sense of ownership for the work among stakeholder advisory group members. It also can help them see beyond the project on which they are involved to a bigger picture of the research–practice partnership. Finally, in having stakeholder advisory group members represent the work, the research–practice partnership will gain a more varied perspective on the work than if research staff continually represent it.

Stakeholder advisory group members may not be direct members of a research–practice partnership. Rather, they may be recommended for the stakeholder advisory group by colleagues in the research–practice partnership. In these cases, it is often necessary to support communications between colleagues in the same partner organization so the research–practice partnership member remains up-to-date about stakeholder advisory group activities. For example, a research–practice partnership consisted of English learner (EL) directors across a number of school districts. One of the research–practice partnership projects was a study of the time it took for EL students to move out of bilingual support programming in one of the member districts, District A. The stakeholder advisory group for that study consisted of the data director from that District A (champion), a school leader from the District A (informant), and an EL director from another district, District B (learner). The EL director, data director, and school leader from District A did not interact regularly during the course of their work. Therefore, the project lead provided summaries of all stakeholder advisory group meetings to the EL director of District A to keep him informed about the project progress and decisions made with the stakeholder advisory group. Although the District A EL director would have learned of the project update through research–practice partnership membership, it was important to prioritize those communications given the significant contribution of the district to the project.

Giving Stakeholder Advisory Group Members Co-Ownership

Although some stakeholder advisory group members are recruited onto a project specifically for their role as a boundary spanner, all members have the ability to connect the work to their professional networks. Tapping into stakeholder advisory group member networks is an important way to share project findings and raise awareness of the work under way. Often, stakeholder advisory group members just need a reminder of the benefits of sharing this work with their colleagues within their organization and in their extended networks. By making their connector role explicit, they are empowered to think about existing opportunities they have at their disposal to share the work. In addition, project teams can develop opportunities for stakeholder advisory group members to represent the work beyond the research–practice partnership. Including stakeholder advisory group members in conference presentations and panels helps expand their professional networks while also bringing practitioner perspectives to the conversation. Finally, it is important to recognize the contributions of stakeholder advisory group members in project publications. Some research–practice partnerships provide recognition through an acknowledgement on the inside front cover of a publication. Others provide a byline on the front cover. Public recognition of the many contributions of the stakeholder advisory group members increases the shared ownership and distribution of the work.

NOTE

1. https://www.virtuallearningalliance.org/applying-lessons-learned-from -online-learning-research/

ABOUT THE EDITORS

Erin F. Haynes, founder of Engage Language, LLC, is a theoretical linguist with expertise in second-language acquisition and education technology, with an emphasis on English learners. She has worked in education research and evaluation for over 10 years, leading and contributing to projects for federal, state, district, and foundation clients. Recent projects include the rewrite of the Los Angeles Unified School District's *2018 Master Plan for English Learners and Standard English Learners,* and English learner curriculum development for teachers in New York. Previously, she was a senior researcher at the American Institutes for Research, where she led an Institute of Education Sciences-funded randomized controlled trial of Descubriendo la Lectura, a literacy program for English learners, and co-led a Regional Educational Laboratory Southwest study of teachers' access to promising professional development practices. She has conducted research related to English learner language proficiency and teacher knowledge and contributed to English learner curriculum development projects for the American Federation of Teachers and for the New York State Education Department. She holds a PhD in Linguistics from the University of California, Berkeley.

Pamela Spycher, WestEd, is an educational linguist with expertise in disciplinary language and literacy development, scaffolding academic content learning, and professional learning for teachers and leaders, with an emphasis on multilingual students and English learners (ELs). Her partnerships with schools, districts, state departments and county offices of education, and nonprofit and national organizations has integrated these interests. Her work with the California Department of Education has result-

Culturally and Linguistically Diverse Learners and STEAM, pages 389–390
Copyright © 2019 by Information Age Publishing
389

ed in new standards (English language development, visual and performing arts), curriculum frameworks (ELA-ELD, science, health education), and practitioner manuals (ELs with disabilities). Her most recent educational research includes leading two EL-focused, federally funded research grants: *Leading With Learning: Systemically Transforming Teaching for English Learners* (Grades PK–6) and *College Ready English Learners: Preparing Teachers to Foster English Language Development With the Expository Reading and Writing Curriculum* (Grades 9–12). She began her career as an elementary bilingual teacher and secondary English language development and world languages teacher. She holds a PhD in education (language, literacy, and culture) from the University of California, Davis.

ABOUT THE CONTRIBUTORS

Zenaida Aguirre-Muñoz is an associate professor in the Department of Psychological, Health, and Learning Sciences at the University of Houston. Her research focuses on issues related to opportunity to learn in multilingual classroom settings. This interdisciplinary approach centers on the intersection of cognition, learning, assessment, and language development of ELLs at the K–12 level. Dr. Aguirre-Muñoz's work has been funded by multiple funding agencies such as the National Science Foundation, the Department of Education, and non-profit foundations.

Will Andrews is the academic advisor and coordinator of internships in the iLab Program at Winooski Middle and High School in Winooski, Vermont. He is also a social studies teacher. Will has received his MEd in curriculum at Saint Michael's College and his master's thesis was entitled *How Are They Engaged? Three Programs Explore Personalized Learning* in which he investigated how three high school programs addressed the educational reforms of Vermont's Flexible Pathways Initiative.

Lauren Artzi is a senior researcher in education at the American Institutes for Research working across the areas of second language education, special education, and multi-tiered systems of support. Dr. Artzi directs early literacy projects and provides national technical assistance on topics related to literacy instruction and education policy. Previously, Dr. Artzi served on literacy research teams at the Center for Applied Linguistics and University of Maryland and worked as a middle school ESOL teacher.

Culturally and Linguistically Diverse Learners and STEAM, pages 391–399
Copyright © 2019 by Information Age Publishing
391

Diane August is a managing researcher at the American Institutes for Research, where she is responsible for directing the English-language learner work for the Center on English Learners. Her area of expertise is policy, research, and technical assistance related to the education of preschool and school age second-language learners. Dr. August has worked as a teacher, school administrator, legislative assistant, grants officer for the Carnegie Corporation, and director of education for the Children's Defense Fund.

Mary A. Avalos is a research associate professor in the Department of Teaching and Learning at the University of Miami, Florida. Her research interests include second language and multilingual teaching and learning in public schools, as well as teacher development and effectiveness in diverse, urban classrooms. Dr. Avalos has worked with teachers to develop interventions that provide explicit instruction for the language of schooling in reading/language arts, mathematics, and social studies content areas.

Noehealani Bareng-Antolin is a doctoral student in the University of Nevada, Las Vegas' Public Health Program. She is the program coordinator for the National Institute of Health Short-Term Research Experience for Underrepresented Persons program, and works with Nevada IDEA Network of Biomedical Research Excellence as an evaluator. She worked as a certified lead risk assessor and healthy homes specialist on a Housing and Urban Development Grant providing lead-based paint and healthy home inspections to low-income Nevada residents.

Lena Baucum, Pacific University, is a former school administrator and district level instructional coach working with veteran teachers to plan content-area instruction to infuse literacy support.

Kevin Carr, professor of science education at Pacific University–Oregon. Dr. Carr has worked for 20 years preparing new and veteran STEAM teachers for service in linguistically diverse K–12 schools. He directs the Pacific University Preparation of Culturally and Linguistically Diverse STEM Teachers program, located at the Pacific University Woodburn Campus.

Harry H. Cheng is a professor in the Department of Mechanical and Aerospace Engineering at the University of California, Davis. Dr. Cheng is the director of the UC Davis Center for Integrated Computing and STEM Education (C-STEM).

Luciana C. de Oliveira is chair and professor in the Department of Teaching and Learning in the School of Education and Human Development at the University of Miami, Florida. Her research focuses on issues related to teaching ELLs at the K–12 level, including the role of language in learning the content areas and teacher education, advocacy, and social justice. She is the author of numerous books, refereed journal articles, and book chapters. Currently, Dr. de Oliveira's research examines scaffolding practices in elementary classrooms. She is president (2018–2019) of TESOL International Association.

Suzie Dollesin, is a doctoral research assistant, serving as the associate editor of the *Journal of Transformative Leadership and Policy Studies* at the California State University, Sacramento.

Thea Fabian is a teacher on special assignment in the Fresno Unified District in California and a faculty member at Fresno State University (economics). Previously, she was an administrator for English Learner (EL) and Migrant Services in Central Unified (California) and a high school history and world languages (Spanish) teacher in Clovis Unified (California). She believes wholeheartedly that with the right kind of scaffolding, ELs can succeed at the highest levels and works daily toward that outcome. She holds an MA from Fresno State University in international relations.

Carolee Dodge Francis is a Native American social behavioral researcher and a member of the Oneida Nation of Wisconsin. She is the executive director of the American Indian Research and Education Center and an associate professor within the School of Community Health Sciences, University of Nevada, Las Vegas. She is nationally recognized for her qualitative research, programming, evaluation, and curriculum development in Type 2 diabetes and health education. Dr. Dodge Francis is the principal investigator for current federal grants.

Danielle Garegnani is a middle school assistant principal in the Lemon Grove School District (California). Her areas of expertise include disciplinary language and literacy development and supporting teachers, principals, and district staff to implement standards-aligned and research based pedagogical practices for EL students. Previously, she was a school and district improvement facilitator with a specialization in English learner (EL) support at WestEd. She holds an MA from San Diego State University.

Rachel Garrett is a senior researcher at the American Institutes for Research. She has major areas of interest and expertise in English Learner students, teacher professional development, and program and policy evaluation. She holds a PhD in public policy from the University of Chicago, and a BA in economics from Barnard College, Columbia University.

Marcelle Goggins is a research associate for the Science and Integrated Language (SAIL) and SAIL+CTM projects at New York University. She is also a master's student in the Department of Applied Statistics, Social Sciences, and Humanities at New York University, focusing on education policy. Before coming to New York University, she worked as a stem cell and developmental biology researcher at Harvard University.

María González-Howard is an assistant professor in STEM Education at the University of Texas at Austin. Her research explores the intersections of teaching and learning science with bilingualism development. Specifically, she focuses on supporting culturally and linguistically diverse students' engagement in science practices. Prior to receiving her doctorate from Boston College, she was a middle school science teacher in regular, advanced, and sheltered English instruction classrooms. She has designed and led professional development for preK–12 teachers.

Scott Grapin is a doctoral candidate in teaching English to speakers of other languages at the Steinhardt School of Culture, Education, and Human Development at New York University. His research interests include the integration of content and language learning, multimodality, and language assessment. Currently, he is working as a graduate research assistant on the Science and Integrated Language project. Previously, Scott was a high school Spanish and English as a second language teacher.

Maria O. Gregory is a bilingual elementary school teacher at the Lubbock Independent School District. She received her master's degree in bilingual education from Texas Tech University (TTU). Ms. Gregory also holds a graduate certificate in multidisciplinary science and has taught for 7 years in grades K–4. She is also a part-time instructor for TTU in the bilingual certification program.

Erin F. Haynes, founder of Engage Language, LLC, is a theoretical linguist with expertise in second-language acquisition and education technology, with an emphasis on English learners (ELs). She has worked in education research and evaluation for over 10 years, conducting research related to EL language proficiency and teacher knowledge, and developing curriculum for ELs.

Jennifer Letcher Gray is an associate professor of education at Marymount University in Arlington, Virginia. Prior to coming to Marymount, she taught both undergraduate and graduate courses at the University of Maryland, worked as a first and second grade classroom teacher, served as a K–3 reading specialist with the Chicago Public Schools, was an ESOL instructor for both children and adults, and served as an adult literacy program coordinator.

Alison Haas is the project manager for the Science and Integrated Language (SAIL) and SAIL+CTM projects at New York University. She began working with Okhee Lee and Lorena Llosa in 2012 on the National Science Foundation-funded grant, Promoting Science Among English Language

Learners. She is a part-time doctoral student in childhood education with a focus on science curriculum development and educational technology at New York University. Previously, she taught 5th grade in New York City.

Rita Januszyk is a professional development provider and science curriculum developer for K–8 teachers in the Next Generation Science Standards. She is the lead curriculum writer on the Science and Integrated Language project. She holds a degree in biological sciences and worked at Argonne National Laboratory as a scientific assistant. She has teaching and leadership experiences from pre–K to middle school, and was a member of the writing team to develop the Next Generation Science Standards.

Loren Jones recently earned her PhD from the Department of Teaching and Learning at the University of Miami, Florida and is now a clinical assistant professor at the University of Maryland, College Park. She is bilingual in English and Spanish and has 7 years' experience teaching Spanish at the secondary level. Her research focuses on best practices for literacy and language instruction to support linguistically and culturally diverse students in the primary grades.

Julie Reed Kochanek is a managing director at the American Institutes for Research and director of the Regional Educational Laboratory Midwest. She also serves as director of the Education Systems Practice Area, which includes work on research-practice partnerships, school choice, district and school improvement and measurement and statistics. Dr. Kochanek has nearly 20 years of experience in research and evaluation of school reform efforts, focusing on the social and organizational conditions surrounding schools and districts.

Okhee Lee is a professor in the Steinhardt School of Culture, Education, and Human Development at New York University. Her research areas include science education, language and culture, and teacher education. Dr. Lee is currently leading collaborative research between New York University and Stanford University to develop instructional materials aligned with the Next Generation Science Standards in order to promote science learning and language learning of elementary students including English learners (SAIL project).

Karin Linn-Nieves, director of Language and Literacy for the San Joaquin County Office of Education, has facilitated professional learning for educators of English learners for the past 25 years. Most recently, she served on the California English Learner Roadmap workgroup, a recently adopted state policy to strengthen comprehensive educational policies, programs, and practices for English learners. She holds an MA in Spanish from Sacramento State University, California.

Porfirio Loeza is a professor in the Sac State College of Education and Doctorate in Educational Leadership Program. Dr. Loeza is the editor of the *Journal of Transformative Leadership and Policy Studies.*

Lorena Llosa is an associate professor of education in the Steinhardt School of Culture, Education, and Human Development at New York University. Her work addresses English learners' content and language proficiency in K–16 contexts. Dr. Llosa is the co-PI on the Science and Integrated Language (SAIL) and SAIL+CTM projects. Her recent studies have focused on validity issues in the assessment of academic writing and the integration of language and science in instruction and assessment.

Katherine L. McNeill is a professor of science education at Boston College. A former middle school science teacher, she received her doctorate in science education from the University of Michigan. Her research focuses on supporting students with diverse backgrounds in science, with a particular focus on explanation and argumentation. Dr. McNeill has worked on a number of projects focused on curriculum, assessments, and other resources to support students, teachers, and instructional leaders in science practices.

Barbara J. Merino a former second-language teacher and professor of education at the University of California, Davis, with a doctorate in educational linguistics from Stanford University, specializes in second-language acquisition, instruction, and assessment in children and adults. The former director of teacher education at the University of California, Davis, she has worked with beginning teachers on their master of arts degree inquiry projects in literacy, math, and science for over 20 years.

Jason Moore is assistant professor of reading and language arts at Oakland University in Rochester, Michigan. His research focuses on ways to support elementary students to read and respond to challenging, subject-area texts in analytical and engaging ways. He has collaborated with elementary and secondary teachers in Dearborn and Detroit to identify ways that linguistic concepts might support English learners' engagement with academic content. Prior to earning his doctorate at the University of Michigan, he was a classroom teacher in Colorado.

James Nagle is an associate professor of education at Saint Michael's College. He serves as co-director of the Middle Grades Collaborative, a professional development organization serving middle school teachers throughout New England and is co-editor of the *Middle Grades Review.* Dr. Nagle's research interests are teacher learning and collaboration, secondary literacy and personalized learning. He is a former science educator in the San Francisco Bay Area.

Michael Takafor Ndemanu is a scholar of multicultural education, curriculum theory, comparative education, and social foundations in the Department of Educational Studies at Ball State University. His research focuses on multicultural education, transformative education, African American Vernacular English, English learner pedagogy, transnational education, translingual literacy, social justice, and peace education. Prior to earning his PhD, he taught French and English in Cameroon public schools for over 8 years before immigrating to the United States in 2006.

Sherilynn Nidever-Jordan is an educator in English, writing, English as a second language, and TESOL (teacher training). She earned her PhD in literacy, culture, and language education from Indiana University in 2013. Her scholarship has focused on immigrant sociocultural identities and narratives, ESL pedagogy, and multicultural education.

Catherine O'Hallaron has a PhD in literacy, language, and culture from the University of Michigan, Ann Arbor. She studied the writing of elementary school children supported by systemic functional linguistics (SFL) and has demonstrated that even young students who are English learners are capable of constructing effective arguments when supported with explicit instruction about the structural, logical, and linguistic features that contribute to strong argumentation.

Alandeom W. Oliveira is an associate professor of science education at the State University of New York at Albany. He earned a PhD degree in science education at Indiana University Bloomington (2008). He has taught science education courses to teachers in Brazil and the United Statesand has coordinated multiple professional development programs for school teachers. His research interests include cooperative science learning, inquiry-based teaching, and classroom discourse.

Annemarie Sullivan Palincsar is the Jean and Charles Walgreen Jr. Chair of Reading and Literacy, Arthur F. Thurnau Professor, and a teacher educator at the University of Michigan. Dr. Palincsar's primary research interest is in supporting students to learn how to engage in knowledge building with informational text, especially in the context of project-based scientific inquiry. She has used design-based research to investigate the process and outcomes of teaching English learners the use of functional grammar analysis as a means of supporting them to interpret and learn from narrative and informational text.

Cristina Poindexter is an assistant professor in the area of Water Resources Engineering in the Department of Civil Engineering at Sacramento State University. She worked as a professional water resources engineer for 5 years prior to obtaining her doctorate in civil and environmental engineering from the University of California, Berkeley. Dr. Poindexter has also worked with teachers to develop lessons that integrate engineering into life science courses at the elementary and secondary level.

Mary Schleppegrell is professor of education at the University of Michigan. She is a linguist who uses systemic functional linguistics to study the challenges of language in school subjects and the language development of second language learners of English. She led the *Language and Meaning* research group in work with elementary school teachers to support them in connecting language and meaning. She is the author of multiple books and journal articles related to language and literacy in first and second languages.

Carrie Scholz is a principal researcher at the American Institutes for Research, where she oversees five research-practice partnerships funded by the Regional Educational Laboratory program. These partnerships are composed of practitioners, policymakers, researchers, and other education stakeholders across the Midwest region. Dr. Scholz supports the partnerships as they develop and implement research agendas addressing specific educational needs, questions, and problems of practice. She also leads a national working group, funded by IES, that focuses on collaborative research partnerships.

Pamela Spycher is an educational linguist with expertise and interests in disciplinary language and literacy development, scaffolding academic content learning, and professional learning for teachers and leaders. She has worked in education for several decades, including as an elementary bilingual teacher and high school ELD and world languages teacher. Dr. Spycher's educational research partnerships with schools, districts, state departments and county offices of education, and nonprofit and national organizations focuses on educational equity for multilingual students and ELs.

Kira Tran earned her bachelor's degree in public health at the University of Nevada, Las Vegas and is currently pursuing a Master of Public Health degree with a concentration in Social and Behavioral Science. She currently works with the NIH/NIDDK Short-Term Research Experience for Underrepresented Persons (STEP-UP) Program and the NIH Nevada IDeA Network of Biomedical Research Excellence (INBRE) Program as a graduate research assistant.